D1269549

THE SYMPHONY
OF LIFE

by

Donald Hatch Andrews

NITY BOOKS • LEE'S SUMMIT, MO.

Copyright 1966 by Donald Hatch Andrews

Dedicated to
REBEKAH WEST HARKNESS

CONTENTS

THE NATURE OF THE UNIVERSE

1. The Unseen and the Unheard - - - - - - - 15
2. The Universe of Particles - - - - - - - 38
3. The Universe of Music - - - - - - - - 55
4. The Quest for Meaning - - - - - - - - 71

THE NATURE OF MUSIC

5. The Music of the String - - - - - - - - 99
6. The Music of the Drum - - - - - - - - 113
7. The Music of the Bell - - - - - - - - 135
8. The Meaning of Music - - - - - - - - 161

THE NATURE OF LIFE

9. The Structure of Life - - - - - - - - 181
10. The Dynamism of Life - - - - - - - - 213
11. The Unity of Life - - - - - - - - - 223
12. The Meaning of Life - - - - - - - - 241

THE NATURE OF MAN

13. The Structure of Man - - - - - - - - 261
14. The Dynamism of Man - - - - - - - - 281
15. The Unity of Man - - - - - - - - - 302
16. The Meaning of Man - - - - - - - - 335

THE NATURE OF THE UNIVERSE

17. The Structure of the Universe - - - - - 353
18. The Dynamism of the Universe - - - - - 371
19. The Unity of the Universe - - - - - - 388
20. The Meaning of the Universe - - - - - 409

Preface

The publication in 1963 of the best-seller "Honest To God" by Bishop Robinson brought to the fore the trend in current religious thinking where our increasing scientific knowledge is employed as an argument for rejecting an increasingly large part of our traditional religious beliefs. Of course, it is nothing new for scientists and philosophers to use the evidence from scientific investigation to discredit religion. Antireligious attacks of this sort are as old as science itself. But today there is a kind of new look to the battle, when theologians themselves urge us to see whether there may not be some truth in the thinking expressed by the phrase, "God is dead."

It is fair to say that there is something like a Copernican Revolution taking place in religious thinking today. It is also a valid conclusion that the role of science as a force in this revolution is, so far, largely negative. Exploration with the instruments of modern astronomy has pushed the possible location of Heaven "up there" or "out there" to a distance of, at least, quite a few thousands of millions of light years. More than that, if one is willing to accept the principles of the theory of relativity with the implication of the curvature of space there seems to be no room at all left for Heaven within the conventional dimensions of our universe. Turning from the almost infinitely large to the almost infinitesimally small, it appears at first glance that our modern concept of the structure of the atom leaves no room in the human body as a dwelling place for the soul. So the same kind of argument can conceivably lead to the conclusion that the soul is just as dead as God. But all this merely subtracts from our faith.

Moreover, before accepting these far-reaching negative conclusions as the ultimate truth, it may be well to ask

7

whether the theologians engaged in this new wave of criticism are not expressing their thoughts in too great haste. If one reviews the history of scientific thinking, one is bound to be struck by the fact that scientists as well as men of religion have often jumped to erroneously broad conclusions on the basis of limited evidence. When a scientific discovery is so basic that it opens the door to a vast network of varied and highly effective applications, the enthusiasm of the scientists sometimes exceeds their discretion. During the early part of the nineteenth century, developments in the field of applied mechanics and electrodynamics led to the industrial revolution in world economy. By the end of the century many scientists were proclaiming that essentially everything in the universe could be explained in terms of the principles of mechanics, and the president of the national organization of physicists in America was so bold as to state in the last decade of that century that all the important basic discoveries in physics had been made, and that all that remained to be done was the extension of the precision of measurement to an increased number of decimal places. There could hardly have been a worse time to make such a prediction. Within just a few years, there followed the most startling series of basic discoveries that had ever been seen —radioactivity, X rays, the photoelectric effect—climaxed by the quantum theory and the theory of relativity that completely revolutionized our concepts both of the very small and the very large aspects of the universe. One could hardly find a more effective example of the danger in drawing broad negative conclusions.

With all this in mind, it is natural to ask whether today is not the right time to reexamine our present scientific knowledge in order to see what positive bearing it may have on the nature of man and on what man may know about his basic relation to the universe and to the absolute transcendent that he calls God. Can the perspectives of science give

8

to us any deeper insight into "this infinite and inexhaustible depth and ground of all being" (Tillich)? The attitude of the new theology seems to be that we must take a hard, realistic, searching look at religion and draw the most "honest to God" conclusions, letting the chips, chunks, or even main trunk of our faith fall by the wayside, if that is the way it is. Certainly, a part of this reappraisal should be a searching reinvestigation of the evidence of science, of the pattern of scientific thinking, and of any scientific perspectives that have a bearing on our ultimate faith. The fact is that during these same decades when religion has been suffering such deep pangs of agonizing self-reappraisal, science has been undergoing a revolution as basic if not even more basic. Starting with the quantum theory and the theory of relativity, followed within less than two decades by the discovery of the wave nature of the electron and the proton, science has seen the absolutism of its major concepts and laws swept away; and the familiar vocabulary of ideas based on the particle obeying the laws of Newton's mechanics in Cartesian space and time has been replaced by a syntax of dynamic forms operating in a space-time domain, the structure of which is still largely a mystery.

To sum up the nature of this scientific revolution in a single phrase, we are finding that the universe is composed not of matter but of music. As Teilhard de Chardin puts it, the more we split and pulverize matter artificially, the more insistently it proclaims its fundamental unity; and we find that the periodic table represents a "harmonic series of simple bodies, strung out from hydrogen to uranium on the notes of an atomic scale."

In shifting the basis of our ideas about the universe from mechanics to music, we move into an entirely new philosophy of science. To date, comparatively little progress has been made in exploring this new philosophy but the few considered conclusions which have been drawn are so full

9

of implications in the common ground of science and religion that they present an impelling challenge for immediate study. It is the purpose of this book to present some of these conclusions.

I want to take this opportunity to express my thanks to a number of persons whose encouragement, support, and assistance have been invaluable during the course of the preparation of this book.

First of all, there is no truly adequate way to state my gratitude to Rebekah West Harkness. I have derived the deepest inspiration from my conversations with her; at her suggestions, I was given a grant by the William H. Harkness Foundation, which was instrumental in providing me with the freedom from many distractions during the preparation of the manuscript; her friendship has been a major component in the stimulus for creative thinking.

Next, I want to thank my colleagues associated with the Foundation for Integrative Education for their friendly advice, criticism and whole-hearted encouragement in this undertaking: Professor Kirtley Mather, Professor F. S. C. Northrup, Professor Henry Margenau, and above all, Dr. Frederick L. Kunz, Director of the Foundation. I hope that the result of my efforts will meet their highest expectations.

The interest in my writing has been most heartening. For encouraging advice I express thanks to Mr. Henry Robinson Luce, Dr. Raymond R. Killinger, Jr., Associate of the Fort Lauderdale Psychiatric Group; the Right Reverend Leland Stark, Bishop of Newark; Mr. John N. Forman, Headmaster of the Forman School, Litchfield, Connecticut; Professor and Mrs. Amos Wilder and Professor Paul Lehmann of the Harvard Divinity School; the Reverend Ralph Harper, Rector of St. James Parish, Monkton, Maryland; Mr. Robert Gerle, of New York City; Mr. Theodore H. Keller, Organist of the Lawrenceville School; and Dr. Charles Kent, Director of the Peabody Conservatory of

10

Music. I thank Mr. Leopold Stokowski for his kindness in showing me his collection of Oriental percussion instruments and for his continuing interest in my work. I acknowledge the inspiration that I have derived from many visits over the years with Mr. Sherwood Anderson and Mr. E. E. Cummings, and from discussions with Professor Adolph Meyer, formerly Director of the Phipps Psychiatric Institute of The Johns Hopkins University, and Professor Hermann Weyl, formerly Professor at the Institute for Advanced Study, Princeton, New Jersey.

I am most grateful to Mrs. Dorothy Wilken of the staff of Florida Atlantic University for the excellent illustrations and to Edwina Berlijn Andrews for the painting of the magic color piano keys.

I am deeply indebted to my colleagues at Florida Atlantic University for the opportunity to discuss many of the aspects of my arguments and especially to Professor James McGuire of the Department of Physics for helpful suggestions and criticism.

Finally, I express my deepest appreciation to Mary Frances Alley whose encouragement, criticism and devoted services in the preparation of the manuscript have been a major contributing factor in making the ideas contained in this book at last a printed reality.

In closing, I must acknowledge my lasting gratitude to my wife, Elizabeth Howland Andrews, for her unfailing encouragement and her cheerful endurance of an author in the house for so many years.

Donald H. Andrews

Boca Raton, Florida
6 VI 66

Dear Reader:

I hope that you will enjoy my book. Some of the chapters contain technical details that you may want to skip over. For example, the first two chapters in the section on music (Chapters 5 and 6) may be of more interest to the professional musician and of less interest to the musical layman. Similarly, the first chapter of the section on the nature of life may appeal more to scientists and less to others.

Feel free to skip many of the details, at least on the first reading; they are included in order to reinforce the central argument but are not necessary for its understanding. My primary objective is to give you a *broad* vista of the new and truly revolutionary unity of science and religion that is emerging today. If you can glimpse this, I will be quite content.

The Author

Part I
The Nature of the Unseen

1

The Unseen and the Unheard

I F I COULD wave a magic wand before you and give
you the power to perceive all the invisible sights and
inaudible sounds around you at this moment, what
would you see and what would you hear?

Shall we try it? Close your eyes for an instant. I wave
the wand. Now look around you. The room is ablaze with
dazzling light. The chairs, the tables, the floor, the ceiling,
and the walls are prismatic crystals, sparkling with a thousand shades of red, yellow, green, and blue such as you
have never in your life seen before. Your clothes are on
fire with a million microscopic rainbow flames. Your nose,
your cheeks, your hands are shining ruby, emerald, and
sapphire. You open your mouth and a shaft of amethyst
light beams out before you. The air itself sparkles as if
millions of miniature meteors are darting all around you,
as if a cluster of skyrockets had just exploded. There is a
swift rain of tiny incandescent bullets shooting down from
the ceiling, shooting through the table, through the chairs,
right through your body, and disappearing into the floor.

Almost blinded by this strange blaze of light, you shut
your eyes in bewilderment. I now press the magic wand on
your ears. Suddenly you are aware of a hurricane of sound
beating upon you, as if a thousand symphony orchestras
were magically squeezed into the room and all playing
fortissimo. For every object near you is resonating with its
own strange, peculiar music. The table booms like a hundred big bass fiddles doing a bolero. The lamp is trilling
like a dozen flutes. The carpet is caroling. In this very book

15

you hold in your hand, you hear a chorus of a thousand voices. And your body is vibrant with the most complex music of all. You hear a super-symphony resounding within you—melody, harmony, counterpoint—canon and fugue intermingling in a tapestry of sound with tones millions of times more varied, with texture millions of times more complex than any symphony ever dreamed of by a human composer.

This is the realm of the unseen and the unheard that shines and pulsates around you and within you unperceived during every moment of your life. But though invisible and inaudible, it is just as real as everything that you actually see and hear and feel. It is the domain in which scientists are beginning to discover more and more of the secrets of life and of the universe. For this unseen and unheard is not science fiction. In scientific laboratories all over the world thousands of experiments have been performed that establish the reality of these unperceived phenomena beyond any shadow of doubt, that prove that these waves of unseen "light" and of unheard "sound" are truly around us and within us at all times. What we see, the *visible* light, constitutes far less than a millionth part of all the radiation around us. What we hear, the *audible* sound, is far less than a millionth part of all the vibration constantly beating upon our bodies. And what is even more important, light waves and sound waves make up in their unseen and unheard *totality* only a small part of the truly complete sum of all the kinds of waves that are constantly churning in the ocean of space in which we exist.

There are, for example, gravity waves. Every particle of matter has a field of gravity; if the particle moves then a gravitational wave is set up; thus we live in the midst of a vast sea of these gravity waves.

And there are even stranger kinds of waves around us and within us. Only a few years ago the French physicist,

Louis de Broglie, proposed that in every atom there is a pattern of waves. Thinking in these terms we believe that underlying all the light waves seen and unseen, all the sound waves heard and unheard, all the gravity waves felt and unfelt, there undulates another vast and mysterious ocean of atomic particle waves. It is in the constantly shifting patterns of this atomic surf that the fundamental chemistry and physics of our living is expressed.

Not all scientists are yet willing to say that these atomic waves truly exist. As Bertrand Russell puts it: Atoms are waves of probability, and the physicist says the waves are in his formulae, and his formulae are in his head, from which, however, you must not infer that the waves are in his head! At least, whether confused or amused by this complexity, every scientist agrees today that atoms behave *as if* their patterns of behavior are determined by patterns of waves; and, as far as I am concerned, this aspect of atomic behavior goes a long way toward establishing the *reality* of these waves. We shall discuss at some length the meaning of that enigmatic word *reality* later in the book.

In any case, today it is clear that science must include this wave aspect of matter as a fundamental component of all scientific thinking. Every scientific conclusion must be consistent with this "harmonic" model of the atom. Thus it begins to look more and more as if our universe is constructed not of *matter* but of *music*. The objective of this book is the exploration of the nature and meaning of this music.

Seeing the Unseen

The music of the universe is a cosmic symphony that is almost unbelievably intricate in its complexity. For in its totality this symphony embraces all the waves of sound audible and inaudible, all the waves of light visible and invisible, all the waves of gravity felt and unfelt, and all the waves of atoms explicit and implicit. As the first step in our survey of this vast symphony, let us take a look at the problems that confront us when we begin to explore the invisible radiation that lies just beyond the boundaries of familiar visible light.

What is the best way to "see" the unseen? If this book were an advanced scientific treatise, we would begin by first setting forth fundamental definitions and then describing this invisible "light" with the help of mathematical equations. And if this were to be our procedure, I feel sure that you and almost everyone else starting to read this book would sigh and close its pages right at this point, for, unfortunately, there are very few of us sufficiently familiar with the advanced algebra and calculus required to enable us to profit from such a mathematical treatment. Most of us do our thinking far more with the help of visual images than with x's, y's, alpha's, beta's, pluses and minuses, and integral signs. For this reason I want to begin our exploration by portraying the unseen and the unheard not in algebraic equations but in *visual* images. For most of us, *seeing* is the first and best step toward *understanding.* In his profound treatise on "The Phenomenon of Man," Teilhard de Chardin expresses this thought in a vivid and arresting way. He remarks: *"Seeing.* We might say that the whole of life lies in that verb—if not ultimately, at least essentially." Again he says: *"To see or to perish* is the very condition laid upon everything that makes up the universe, by reason of the mysterious gift of existence. And this, in superior measure, is man's condition." Alfred North Whitehead also comments on this problem of attaining understanding through the deepening of the modes of perception. In his book "Adventures of Ideas," he remarks that the whole body is the true organ of sensing. He is especially competent to discuss this dilemma of charting the golden mean between mathematical expression on the one hand and pictorial image on the other, since in early life he achieved great distinction as a mathematician and at the close of his career was recognized as one of the world's most eminent philosophers. I will quote him at length in many passages later in the book.

I agree with Whitehead that we have to grasp these new ideas about the unseen and the unheard with our total power of perception. Whitehead says of the eighteenth century philosopher, Leibniz, that he taught us "what it must be like to be an atom." That is exactly the sensation that I hope I can help you to feel. And *seeing* is a major step toward *feeling*.

Obviously the visual approach has its dangers; and many of my colleagues may be offended by some of my visual descriptions of the unseen. But if the objection is raised that a visual description gives a false impression of the true nature of light waves, gravity waves, and atomic particle waves, I reply that even the most advanced mathematical description has a component of artificiality. Whether we use the crudest visual picture or the most advanced mathematical symbolism, we are still building a model of nature, not reproducing nature itself. When an artist paints a portrait of a human being, say a beautiful woman, all he can hope to do is put on the canvas just a partial representation of the real living beauty. The painter may achieve this with comparatively few strokes of the brush if the picture is in the impressionistic style; or he may spend weeks and months making thousands upon thousands of tiny shadings if he is striving for the greatest possible realism. But no matter how long he labors he never can create the actual flesh. The woman will never step out of the picture. What he paints is, at best, only a partial representation of living reality. And the same limitation will always be inherent in the most advanced mathematical description of our actual real world.

Again, some of my colleagues complain that it is misleading to speak of *seeing* this invisible radiation, because we never can develop a human eye with greater power of perception than that which nature has already given us. Later, when I suggest what an atom *might* look like if we *could* see it, they may reply that the very nature of the universe is such that radiation can never give us directly a *picture* of an atom. Well, after all, most chemistry texts are filled with imaginary pictures to help the students understand atoms by visualizing their structure. If I push the pictorial aspect a little farther than usual, I hope that it will not be misleading, as long as we both keep in mind that this is only "seeing through a glass darkly," that it is only the *first* step on the journey toward understanding and that we must be ever mindful of the limitations that inevitably go hand in hand with the elements of truth that are being revealed in these pictures. Remember especially that the limitations themselves will be the basis for a much more extended discussion later in this book after we have achieved our first "bird's-eye" survey of the invisible and are then better prepared to search for its deeper meaning. As the country preacher said at the beginning of his sermon one Sunday morning, "My friends, today we are going to try to see the unseeable, hear the unhearable, and unscrew the unscrutable." So, until you and I have progressed in our survey to the point where we can scrutinize our scrutiny, I hope that you will accept my impressionistic images in the spirit in which they are offered: exercises in the training of the *inner* eye to enable it to look farther and deeper, and ultimately to see more clearly so that, according to Teilhard de Chardin, we can understand the immensity around, behind, and in front of us.

The Nature of Seeing

Let us first consider briefly the nature of the light by which we actually do see. It has been known for something over a hundred years that light has a wavelike character. As light comes in through the window and passes into your eye, it is much like a stream of little ripples resembling the ripples you see when you drop a stone into the surface of a pond of water. If there is a leaf floating on the pond as the ripples go by, you may notice that the big broad ripples make the leaf rise and fall slowly. By contrast, little ripples where the ridges are close together make the leaf move up and down much more rapidly as they pass under it. The "rapidity" with which the leaf moves up and down we shall call the *frequency* of the motion. Thus, the larger ripples that make the leaf move more slowly might cause it to move up and down twice during each second of time. In this case we say that the frequency is two vibrations per second. The smaller ripples, by contrast, might make the leaf move up and down eight times during each second. Here, we say that the frequency of the motion is eight vibrations per second.

Suppose that you have in your room two lamps, one of which gives off light which is deep red in color while the other lamp shines with light which has the color of deep violet. Suppose that through the magic eyesight that I conferred upon you just a few minutes ago, you can actually see these ripples of light coming toward your eye. Suppose also that you can put a magic speck of dust in the air so that these ripples make the speck move up and down like the ripples on the pond disturbing the leaf. You observe that the ripples of the red light are spaced further apart and make the particle of dust move up and down in a way that is slow compared with the up-and-down movement when the violet light disturbs the dust. If you count the number of movements up and down per second (and this really would take some potent magic as the ripples of light are almost unbelievably fast in their up-and-down motion, over one hundred trillion vibrations per second), you would observe that the dust wiggles up and down almost exactly twice as fast when the violet light hits it as it does when the red light hits it. If you have other lamps that give out orange, yellow, green and blue light, you can perform the same experiment and find that all the different colors of visible light have vibrations that in their frequency lie between the slow frequency of the red and the fast frequency of the violet. Because violet light vibrates just about twice as fast as red light we can say, using musical terms, that the range of visible light from the deep red to the deep violet covers one *octave.*

The resemblance between the vibration of light and the vibration of sound can be so helpful in understanding many of the musical or harmonic relationships in nature that I now want to explore it in some detail. Let's imagine that we have a piano with a keyboard made up of translucent keys through which colors glow. There is a little magic electric light placed just under the ivory slab on each of the keys and the color of the light is adjusted to be "in tune" with the sound of the note when it is played. By this, I mean that the frequency of the light seen varies proportionally with the frequency of the sound heard. Let's arrange it so that the piano key which, on being struck, sounds the note of middle C, glows with deep crimson light. In the key of C major, this is the *do* of our scale of *do, re, mi, fa, sol, la, ti, do.* The key just above *do* which sounds *re,* glows with a bright red light. The *mi* key has an orange color; *fa* is yellow; *sol* is green; *la* is blue; *ti* is violet. Thus the colors are adjusted so that the frequency of the light is exactly in proportion to the frequency of the sound. For example, the *sound* of the note *sol* has a vibration just fifty percent faster in frequency than the original note *do* below it; the green *light* coming from the ivory key corresponding to *sol* vibrates exactly fifty percent faster than the deep crimson light coming from the ivory key corresponding to the original *do.*

But what about *high do* one octave above the original *do?* In the sound of *high do* we hear a note that sounds like the original *do* at middle C and yet is different. Our ears recognize the close family resemblance between these notes that are an *octave* apart; but our ears also detect that the notes are *different; high do* sounds *higher* than *middle do.* If the frequency of the light coming from *high do* is still proportional to the sound frequency, what is the color of this note? It is a deep violet-purple that has a family resemblance to crimson but is still recognizable as a different color. Thus from *do* to *high do* we have one octave of sound and one rainbow of color, crimson to violet.

Purplish-violet is as far up the scale of color as the normal human eye can perceive. If we strike *high re* above *high do,* our ear hears this note with perfect clarity; but the light coming from this note, with color frequency proportional to the sound, is invisible to us. For we have gone up the color scale across the one octave rainbow of visible light and have now passed into the realm of *invisible* light that is called the *ultra*violet (because it lies beyond the visible violet at the right edge of the rainbow). But although we don't see this light, it exists nevertheless. In the radiation from our sun there is a great deal of this invisible ultraviolet light in the octave of color above the visible octave. In fact, it is this invisible ultraviolet light that gives us a suntan when we lie on the beach.

Now what about the notes *below* middle C? If each were lighted with a color whose frequency is proportional to the frequency of the sound, the light coming from these lower notes also would be invisible; it lies in the invisible *infrared* part of the spectrum, which is given this name because it lies in the range *below* the visible red in the same way that invisible ultraviolet light lies *above* the visible violet. In our experiment with magic vision described at the beginning of this chapter, we were imagining what these invisible colors would look like, *if* you had the power to see them. We were also imagining that your mental capacity of awareness of radiation was enlarged so that you could perceive many octaves of color and recognize *color* harmony in the same way that you recognize *sound* harmony. Just as a high G frequency, twice as fast as middle G, sounds like middle G but is *different* by being higher, we will now imagine that the invisible color of light corresponding to high G will be recognized as similar to the green color of middle G, but at the same time will be perceived as a *different* kind of green because it is an octave higher in frequency.

We also imagine that you have a new *sense* of color harmony. Whereas in the ordinary act of seeing, three colors blend and give the appearance of being a single color, now in your magic seeing you perceive both the harmony of the colors as a kind of color chord *and* you also see the presence of each individual color—just as you are aware of the three tones in a musical chord of three notes and perceive their blend, both as harmony and as three individual tones. Thus for the major triad of *do-mi-sol,* you see red, orange, and green as a chord of color and not just as a single, completely blended color.

Ultraviolet: High Soprano

Now let us go on up the piano keys above high C and find out what their colors look like with your new magic vision that permits you to see invisible "light." On the piano we have three octaves of keys lying above middle C. With your magic vision you now see these keys glowing with new colors of a sort that you have never seen before, a new kind of crimson, a new kind of bright red, new oranges, yellows, greens, blues, and violets as your eye wanders up the keyboard from *high do* to the higher *re, mi, fa, sol, la, ti, do,* and the even higher octaves. Hold your hand over the octave just above high C and you get a suntan from the ultraviolet radiation coming from these keys. Hold your hand over the very highest notes on the piano and you see the light from these keys actually passing right through your hand. For in these high ranges of radiation frequency, we are in the X-ray region, where the light has such a high-pitched "tone" that it can penetrate directly through your flesh, making the bones appear as shadows.

If we move still higher, we will go off the top of the keyboard of an ordinary piano; but we still have not reached anywhere near the top range of frequency of radiation that has been observed in scientific experiments. So let us imagine that, instead of an ordinary piano, we have one with the keyboard extended to the right by twenty-five feet, with some twenty-five octaves of keys lying above middle C. As you keep on looking farther up this extended keyboard, you see rainbow after rainbow of these strange new prismatic X-ray colors. The radiation becomes more and more penetrating and it would actually give your skin a severe burn if you were exposed to this radiation for any great length of time. These are the "colors" of radiation used in cancer therapy to destroy malignant tissue. The "sounds" from these higher keys on the extended piano are also inaudible to the normal human ear when we go about two octaves above the top note on the piano. Beyond that, animals and insects can detect some of the notes, but you will need your magic ears to hear them all.

At about the twentieth octave above the range of visible light we pass into the region of the spectrum where the radiation is called "gamma rays." These rays are emitted when certain "explosive" transformations take place in the nuclei of atoms. Frequently these gamma rays in penetrating other atoms cause them also to emit X rays. In my description of the invisible light coming from the walls of the room, I spoke of the scintillation of colors, tiny sparkling points of light appearing and disappearing as if the walls were covered with fireflies. These scintillations are the X rays and gamma rays coming from the walls because of the slight amount of radioactivity that is present in any material.

But how about the shower of incandescent bullets coming down through the ceiling and penetrating everything they hit? These bullets are bits of radiation lying in the highest ranges of frequency that have ever been experimentally observed, some twenty-five octaves above the range of visible light, more than twenty-five octaves above middle C on our magic piano. They are referred to generically as "cosmic rays." The primary origin of this kind of radiation is somewhere out in space among the stars.

Perhaps these cosmic rays are faint echoes of the cosmic thunder that shook the universe in the birth pangs of its creation which many cosmologists believe occurred about ten billion years ago. Whatever or wherever their origin may be, cosmic rays contain fantastically large amounts of energy; these radiant "bullets" have such power that they shoot right through the roof, through the ceiling, through your body, down through the floor, and penetrate many feet into the earth before finally being absorbed. As you read this, one of these cosmic bullets is shooting through your brain about once every second. Fortunately it does you no harm; though if you feel queer someday, perhaps you can blame it on one of these cosmic bullets that has hit a sensitive spot in your cranium.

The Unseen Baritone

Let us now turn from the high *soprano* tones in the cosmic symphony and consider the *baritone* range, the invisible radiation that lies just below the red light that we can perceive with the unaided human eye. As I stated before, this range of radiation is called by the name *infrared*. If you look at the glowing keyboard of our magic piano with *ordinary* human vision you see only the single rainbow of color running from the violet at *high do* down through the blue at *la,* the green at *sol,* the yellow at *fa,* the orange at *mi,* the flame-red at *re,* and the deep crimson at *middle do,* which is middle C on the keyboard. Below this octave the eye does not detect any light coming from the lower notes down to the far left end which represents the bottom of our piano scale. But hold your hand over the keys just below *middle do* and you will feel heat coming from them; for your skin detects these invisible infrared rays even though you cannot see them.

Since these infrared rays give you the sensation of heat, you may suspect that their emission is related to temperature. To see this relationship let's do a few experiments with an ordinary kitchen frying pan. As the pan hangs on the kitchen wall, you do not detect any heat coming from it. For the pan is at room temperature, close to the temperature of your hand; and although the pan actually is radiating at your hand, your hand is also radiating back at the pan; and we are so used to having this invisible radiation fall on our skin that we are insensitive to it when it comes to us from other objects that are at room temperature.

Now light a burner on the stove, take the frying pan down and place it over the burner for about twenty seconds. If you now take it off the stove and hold it near your face, you are immediately aware of heat radiating from the pan and falling on your skin. Put the pan back on the burner and leave it for several minutes, and your eye now can detect that the pan is glowing with a deep red color. It is radiating *visible* light. (This is especially evident if you carry on this experiment at night and turn out the kitchen light in order to observe the pan in the dark.)

We may conclude from this experiment that by raising the temperature of an object sufficiently we can make it give off visible light. We talk about a body being *red-hot* when it glows red in the dark, and *white-hot* when the temperature is raised even more and we observe white light coming from it. Actually any object such as a frying pan gives off radiation having a number of different colors. When it is sufficiently hot these colors blend and give us the sensation of white. However, if we could be endowed with magic eyesight and perceive both the blend of color *and* the individual tones of color, then we would see the object giving off whole rainbows of color when it is heated to about five hundred degrees above room temperature.

There are two principal reasons why we do not actually see the objects all around us glowing when we are in a dark room at night. In the first place our eyes are not sensitive to this infrared radiation, this "dark light." In the second place, although the objects around us are actually giving out a faint glow of visible light, our eyes are not sufficiently sensitive to detect this faint glow. But it is important to realize that this radiation actually is coming to us all the time from the objects around us. It is also important to realize that our own bodies are giving out this radiation; each of us is clothed in an invisible aura of thousands of colors during every moment of our life.

In order to understand the origin of this aura let us turn back to the lower part of the glowing piano keyboard and examine it with the help of magic vision. Although with your *ordinary* vision you cannot see any light coming from the notes in the octave just below middle C, you can with your *magic* vision perceive that in this octave there actually is a new repetition of the familiar rainbow in the baritone range; *ti* is glowing violet, *la* glowing blue, *sol* glowing green, *fa* glowing orange, *mi* glowing yellow, *re* glowing bright red, and *do* glowing crimson. We can imagine that these colors, although resembling our familiar visible rainbow, will have a different, darker quality just as the notes of sound in the baritone range have a different, deeper quality than do the notes in the alto range. Let's keep on looking down the keys, now observing the notes in the bass range two octaves below *middle do*. Again the rainbow is

repeated but with even darker colors. On the ordinary piano there is one more octave of extremely low notes that we may call the sub-bass. Again in this range we see the rainbow repeated once more. But even at the end of this third rainbow we have scarcely begun to explore the domain of this invisible low-frequency radiation. So just as we imagined the upper part of the piano extended off to the right beyond the high notes to provide us with about twenty-five octaves *above* middle C, let's imagine now that we can extend the piano keyboard to the left below the bass notes for about fifty feet, to provide us with fifty octaves of keys *below* middle C.

Let us think of familiar visible light and the notes corresponding to it as our *primary* octave; we call the baritone range, lying just below it, the *secondary* octave. Extending this notation, we think of the bass range as the *tertiary* or third octave, the sub-bass as the *quaternary* or fourth octave. We now want to explore the sub-sub-bass below the range of the piano, which we will call the *quinary* or fifth octave.

Darken the room and hold your hand over the glowing piano keys and you will see that the colors coming from these sub-sub-bass keys match the colors that your hand itself is radiating. As you certainly recall, human body temperature runs about 98 to 99 degrees Fahrenheit with skin temperature a little lower. An object with a nonselective radiating surface has the color of its strongest radiation in this range, when the temperature of the object is about the same as normal human skin temperature. The radiation coming from such an object as your hand may be compared with the tones coming from a piano if you strike all the keys at once—but hitting one central key the hardest and then hitting the keys on either side progressively weaker, as you move away from the central key.

Physicists refer to such radiation as "black body" radiation because, in this ideal radiating body, no color is given any preference resulting from the chemical composition or the material structure of the body, and the relative intensity of the colors depends only on the temperature. Actually it is impossible to construct a perfect "black body." Because all material is made of different kinds of atoms put together in many different ways, there are always certain colors that are preferentially favored in the radiation (although a rusty frying pan, blackened by the soot from many fires, does resemble the physicist's ideal "black body" pretty closely). Many objects will radiate nonpreferentially in certain ranges and exhibit preferential radiation in others; but, for the purposes of our broad survey of the types of radiation, such effects will not concern us at this time. In our discussion the main point is that the surface of your own body is radiating at this moment hundreds of different colors in this quinary sub-sub-bass range of invisible light.

Although it is very doubtful whether we will ever be able to see this radiation directly, the day is not far off when we can observe it in considerable detail both with photography and with television. During the 1940s I worked on the development of infrared television in collaboration with the United States Army Signal Corps and later with the United States Navy. The first experiments were crude but they demonstrated clearly the existence of this radiation. As I stood in a completely darkened room before my infrared television camera, the "aura" of radiation from my body was picked up and projected on a television screen. Looking at that screen I saw the glowing image of my body projected by the invisible light I was radiating. It was not a flattering picture; in fact, you never would have been able to recognize me—my image did have human shape, but my face looked more like that of a man from Mars.

The origin of this infrared radiation is primarily in the motions that the atoms of the radiating material undergo because of the heat that is present in the material. We shall examine in more detail later the way in which this invisible radiation is produced. At this time I want to go on to explore the remaining forty-five octaves of radiation that represent still lower tones in our cosmic symphony.

The Hypo-Bass Range

Remember that we have extended our piano some fifty octaves below its normal bass range. As we look down over these dozens of keys we see the familiar rainbow of violet-blue-green-yellow-orange-red repeated over and over again. What is the nature of these hypo-bass tones?

If, in our laboratory for exploring wave phenomena, we have a detector for radar, we will find that the piano keys some fifteen octaves below middle C are giving off radar waves. As we go down farther octave by octave, we get into the range that is used in television broadcasting; and some twenty-five octaves below middle C we find that our piano keys are giving out waves that can be picked up with an ordinary radio receiver. About fifty octaves below middle C we are in the 60-cycle frequency that is used for transporting electrical power. Actually there is no difficulty in making electrical waves at still lower frequencies. The electric organ does this. Our ordinary electronic audio circuits also do this when they reproduce music or voice from a radio, record player, or public-address amplifier. Many of the objects around you at this moment are producing electrical oscillations in this range because thermal energy makes their atoms vibrate and their atoms act like little broadcasting stations. The intensity of this radiation is almost infinitesimally small; but you should not forget that if you *could* see all the radiation around you at this moment, you would perceive your room filled with radar waves, television waves, radio waves, and millions of other low-frequency waves that are produced by the vibrations of all the objects around you as well as the waves that are coming from radar stations and television and radio broadcasting stations.

The molecules of water in the air of your room are also radiating infrared rays. As they dash around at speeds of thousands of feet per second, they are emitting radiation in the quaternary and quinary octaves of the infrared. With magic eyesight that enables you to see this invisible radiation no matter how faint, you perceive these molecules as millions of shooting stars all around you.

In trying to understand this vast range of radiation with frequencies lying below those of visible light, it is frequently helpful to think of *hearing* these waves rather than *seeing* them. So, at this point, we leave the magic piano with its glowing keys and turn to consider what the sensation would be if instead of *seeing,* you could *listen* to the invisible and inaudible waves that surround you.

Hearing the Unheard

There is no doubt that the sudden ability to hear the inaudible waves all around you would be a startling experience, because of their enormous numbers. With the eye you can focus on a relatively small segment of the view that is laid out before you and mentally exclude the rest. It is far more difficult to "focus" the ear. In a crowded room where there may be a dozen conversations taking place, you can concentrate your attention on the one conversation in which you wish to participate directly, but it is difficult to exclude the awareness of other sounds around you. Trained musicians can undoubtedly focus their audible attention on the sounds from a single instrument coming from an orchestra of a hundred players, but they seldom lose consciousness of the other notes. Nevertheless, for our purposes, let's imagine that you can focus your audible attention exclusively on different parts of all these inaudible, unheard waves by which you are surrounded. We also will imagine that you can hear waves such as light and gravity waves that are intrinsically different from sound. Thus, as you sit in your room listening with your magic ears and magic mind, you may be struck first by the "sound" coming to you from some particular object near you—for example, a chair. The sound coming from the chair is extremely small in intensity and comes largely from the motions of the atoms in the chair, motions that take place because the chair contains heat.

Heat and *thermal motion* are synonomous; for an object does not have to be hot to contain heat. Whether we think of something as hot or cold is entirely relative. The top of a stove may feel very hot to your hand but it is cold compared with molten steel. Of course the atoms in the liquid steel are vibrating with a great intensity of thermal motion; but the atoms in a block of ice are also vibrating with thermal motion, although we think of the ice as *cold* rather than *hot*.

In theory we can conceive of a block of metal cooled to such a low temperature that every atom within it has lost all of its thermal motion. This is the temperature we refer to as *absolute zero*. This point on the temperature scale is picked for a logical reason. We think of heat as the motion of the atom and we think of this thermal motion ceasing when all the heat is abstracted from an object. We conclude that nothing can be stiller than being stopped in its motion. So from this point of view there can be nothing colder than the object which has no thermal motion. Therefore, it seems logical to pick this temperature of motionlessness as the absolute zero or base point of our absolute scale of temperature.

We believe that it will never be possible to bring any large numbers of atoms into a condition where they are absolutely stopped as far as their thermal motion is concerned. There are a number of interesting theoretical questions associated with this concept of absolute zero but these involve problems too complex to discuss here. The zero of the temperature scale has been established by measurements with great precision. We believe that it lies 273.15 degrees centigrade below the standard freezing point of water, which is zero degrees on the centigrade scale. On the Fahrenheit scale, which is used widely in the English-speaking countries, absolute zero would lie at 460 degrees below zero Fahrenheit. The important thing for us at this point is that all the objects around us, whether relatively hot or relatively cold, contain thermal energy so that their atoms are vibrating.

Suppose that there is a marble statue of a beautiful woman, standing on a table near you at this moment. The atoms of this marble statue are vibrating. The marble is composed largely of calcium, carbon, and oxygen, and each of these different atoms is moving back and forth, though some move faster than others and the patterns of motion are constantly changing.

Usually scientists are apt to think of this thermal motion of atoms as quite random—almost like the motions of a swarm of gnats, which to our eyes, at least, appear to be quite random and have no significant pattern; though it might be dangerous to assert that there is no significance of pattern visible to a gnat's eye. Actually there is a highly significant pattern in the thermal motion of the atoms in the marble statue, although it is such an extremely complex pattern that at first glance, if you could see it, you might think it as random as the motions of the gnat. The significance of the pattern of the tones in the motion of these atoms was first pointed out by the German physicist Peter Debye. Some fifty years ago he showed that one could calculate this pattern from theories of atomic mechanics and predict how much heat it would take in various temperature ranges to warm an object up. Measurements in a number of laboratories verified Debye's theory and it has become one of the cornerstones of the science of thermodynamics.

To us the important point is that, in the interior of the

object, sound and heat are essentially synonomous; and since every object has heat in it, it also has sound in it and is broadcasting a series of tones that are characteristic of its substance and of its shape.

Take the air around you at this moment for example. The air obviously has a good deal of heat in it. The molecules of oxygen and nitrogen are zipping back and forth, bouncing against your skin and exchanging energy with it. Because the air has a temperature not too different from the temperature of the surface of your skin, you are not aware of the air currents that flow by you; but if the air had less heat in it, if its temperature were lower, you might suddenly exclaim, "I feel a draft." Suppose a friend now calls to you through the door of the room. The motions of his vocal chords set up waves in the air. These waves strike not only your eardrum but your skin. You have the sensation of hearing because of the motion set up in your eardrum and, in turn, because of the resultant impulses in your auditory nerve. This particular part of your anatomy, the ear, is built so that it is extremely sensitive to vibrations in the air and conveys the patterns of these vibrations in a form that your brain recognizes as sounds or speech. But because you do not have a similar sensing device in your hand, you get no sensation of sound from your hand when the sound waves strike it. Now it is only because of a certain rhythmic quality in the sound waves that you get the sensation of sound, while the similar but incoherent bombardment of your eardrum by the air molecules produces no sensation. In other words, sound and heat are both motions of the atoms of air, but the one has a coherent rhythmical pattern while the other does not.

Now let's consider the statue again. Dr. Debye pointed out that inside the statue, the waves of vibration are reflected from the surface as they go back and forth and this produces a certain kind of pattern of vibration. Because of this the statue has, in effect, certain tones within it. We do not hear these tones because our ears are not sufficiently sensitive. But the laboratory experiments prove beyond any doubt that these tones are there. What is even more important, the harmony in these tones is directly related to the shape of the statue. That is why it is correct to say that, as the statue sits there silently on your table, it is actually singing its own peculiar, unique song that is the expression in the domain of music of the space form of the statue. The statue's song is part of the inaudible sound that you hear with your magic ears. Thus every object around you has its own particular harmony dependent both on its shape and the materials of which it is made.

The walls of your room are vibrating, the whole building is vibrating with a harmony that is associated in part with its space form or architecture. The architecture of a Gothic cathedral has been called "frozen music." This is more than a poetic image. In truth, the cathedral walls are actually resonating with a vast symphony that in its billions of chords, melodies, and cadenzas has a dynamic form that is the unique equivalent in the domain of music of the static form of the towers, arches, and ornaments in the domain of space.

The music that you hear vibrating within your own body is partly due to heat, but it is due also to all the untold millions of chemical reactions that are taking place in the life process constantly going forward within you. The tones in this symphony of life are associated with the shapes of the combinations of your atoms just as the tones of the statue are associated with its shape; they also depend on the interaction of the atoms with each other and on the pattern of the waves inside the atoms. In order to understand the nature of this music we have to understand a little more about the nature of the atom. So we turn in the next three chapters to see what an atom looks like and to explore the dynamic patterns of the motions of its parts. In this way we can get a deeper insight into the meaning of this mysterious domain of the invisible and the inaudible, where there are many messages waiting to be deciphered that tell us much about the meaning of life and the significance of human existence.

2

The Universe of Particles

U P TO the time of the third decade of our present century, about the year 1923, scientists agreed almost unanimously that everything in our universe was made of particles. There were the particles of familiar electricity, the electrons with negative electric charges that flow through the wires when an electric current is carried. There were the particles, the protons with positive electrical charge, that make up nearly all the mass of the universe. Each proton carried a positive charge of electricity equal in amount to the negative charge on an individual electron. The electrons and protons grouped together to form the electrically neutral atoms. These atoms were thought of as the basic building blocks of the universe. Fifty years ago chemists had recognized 92 different varieties of atoms and it was concluded that by combining these 92 varieties in different proportions and in different ways all the various material substances of our universe were constructed.

This *particle* view of the universe goes back, of course, to the time of ancient Greece. The philosophers of that era debated whether matter could be sliced finer and finer without any limit to the fineness of division, and they concluded that ultimately there must be a limit to such a process. At first, it was only a speculation but with the advent of scientific experimentation more and more evidence piled up, indicating that the ancient Greeks were right in proposing that basically matter was composed of particles that could not be sliced further—particles called atoms, *a-tom* meaning *un-cut-able* (though as we shall see later, the really un-cut-able particles are not the atoms, but the fundamental particles like the electron and proton from which the atoms are composed).

Of course, no one has ever seen an atom by looking through some instrument like a microscope; but it became clear as more and more experiments were carried out that the diameter of an atom was many times less than the wave length (the distance between the crests of the waves) of visible light; and it was concluded that there was no hope of ever seeing an atom for this reason. Yet by the beginning of this century hardly any scientists doubted the existence of the fundamental particles of which atoms were made; and this *particulate* image dominated most of the scientific thinking in the first half of our present century. It is still a strong underlying influence in a great deal of our fundamental scientific logic.

Although scientists were unable to see atoms, they were able to get all kinds of evidence from indirect observations that served as a basis for constructing a picture of an atom. The first detailed atomic picture containing many elements of truth was proposed by the British scientist Lord Rutherford, in collaboration with a young Danish scientist named Niels Bohr. In order to study this Rutherford-Bohr picture of the atom in perspective, let us conduct another "magic" experiment.

Seeing Atoms

Just as we imagined the possibility of vision extended so that we could "see" all kinds of radiation, let us imagine that we can construct a magic microscope that will enable us to see smaller and smaller objects without limit. As I mentioned, we know that there is a real limit to direct visual seeing. However, in constructing images to convey some idea of the structure of particles that are smaller than we can ever see directly, scientists have boldly visualized and drawn pictures of groups of atoms and even of the interior of atoms. Every chemistry book is full of pictures of this sort that are useful in conveying information to the student even though the student must recognize that the picture portrays something that he can never see directly.

Especially within the last twenty or thirty years, scientists have become more deeply aware that there is a limit beyond which it is unwise to push such visual images. As we go further and further into the domain of the very small we begin to find kinds of relations that do not lend themselves directly to visualization. The attempt to visualize frequently tends to make us forget the truth in the basic relationships and overemphasize the other relationships that are actually superficial.

Bearing all this in mind, I want to take you on a little trip inside an atom and give you a picture of what the interior of the atom might look like if we could see it with magic vision. This gives us a series of images that we can examine later to peer a little more deeply into the truth of the meaning of observations of atoms and the way in which some observations have been misinterpreted.

As a start for this journey of exploration into the atom let us imagine that you have a magic microscope that will permit you to see objects no matter how small and to look inside them with a kind of X-ray vision. Suppose that you put your finger under this microscope with the dial first set for low magnification, so that you see the coarse features of the structure of the skin of your finger. You observe the ridges in the skin with the troughs running between them. If you continue to look carefully you will find little wells running down into the interior of your finger, the pores through which you perspire.

Let us now focus the microscope on the wall of one of these pores and turn up the magnification so that it makes this part of your skin appear ten thousand times larger than it really is. Now you will see that the skin is actually made up of little sacs or bags stacked together with their exterior walls touching and adhering to each other. These are the biological *cells,* the unit structures of living matter that (grouped together) make up the whole living organism. In the world of *animate* substance, the cell is the unit of structure playing a role that is comparable to that of the atom, which is the unit of structure of *inanimate* matter. In the third major division of this book we shall spend considerable time examining the features of this cell structure. Right now, let's turn up the magnification and look at the wall of one of these cells. Setting our dial so that we now see the wall enlarged to a million times its actual size, we notice that it is made up of tiny strands of growth woven together into a network. These strands are the fibrous protein. If we examine them carefully we see that each strand consists of a number of finer threads wound around each other in spiral fashion just like the familiar ropes used to hoist sails on a ship or tie the ship to a wharf.

We now turn the magnification up to a hundred million and look at one of these strands of protein rope. We see that the strand is made up of clusters of little balls strung together like beads in a necklace. If you guess that these balls are the atoms, you are correct. You notice that they are of different sizes, some small and some large, and that they hang together very much like clusters of grapes.

Each of these atoms is only about a hundred millionth (1/100,000,000) of a centimeter in diameter. It is impressive to see all of these ciphers in the number that tells how small an atom is, but for most of us this still hardly conveys any real idea of the extreme minuteness of the atom.

Your Own Atoms

One evening I was trying to think of a way of making the small size of the atom vivid to my own class in chemistry.

I thought it might be interesting, first, to calculate the approximate number of atoms in the average human body. I know my own body weight and I know precisely how much each kind of atom weighs. I also know fairly well what percentage I have in my body of each of the different kinds of atoms. So it did not take me long to figure out that I have in my body about five octillion atoms. Writing this number out with digits it is 5,000,000,000,000, 000,000,000,000,000: five followed by twenty-seven zeros.

Five octillion is obviously a very large number. But again we are rather lost when we try to grasp clearly its size. We are unable to visualize distinctly the difference between, say, a trillion or a sextillion or an octillion. While I was meditating on this difficulty, I noticed some dried peas in a dish on one corner of the kitchen table where I was making my calculations, and I began to wonder what five octillion peas would look like. Suppose I actually had five octillion peas; would they cover several acres, several square miles, or perhaps even several counties?

There was an empty medicine bottle about a cubic inch in volume sitting on the table so I counted out a hundred peas and found that they just about filled this bottle. Knowing this, it was fairly easy to calculate that a million peas would fill our household refrigerator, a billion peas would fill our house from cellar to attic, and a trillion peas would fill all the homes in the town of Bel Air, Maryland, near where we were living. Bel Air at that time had a population of about ten thousand and I could make a guess at how many peas it would take to fill all the houses there.

I next calculated that with a quadrillion peas I could come close to filling all the buildings in the city of Baltimore, which was the nearest large metropolis. You see how we are progressing: million, billion, trillion, quadrillion, adding three ciphers at a time.

I saw that I was going to run out of buildings pretty

soon so I searched for another measure for the peas. We were living just south of the Mason-Dixon line, the boundary between Maryland and Pennsylvania. The state of Pennsylvania is roughly rectangular so I decided to take that as my next measure.

Suppose that there is a blizzard over Pennsylvania but instead of snowing snow, it snows peas; and we get the whole state of Pennsylvania covered with a blanket of peas four feet deep. You can imagine what it would be like under these conditions driving out on the Pennsylvania Turnpike, seeing peas banked along the roadside, drifting up against the houses, peas off to the horizon in every direction, peas covering the entire state, from Maryland up to western New York and from New Jersey out to Ohio. Pennsylvania thus covered with peas four feet deep would contain just about a quintillion peas, the next rung on our ladder of ascending numbers.

For the next step we need to imagine this blizzard of peas taking place over all the land areas of the entire earth. We have to have North America, South America, Europe, Asia, and Africa all covered with peas four feet deep. This pea blanket would contain about a sextillion peas.

For our next figure we must go out among the neighboring stars, collect two hundred and fifty planets each about the size of the earth, cover all these planets with peas four feet deep—and then we will have a septillion peas.

Finally, we go out to the farthest reaches of the Milky Way; we collect one million, two hundred and fifty thousand planets each the size of the earth; we cover each of these planets with peas four feet deep; and then, at last, we have the number of peas corresponding to the number of atoms in an average human body. So now perhaps you have some idea of how small an atom is and, incidentally, an idea of how complicated you are.

The Inside of the Atom

In spite of the incredibly small size of the atom, it has been possible in scientific laboratories to make observations with a number of different kinds of instruments and get evidence that shows us pretty conclusively what the inside of the atom might look like if we could see it. To show you this I want to conduct another imaginary experiment. Suppose that I can swallow an Alice-in-Wonderland growing pill that makes me grow with the speed of light; and, of course, any particular atom in my body will grow in proportion. Let's focus our attention on an atom of calcium in the tip of the bone of my forefinger. I now swallow the pill and start shooting up into the air. I shoot through the ceiling, through the roof, up into the sky, past the clouds, through the stratosphere, out past the moon, way out past the sun until I am a little over one hundred and fifty million miles in height. Meanwhile, this atom of calcium in the tip of my finger has swelled from its very small size into a sphere about one hundred yards across. It is now something like a balloon so big that you could put a football field inside it. So imagine that you can step into this gigantic calcium atom and have a look at it. We will suppose that you are wearing magic glasses to enable you to see some of the rapidly moving atomic parts and that you are getting a picture similar to that which Rutherford and Bohr envisioned some fifty years ago.

You may notice first some twenty luminous spheres about the size of basketballs moving in great circles over your head, down at the side and under your feet. These are the electrons, the particles of negative electricity that through their motions create the forces of attraction that bind the atom of calcium to the neighboring atoms of oxygen and phosphorus and thus make up the solid structure of the bone of the finger. As we shall see later, it is somewhat meaningless to talk about the size of an electron because an electron is spread out from its center and thins out gradually. However, for many purposes one can think of an electron diameter and this picture of the electrons as orbiting basketballs gives a fair idea of the kind of atom that Rutherford and Bohr were proposing.

Since these electrons are moving very much like planets, you may ask whether there is anything corresponding to a sun at the center of the atom to hold these planetary electrons in their orbits. Remember you are standing just inside an atom that is approximately one hundred yards across, big enough to hold a football field. Imagine that you look down at the center, which would be like the fifty-yard line on the football field; there at the center you see a tiny whirling point of light that, even on this scale ten trillion times actual size, is still hardly larger than the head of a pin. This is the atomic nucleus, the atomic sun that contains a charge of positive electricity. The attractive force between this positive charge on the nucleus and the negative charges on the circulating planetary electrons holds these electrons in orbit very much as the force of gravity emanating from the sun holds the planets of our solar system in orbit around the solar center. You see what an almost incredible picture of an atom Rutherford and Bohr proposed. Yet the evidence seemed most convincing. They had shot little atomic bullets through atoms and counted the number of times these bullets collided with this nucleus at the center. This proved beyond doubt that the picture was correct, that if an atom were enlarged ten trillion times so that it was one hundred yards across, large enough to hold a football field, the nucleus would still be only of a size varying from the head of a small pin to a small marble, depending upon the particular atom considered. Of course, there is difficulty in defining precisely what we mean by the size of a nucleus just as there is difficulty in defining the size of an electron, but the collision experiments do give us a rough idea of size; so this picture of the nucleus as about the size of the head of a pin, compared with the atom one hundred yards across, shows us their relative sizes.

One of the most striking features of this Rutherford-Bohr picture of the atom was its emptiness. Here we have these few electron basketballs circulating in orbits of about a hundred yards across around this pinhead nucleus at the center, and everything else just empty space. This means that because we are each of us made of atoms, we are nothing much but empty space, too. If I were Superman and could take your body in my hands, squeeze you down, squeeze these atomic holes out of you the way you squeeze the holes out of a sponge, you would get smaller and smaller until, when the last hole was gone, you would be about the size of the smallest speck of dust that you could see lying on a piece of paper. One of my friends remarked that such a squeeze is certainly the ultimate in "reducing." At least, it shows us how insubstantial we really are in terms of the Rutherford-Bohr picture.

This model of the atom with its planetary electrons was based on experiments carried out in Rutherford's laboratory at the University of Cambridge in 1909. This model explained the results of many previous experiments for which there had been no adequate interpretation. Many more experiments were carried out in the decade following the proposal of this model and almost all of the results indicated that there was a great deal of truth in this picture of the atom as a small planetary system.

The Atom as a Machine

In many ways it is fair to say that this explanation of atomic behavior was the culminating triumph of the theories of mechanical action which had been developed by physicists over the previous centuries stretching back to the time of Sir

Isaac Newton and even Galileo. Over these hundreds of years there had been a growing conviction among scientists that if any phenomenon could be explained as mechanical action, then it was really understood. Sir Isaac Newton's famous "laws of mechanics" had enabled the astronomers to calculate with almost unbelievable precision the motions of the planets around the sun. The time of an eclipse could be predicted dozens of years in advance and, when the event took place, the light of the sun faded out exactly at the minute calculated according to Newton's equations. All this showed that the laws of mechanics correctly explained actions that spanned planetary space.

Another great triumph for the theories of mechanics had been the development of the machines that revolutionized the industries of the world during the course of the nineteenth century. An understanding of the way in which force was transmitted by the lever, the wheel, the gear, the axle, and the screw was the most significant single factor that made possible the design of the thousands of varieties of machines that stepped up the production of our world economy by a ratio of increase running into hundreds or even thousands. An understanding of mechanics enabled engineers to *do* things. Now a set of theoretical laws that enabled anyone to accomplish tangible acts, to produce material goods, had a ring of authentic truth. It was natural for scientists to feel that if some phenomenon of nature could be explained in terms of mechanics, this explanation gave us the *true* picture of this phenomenon.

In science, another great triumph of mechanics was the development of the kinetic theory of gases during the latter part of the nineteenth century. The simplest gases like helium and its chemical cousins, neon, argon, and xenon, had been shown by a number of experiments to consist of individual atoms that moved about freely in space with very little attraction for one another. It was postulated, for ex-

ample, that an atom of helium behaved like an extremely
tiny tennis ball or a billiard ball. This tiny elastic sphere
bounced off a wall exactly like a tennis ball bouncing off the
backstop of a tennis court, or a billiard ball rebounding
from the cushion of the billiard table. When one atom collided with another it was exactly like one billiard ball colliding with another, and it appeared that the angle at which
the two atoms parted after the collision could be predicted
and was similar to the angle between two billiard balls that
had just struck one another.

Of course, it was impossible to observe any individual
pair of atoms colliding with each other and rebounding. In
a boxful of gas untold millions of these collisions took place
every second. But just because there were so many atoms
involved having so many collisions with each other, it was
possible, on the basis of statistical theory, to make accurate
predictions of such things as the rate of escape of atoms of
the gas through a pinhole in the side of the box. Such predictions are based on the branch of physics called *statistical
mechanics*. While the more familiar gases like the oxygen
and the nitrogen in the air around us did not consist of
billiard-ball-shaped atoms, but rather of pairs of atoms
linked together like little dumbbells, still the kinetic theory
of gases with the help of the principles of statistical mechanics enabled scientists to make startlingly accurate predictions of behavior that were confirmed by thousands of
experimental observations. Since in the collision of billiard
balls it is the elastic property of the exterior surface of the
ball that is involved in the collision, one could say that this
kinetic theory of gases extended the principles of mechanics
to the *exterior* of the atom. The Rutherford-Bohr theory of
the atom as a planetary system carried this development one
step further and explained the *interior* of the atom in terms
of mechanics.

With such a series of triumphs attributable to these laws

of mechanics, it is understandable that the majority of scientists felt that in these laws they had found the key that unlocked the door through which they could pass to a complete understanding of the entire structure of the universe. There was considerable evidence that not only gases, but liquids and solids had structures that were essentially mechanical in nature. The atoms grouped together in these more condensed forms appeared to obey laws that were part of the whole mechanical theory. With astronomers, physicists, and chemists achieving such triumphs along with the engineers, it is understandable that the biologists wanted to climb on the same bandwagon. They pointed out that obviously living matter was made of atoms, and atoms had now been shown to behave like little machines. The principles of mechanics appeared to be the basis of the behavior of matter all the way from planetary systems thousands of millions of miles in diameter down to atomic planetary systems a hundred millionth of a centimeter in diameter. Wasn't it logical then to believe that the phenomenon of life was really mechanical in nature also? Why should one postulate any special vital force, any *elan vital,* when the concept of familiar mechanical force had explained so much, all the way from planets to planetary electrons?

A Cosmic Carousel

Of course, this led to some rather uncomfortable conclusions. One of the cornerstones of these mechanical principles is the law of cause and effect. This law states that if one knows the exact mechanical situation before an event takes place, then one can predict with absolute certainty the outcome of the event. For example, if one knows the exact weight, shape, and elasticity of two billiard balls, the precise direction in which each is traveling, and the precise speed, then when they collide, in theory one can predict with absolute accuracy the angle between their departing paths and the speed and direction along which each will travel as they go on their separate ways.

Moreover, if these billiard balls are perfectly elastic and rolling on a perfectly smooth table with no loss of energy to the surroundings—a situation comparable to the spherical elastic atoms of gas colliding—then the outcome of a series of collisions can be predicted just as precisely as the outcome of a single collision. In adding together the factors involved in each collision one does not change the essential nature of the picture, one does not lose any predictability with regard to the final result. Thus, in mechanics, one can say that *the whole is equal to the sum of the parts.* Applying these principles to the life process, one then argues that the atom is a little machine; and when atoms are combined to form animate matter, one then has in the organism or even in the human being only a somewhat bigger machine. And since the universe is made of atoms, the universe is just a supermachine. And when one asks about the chain of events as time rolls on, one is forced to conclude that the exact outcome is predictable from a knowledge of the initial beginning, whether one is dealing with a single pair of atoms colliding once, an octillion of atoms constantly interacting as in the human body, or a collection possibly reaching almost to a vintillion of atoms as in the entire universe.

One is forced to conclude (assuming the acceptance of these principles) that if a billion years ago there had been a supernatural, superenormous, supercomplex, supersensitive moving-picture camera that could have photographed the position and velocity of every particle in the universe, then a superintelligence with a supercomputer could have predicted with complete precision that the universe now at this particular instant would be in the exact shape in which we find it. It could have been predicted a billion years ago that you would be sitting right where you are sitting and that you would be reading these exact words in this book at this moment. Putting it another way, this picture of the universe would lead us to believe that it is just a mechanical cosmic carousel and that human beings are only robot punchinellos riding on its mechanical steeds. In such a picture there is no room for the concept of free will, of the human soul or spirit, or of moral or human values that stem from the idea of man as something more than mechanical.

There is no doubt that many scientists at the beginning of this twentieth century professed to believe in this kind of universe. They stated in no uncertain terms that they felt that the phenomenon of life was only physicochemical action obeying the laws of mechanics, with the result always completely predictable from a knowledge of the cause. It is a little remarkable that men who sincerely believed this could still be so possessed with scientific curiosity, could still work such long and late hours in the laboratory and be so eager to publish their findings and win the approval of their fellow scientists. Of course, they could reply that they could not help themselves, that this was just all part of the pattern of life which this inescapable deterministic fate had decreed.

There are still thousands of scientists who maintain pretty much the same position today. This is one of the reasons why I feel that it is important to write this book. I am convinced that a careful examination of the newer developments in chemistry and physics which have taken place since the 1920s force us to view the nature of the universe in terms far different from this deterministic, materialistic picture that was drawn on the basis of the chemistry and physics preceding that date.

The Creaking Machine

At this point, it must be stated that nearly all scientists in the early 1920s recognized that there were still important unexplained features in the picture of the atom as a mechanistic planetary system. Although a number of scientists felt that these difficulties eventually would be solved satisfactorily in terms of the principles of familiar mechanics, others were inclined to keep open minds and not generalize too far until the rest of the picture could be filled in.

One of the most puzzling problems centered on the kinds of orbits in which these planetary electrons moved. According to the laws of mechanics the planets of the solar system might be found moving in orbits giving them any conceivable value of energy of motion. Take the earth, for example. It is moving in an orbit around the sun with a definite pattern of velocity so that about three hundred and sixty-five days are required for the complete trip around the sun. As far as we know from the principles of mechanics, there is no reason why the earth could not move faster or more slowly. Now its energy of motion will be related to its speed by the familiar equation of Newton which states that the kinetic energy of motion is equal to one-half the mass of the moving object multiplied by the square of its speed of motion. Thus, there is nothing to prevent this energy from having any value whatsover. As the mathematicians say, there is a *continuous* range of values that can be assumed by the energy.

If the electrons in the atomic planetary system obeyed these same laws, one would expect that the electrons also could take on any values of energy. But the experiments indicate otherwise. There appear to be only a certain few discreet values of energy which the electrons are permitted to have and so they must move in just a few select orbits. All the other infinitely varied orbits are forbidden to them for some strange reason.

The behavior of the electron differs from that of the planets in another respect. The planets are essentially electrically neutral bodies, while the electrons each possess a negative charge of electricity. When an electrically charged particle undergoes rhythmic motion like the electrons moving around the atomic nucleus in planetary orbit, radiation should be emitted according to the accepted laws of physics deduced on the basis of experiments carried out largely during the 1800s. According to these laws, the electrons should be radiating continuously. Radiation contains energy. When radiation from the electric light strikes your eye there is energy in this radiation that brings about the photochemical action enabling you to see. In the invisible part of the radiation from the electric light that lies in the infrared part of the spectrum, the unseen "light" that we discussed in the previous chapter, you can feel the energy in this radiation as heat. If the electron in revolving around the atomic nucleus like a planet going around the sun continuously gave off this radiation as it should do according to the laws of earlier physics, then it should move more and more slowly and finally, having lost its radiation, plunge into the nucleus under the electrical attraction existing between the electron's negative charge and the positive charge on the nucleus. But this does not happen. All the evidence shows that the electron continues to move round and round the nucleus like a little planet without losing any energy whatsoever until the moment comes—we do not know when or why—the moment of change during which the electron may suddenly emit a burst of light and then drop down to an orbit with lower energy. Under these conditions its orbits are said to be quantized. The electron emits its energy by jumps, *per saltum,* as the Latin phrase goes.

This discontinuous aspect of the behavior of matter was first pointed out by the German physicist Planck in his study of the nature of radiation made at the beginning of the present century. Shortly afterward Einstein showed that when light strikes the surface of a metal and electrons are thereby expelled from the metal (the photoelectric effect), there is a similar quantization.

The scientists prior to 1920 recognized that these were fundamental aspects of the universe. Such facts could not be shoved aside and ignored in trying to draw basic conclusions about the nature of matter, the nature of energy, and the pattern of behavior of the universe, whether one focused one's attention on the atom, on man, or on the total cosmos. So in looking back half a century, I am inclined to think that the scientists who refrained from believing that the universe was conclusively mechanistic were wiser than those who shouted their enthusiasm for the omnipotent rule of mechanics and their disdain for the possibility of the existence of any dynamic structure of the universe, such as one that contained the components of human free will.

At any rate, only fifteen years elapsed between Rutherford's experiments pointing toward a mechanical explanation of the inner nature of the atom and a new series of experiments in the mid-1920s pointing toward a completely new and different picture. It is to this new picture of the atom (first proposed by the French physicist Louis De-Broglie) that we now turn in the next chapter.

3

The Universe of Music

YOU ARE now going to take another imaginary journey into the inside of the atom; but this time you will wear more powerful glasses and take along a magic hearing aid. With your new glasses you will see the atom as it is pictured by science today.

Let's first step up to this magnified calcium atom from the tip of the bone of my forefinger—the atom that you saw in the last chapter as a kind of planetary system with the electrons circling around the atomic nucleus. As you approach this atom, looking through your new and more powerful glasses, you no longer see individual electrons moving in orbit; instead the atom looks like a great ball of luminous fog. As you look more closely, you see that this glowing fog is filled with waves and ripples, much like the ripples you get when you drop a stone into the surface of a pond. You now turn on your magic hearing aid and strange music begins to resound all around you. From the deepest interior of the atom there are shrill tones dozens of octaves above the highest tones of a violin. This is the music of the atomic nucleus, the tiny particle at the center of the atom that was like the sun in the atomic planetary picture discussed in the last chapter. You see it now as the center of this great ball of glowing fog. As you look more closely you note that this center is surrounded by layers where the fog is somewhat more dense, layers very much like the concentric skins of an onion. From these spherical layers you detect certain musical notes that form familiar major and

minor chords related to the chords you hear when a hymn
is played on a church organ.

But as you listen more closely you are aware that this
music of the atom is far more complex than familiar church
music. There are many dissonant chords like those found in
the music of today's modern composers. You hear finer intervals of harmony, quarter tones, eighth tones, and six-
teenth tones such as we find in the music of the Orient. And
beyond these there are even stranger intervals that an expert
in accoustics might recognize as representing some of the
irrational numbers in mathematics.

As you study the shapes of the waves in the fog, you see
that there are many wave patterns not simply spherical but
having designs of complex symmetry. There is one striking
pattern just outside the second spherical shell with pear-
shaped arms, one at the left and one at the right, and two
more, one pointing upward and one pointing downward,
so that these form a cross with the nucleus of the atom at
the center. As you look more closely you see also that there
is a pear-shaped arm pointing toward you and another pointing backward behind the nucleus, so that there is really a
triple cross traced out in three dimensions.

While you have my finger under this enormous magnification, move the focus of your attention from this calcium
atom to some of the neighboring atoms and explore other
parts of the whole structure. Close by the calcium atom you
see atoms of oxygen and atoms of phosphorus. These are also
spheres of rippling fog each with an atomic nucleus at the
center. The oxygen is considerably smaller, having only
eight electrons constituting its fog while the phosphorus
has fifteen electrons. In the picture of the atom that we discussed in the last chapter it would have been relatively easy
to count the number of electrons as they circulated around
the nucleus like planets. But with the electrons appearing
like fog this is not so easy. We see that the atom has lost a

certain aspect of simplicity; the electrons are spread out in these fog patterns that merge into one another and make the identity of the electron difficult to define and any idea of a precise location for an electron almost meaningless.

You notice that there is a bridge of this electron fog joining the phosphorus atom to the several oxygen atoms that surround it. In other words, an electron has changed from a kind of point particle circulating like a planet around the nuclear sun and has become not only a ball of fog enveloping this sun but has spread out into an even more diffuse fog pattern that can embrace two or more atomic centers.

If you observe even more closely you see that the more attenuated parts of these electron-fog balls not only spread out into other neighboring atoms, but also extend far beyond what we had thought of as the original single atom; in fact, not only is my finger one total mass of intermingled atomic fog, my whole body is a mass of these intermingled electron-fog waves.

We thus begin to get a visual image of the unimaginably vast complexity of the human body. In my finger bone there are some quintillions of atoms. Think back to our story about the peas in the last chapter. A quintillion peas would be enough to cover all the land areas of our globe with a pea-blanket four feet thick. Here in this bone of my finger there are more than a quintillion atoms each with its rippling cloud of electrons and the waves from each electron interpenetrating with those of all the rest.

A Symphony of Anatomy

If you listen with your magic hearing aid, you also can get an audible idea of this same complexity, as you become aware of the almost infinite intricacy of the tones that you hear coming from this single finger bone. Listen first to the shrillest soprano tones. These tones come from the nucleus

of each atom. Below these there are somewhat lower tones
coming from the motions of the individual electron clouds.
Still further down the scale there are tones coming from the
synchronous vibration of the nucleus and the cloud that
come from atoms moving toward and away from each other.
There are still lower tones that come from mass movements
of atoms, whole groups of atoms swaying together like the
leaves of a tree moving together in the breeze. And, of
course, you hear the waves in the bone intermingled with
the waves from the other bones and the waves from all the
other parts of the body—the muscles, the nerves, the arteries,
the veins, the blood, the skin, the entire flesh vibrating together. And these tones reflect not only the vibrations due
to the energy of the atomic nuclei, the energy of the atom's
electron, the energy of the total atomic motion; they also
reflect the energy of the impulses in the nerves, the circulation of the blood, the chemical dynamics of the cell metabolism and replication, the total dynamics of the life process. This is the symphony of life, this unimaginably complex tapestry of music that is sounding within us every moment of our life. And this symphony not only is singing
within us, it is actually radiating from us in terms of all the
mysterious waves that these actions set in motion in the space
surrounding our bodies. How far this broadcasting of our
individual symphony penetrates out into the universe in a
significant way, we do not know.

I have often wondered how the poet T. S. Elliot came
to write the lines in the second part of the first poem of his
"Four Quartets":

> The trilling wire in the blood
> Sings below inveterate scars
> And reconciles forgotten wars.
> The dance along the artery
> The circulation of the lymph
> Are figured in the drift of stars.

The Reality of Electron Waves

You may want to stop and ask at this point to what extent the picture I have just drawn is really true. Does the blood trill? Do these electron waves truly exist? Does it make sense to picture the electron as a bundle of waves instead of as a point particle circulating like a planet around the atomic sun?

First of all, we must be clear about what we mean when we say, "Do these waves exist?" The meaning of this word *exist* is the focus of one of the hottest and most protracted debates in philosophy. And these new discoveries in physics which give us this new picture of the atom certainly intensify the need for a clearer understanding of the meaning of this word. We'll talk about that later on. At the moment, I only wish to point out that the validity of the experiments establishing a wave-character for the electron are today beyond question.

Let me describe briefly one crucial experiment. Shortly after the French physicist Louis de Broglie proposed that the electron had this wavelike behavior, two American physicists, C. J. Davisson and L. H. Germer, arranged a device so that a stream of electrons could be bounced off the surface of a crystal. Think of the electrons as resembling tennis balls shot by compressed air out of a tube in rapid succession. The electrons hit the wall of the crystal at an angle which is called the angle of incidence. If the electrons are behaving like particles we expect them to bounce back just like tennis balls bouncing off a wall, with the angle of incidence equal to the angle of reflection at which they leave the surface. On the other hand, if De Broglie's suggestion is correct, that the electrons are more like waves in this experiment than particles, then we might expect the reflection to obey an entirely different law.

The nature of this other kind of "bounce" can be seen

by thinking of the kind of reflection we get when waves come in from the sea and strike against the regularly spaced pilings of a fishing pier. Earlier experiments with X rays indicated that the atoms in the crystal are regularly spaced in a manner similar to the pier pilings. Under these conditions the intensity of the reflected wave depends on the angle at which the waves approach the pier. For certain angles we find a high intensity in the reflected waves and at other angles an intensity approaching zero.

It was exactly this variation in intensity with angle that Davisson and Germer found. And reading the results, all physicists agreed that this established the wave character of the electron beyond any shadow of doubt. Since that initial observation, the experiment has been repeated many times with many variations and there has never been any evidence to raise any doubt about the wave character of the electron under these circumstances.

Another less direct but equally convincing proof of the wave character of the electron comes from the study of the light that an electron emits when it changes from one pattern of motion to another as it is associated with the nucleus of an atom. It is found that there are only certain selected frequencies of light or colors of light emitted. In terms of the picture of the atom as consisting of electrons circulating like planets there was no way to explain why these frequencies and only these frequencies or colors were found. In terms of the electron as a wave pattern there is a simple and direct explanation of the values of these colors that are emitted.

The electron "vibrates" much as a round rubber ball does. The "tones" of the vibrating ball are in turn related to the tones of the violin string and the tones of the drum. We want to explore this relationship in the next division of this book, where we show that the similarities between electron vibrations and music not only help us to understand the nature of the atom but also open up vistas for new kinds of music. The music of the atom has far richer tones and more subtle intricacies of form than have ever been achieved heretofore in our familiar music. But before we explore the nature of this atomic music further, I want to go over briefly some of the questions raised by shifting our concept of the electron in the atom from a *particle* picture to a *wave* picture.

The Electron Delocalized

One of the first and most obvious questions is associated with our difficulty in locating a wave-electron in an atom. Where is an electron if we think of it in wave terms?

What do we mean when we say *where* something is? Usually the meaning is pretty obvious when we are talking about familiar objects in familiar space. Where are you at this moment? You may reply that you are seated in your living room, that your living room has a location that can be described precisely with respect to your house or your apartment building, that the building is located at a definite point on a certain street, that this street is located definitely in a certain part of a certain city and that the location of this city can be specified in terms of latitude and longitude so you know exactly where you are. But if I want to pin you down even more closely and ask you to tell me just how far you are from the north wall of your living room and just how far you are from the east wall of your living room, and if I demand this information with a precision of a hundredth of an inch, then it is necessary to specify more precisely what you mean by *where*. If you say that you are five feet and six inches from the north wall of your living room, are you measuring this distance to the top of your head or to the point of your shoe? Would it be better to determine the center of gravity of your body and then state the measurement of the distance from the north wall in terms of the distance from that wall to your center of gravity? You can see that even with objects of familiar size like your own body it takes a little care to state precisely where an object is located.

Now come back to the problem of the electron and its location with respect to the nucleus of the atom. We can say quite precisely where the nucleus is at any given moment. The nucleus is spherically shaped and we can conceive of a point at its center. Let's forget at the moment that the nucleus too is actually a bundle of waves and let's ignore the ambiguity of location entailed by this fact. If the electron were really a point particle moving around the nucleus and we had a magic camera by which we could photograph the electron, we could say that the electron was at a certain moment of time exactly such-and-such a distance from the nucleus in exactly such-and-such a direction. But if instead of being a particle, the electron is a series of ripples that spread out from the nucleus, decreasing in amplitude and reaching to infinity, how can we say where the electron really is? For we can no longer give it a precise *point* of location. The electron has been delocalized. The precise location no longer can be specified like latitude and longitude. What is even more important, we are no longer nearly as much *concerned* with location as we were in the picture of the electron as a point-particle moving in orbit around the nucleus.

In trying to understand the pattern of behavior of the electron in terms of the point-particle picture, we used the formulas of the so-called *classical* mechanics, that branch of physics that goes back to the time of Sir Isaac Newton and his famous laws of mechanics. To express the effect of these laws on the pattern of behavior of the electron we had to write certain mathematical equations which contained symbols like x, y, and z—symbols that represent the precise location of the electron in space. The energy of the electron was expressed in terms of the motion and speed through space. With a wave the situation is quite different. We are now more interested in the symmetry of the wave pattern and far less concerned with any specification of the points of location of the wave. We have *delocalized* the electron and are less interested in its location than we are in the character of its "shape." We are far more interested in the pitch of the note that it is singing than we are in where it is. We are far more interested in the kind of harmony its tone forms when merged with its neighboring electrons than we are with its space relations in respect to its neighbors. We are more interested in its music than in its motion. We are far less interested in *drawing* a picture to show where the electron is and far more interested in writing the music of its song. The nature of our thinking has shifted from visual images to audio images.

There is also a kind of delocalization in time accompanying this delocalization in space. We can express the space delocalization by saying that a wave has to be spread out in space. Unless it repeats itself as its observer moves through space it can scarcely be said to be a wave, for it will not have wave behavior. It must have a series of wave crests and wave troughs to be really wavelike. And the same relationship is true in *time*. It is the repetition of a pattern of motion, the same kind of up-and-down motion over and over again as time moves on, that enables us to say that we have a wave pattern in time. And we cannot say "when" the wave is any more than we can say "where" the wave is. Suppose we are watching the leaf bobbing up and down on the surface of the pond as the series of waves passes under it. We cannot associate any one bob-up as the time of the wave pattern any more than we can call a bob-up some moments later the time of the wave pattern. So the wave is delocalized in time as well as in space.

The Demechanized Atom

In the last chapter we commented that portraying the atom as particle electrons moving in orbits around the nucleus was the equivalent of saying that the atom is a little machine. We also commented that the shift to the wave picture of the atom forced us to view the atom in a less machinelike perspective. Let us now examine this change in perspective.

We think of the machine in terms of certain general laws and principles. We say that *the whole is equal to the sum of the parts.* We say that the machine will obey the laws of mechanics, and we expect each effect to be predictable from its cause. We say that the machine in its operation has a deterministic pattern of behavior, that if at one time we know completely the position and motion of each part then we can predict with absolute certainty what the position and motion of each part will be at a subsequent time.

You certainly may be puzzled by the wave description that we have given so far and unable to see why the wave atom should be less mechanistic than the planetary-electron atom. One of the differences between the new "wave mechanics" and the *classical* mechanics resting on the laws of Sir Isaac Newton is associated with the principle of *indeterminacy* or *uncertainty* first enunciated by the German physicist Werner Heisenberg. Again I do not want to take the time at this point to go deeply into the nature of this indeterminacy or uncertainty principle. Like the debate on the meaning of the word *exist,* there is still a wide debate on the meaning of the uncertainty principle. The distinguished American physicist Samuel Goudschmidt once remarked to me that he felt there was more uncertainty *about* the uncertainty principle than there was *in* it. I quoted this remark when I was introducing another distinguished physicist, John Von Neumann, to the audience at a meeting of the faculty and students of the "History of Ideas Club" at The Johns Hopkins University some years ago. Von Neumann then began his remarks by saying: "Ladies and gentlemen, tonight I shall speak on the *principle of indeterminacy,* which is sometimes vulgarly referred to as the *uncertainty principle.*" After this (for me) somewhat shattering experience, my self-confidence was partly restored by the appearance a few weeks later of the American translation of one of Heisenberg's books in which reference was made to "The Uncertainty Principle."

In any event, without worrying about its proper name, let me try to state this principle simply. When one of these electron waves interacts with another wave, we cannot predict with exact certainty what the outcome will be. We can only say that there is a certain *probability* that one result will be found, another probability that another result will be found, and still another probability that still another result will be found. We can catalog all the possible results and assign to each the probability that it will be found; but we cannot say with certainty *which* result will be the answer, although we may know that, among all possibilities, the end result must be in a clear-cut fashion one of these possibilities.

One simple example of such a situation is the spinning of a coin. Suppose I have an ordinary fifty-cent piece and stand it on edge on a smooth table top and start it spinning with a flick of my finger. Unless I am endowed with supernatural powers, I cannot predict whether, when it stops spinning, it will be found "heads up" or "tails up." I can be reasonably sure that if I spin the coin a thousand times it will come up "heads" just about half the time and "tails" just about half the time. I can be reasonably sure that it is correct for me to say that the probability of "heads" turning up is 50% and the probability of "tails" turning up is 50%. Since these two probabilities add up to 100% I can say that

I have exhausted the possibilities of outcome for the spin of the coin, that it must come up "heads" or "tails," but that I cannot say with any certainty that it will be surely "heads" (or surely "tails") on any particular spin.

There is always a certain inherent danger in making statistical analyses of this sort. I recall an incident many years ago when I was a postdoctoral fellow at the University of California, living at the Alpha Chi Sigma fraternity house with a group of graduate students. One evening after dinner a few of us were trying to decide which of two moving picture theaters we would visit that evening. Someone suggested that we spin a coin. If it came up "heads" we would go to see the Western movie; if it came up "tails" we would go to see the musical comedy; and someone added facetiously that if it stood on edge, we would stay home and study. The coin was spun and, as it revolved more and more slowly, we suddenly realized that this third alternative was a real possibility. As the last bit of spinning motion ceased, the coin remained standing perfectly stable, on its edge in the middle of the table. As you can surmise, we were much too shaken by this unheard-of event to consider staying home and studying; we went to see the musical comedy.

In the experiment with the spinning coin, any physicist would agree that in the case of *one particular spin* it is impossible in actual practice to predict with certainty whether the coin will fall "heads up" or "tails up." Fifty years ago he would have ascribed this uncertainty in the prediction to insufficient knowledge of the amount and direction of the force applied to start the coin spinning, of the shape and distribution of the mass of the coin, of the elasticity of the coin, of the smoothness and elasticity of the table, and so on. He would have maintained that, given precise knowledge of all the mechanical factors involved and unlimited mathematical skill, an exact prediction could have been made telling with certainty whether the coin would come to rest "heads up," "tails up," or standing on edge: He believed that in theory the effect was completely determined by the cause.

Heisenberg's principle of uncertainty has at least raised some doubts with regard to the validity of this conclusion. Let me quote a passage from *"Matter and Light,"* by Louis de Broglie, the scientist who gave us the first ideas about this strange wave character of the electron. The translation is by W. H. Johnston; the passage below is from a twenty-page excerpt from de Broglie's book that appears in Heisenberg's own book, *"The Physicist's Conception of Nature"*:

"The development of Wave Mechanics, then, has compelled physicists to give an ever wider and wider scope to their concepts. For according to the new principles, the Laws of Nature no longer have the strict character which they bear in classical Physics: phenomena (in other terms) are no longer subject to a rigorous Determinism; they obey only the Laws of Probability. The famous Principle of Uncertainty advanced by Heisenberg gives an exact formulation of this fact. Even the notions of Causality and Individuality have had to undergo a fresh scrutiny, and it seems certain that this major crisis, affecting the guiding principles of our physical concepts, will be the source of philosophical consequences which cannot yet be clearly perceived."

Is there really uncertainty in the outcome of a physical action; or is the uncertainty only in our *ability in theory to predict* the outcome? Some physicists argue that Heisenberg's principle merely defines the limit of the degree of fineness of detail of our knowledge; they maintain that when we try to observe the electron in order to get the knowledge we need to predict with certainty what the electron will do, the very act of observation disturbs the electron and results in a different and unpredictable outcome. They conclude that nature if left to itself undisturbed by peeping scientists will go forward on a completely deterministic course. Thus we see the uncertainty *about* the uncertainty principle!

Ultima Thule

With the particle, generally speaking, we know the answers to the questions implied by the words *where* and *when.* As we can specify the position of a ship by latitude and longitude, we can specify the position of the particle by its coordinates. And we can say the time at which it has this position. We think of the forces that may affect the future pattern of behavior of the particle as forces acting on the particle at the place where it is and at a specified time. Not only is the aspect of the particle localized, the action upon it is localized.

By way of contrast, a wave is delocalized, it is spread out. It reaches through a wide volume of space. By way of contrast, the factors that play the most significant part in determining the future pattern of behavior of the wave are factors frequently found at the far boundaries of the space where the wave exists. Technically speaking, we refer to these as the *boundary conditions* of the wave. The waves of vibration in the violin string are determined by the position of the pegs or ridges that limit the free motion of the string. The pattern of vibration in the drumhead is determined by the shape and location of the rim over which the drumhead is stretched. And similarly, instead of focusing on a point as we do in studying the behavior of a particle, we have to look way out to the boundaries of the wave to study the behavior of the wave. We must journey to *ultima Thule* to discover the secret of *home.*

This brings us to the second important feature of the wave that distinguishes it from the particle, the necessity of studying the aspect of the wave as a *whole.* This is another focus of debate in the study of the underlying philosophy of atomic behavior. It is correct to say, of the atom regarded as a planetary system, that the whole is essentially equal to the sum of the parts. The prediction of the behavior of the whole planetary system is possible if we understand completely the behavior of each of its parts. By way of contrast, is it correct to say that in the atom regarded as a complex of waves the whole is essentially more than the sum of the parts? In the next chapter we shall examine the conflicting opinions of a number of the experts in this field. At the moment I want to quote an outstanding scientist, Hermann Weyl, who spent the latter years of his life with Einstein at the Institute for Advanced Study at Princeton. In his book on the philosophy of mathematics and the natural sciences, in speaking of the atomic pattern of waves, he says that the whole is always more, is capable of a much greater variety of wave states, than the combination of its parts. Again in this same book he says, "In this very radical sense, quantum physics supports the doctrine that *the whole is more than the combination of its parts.*"

If, at the very least, we have to examine the possibility that the whole is more than the sum of the parts, what are these *wholes?* This certainly seems to imply that there is a *whole* that has a claim to existence above and beyond the claims to existence of the individual parts. This brings us right up against the question of how we identify the things we are talking about as existing. This opens the door to any number of deeply probing questions that force us to reconsider some of the ideas that we have taken for granted for so many centuries such as our concept of space with its three dimensions of length, breadth and height and our concept of time as flowing simply along a single course that can be marked off with seconds, minutes, hours, days, years.

To sum it up, if we are to accept the suggestion of de Broglie that many of the patterns of behavior of matter are more properly explained by thinking of matter as waves rather than particles, if we are to accept the correctness of the results from experiments like those of Davisson and Germer, then it appears that we are forced to reexamine a number of the most fundamental concepts in scientific thinking. The observations of astronomy made it clear that the only sensible way to think about the motions of the earth and its sister planets was not in terms of sun and planets revolving around the earth but of the earth as only one of the total group of planets revolving around the sun. Thus took place the Copernican Revolution in scientific thought. We gave up the idea of a flat earth and accepted instead the idea of a spherical planet moving in orbit. It appears that we are now in the midst of another, even more drastic revolution in scientific thought. In the next chapter we want to examine what a number of scientists have said about this revolution and why it is so important today for both scientists and laymen to become aware of the implications of this revolution.

4

The Quest for Meaning

WHAT DO all these strange pictures of the atom add up to? Do they tell us anything that is worth stopping to think about in this hectic world of the 1960s? Well, we have seen that the instruments of science reveal that the inner structure of matter is far different from the outer structure which we observe in the familiar objects that we see and touch in everyday life. We have seen that in exploring this inner structure, science has found that the building blocks of matter, the atoms, do not resemble things like billiard balls reduced to a very small scale, but instead must be described in terms of unfamiliar concepts like probability waves. To sum it up, science has pulled back the curtain and revealed that in the unseen and unheard there is a vast ocean of reality in which the familiar seen, heard, and felt account for only a very small part of the whole.

Having considered these strange sights and sounds we now turn and ask again, "What do they signify?" For a human being who is trying to get a better idea of his own particular role in the great cosmic drama, *what is the meaning of matter?*

In trying to see what any picture means, we should first examine the means by which the picture is seen. When you photograph a landscape, the nature of the image that you get on the film will depend on the nature of the camera lens through which the light passes to make the image. The nature of the picture on your television screen depends on the nature of the circuits through which the electronic impulses

71

pass to produce the picture. And you must remember that
the pictures of the unseen and unheard, which I have described in the previous chapters, actually are revealed to us
through the instruments of science, instruments that in their
nature reflect in turn the nature of science. So we now must
take a brief look at the nature of science in order to understand better the meaning of this picture of matter that
science has drawn for us. And to understand the nature of
science, we have to take a look first at the scientists themselves.

The Nature of Scientists

I think that everyone today recognizes that all scientists
are, to a degree, prejudiced. Perhaps prejudiced is not quite
the right word. I do not mean to imply that scientists will-
fully distort the picture of nature which they draw, or that
they deliberately suppress or ignore part of the truth. I am
just pointing out that the very nature of any scientific observation is influenced by the pattern of ideas in the mind
of the scientist making that observation. To a certain extent
he sees what he wants to see; and what he wants to see is determined by the closely interwoven texture of the ideas
that constitute the mechanism of his scientific thinking.

For several centuries scientific thinking has been dominated by a mechanistic slant. Some people like to call it a
geometric slant. Many of the relations in mechanics are best
expressed in terms of geometry, and in pictures of geometric
lines and curves that display these relations in a visible way.
So to see in proper perspective these geometric lenses
through which most of us look, let us examine some recent
changes in our geometric thinking.

One of the great triumphs of nineteenth century science
was the achievement of more flexibility in geometric thinking. And it is well to remember that there were many growing pains as this increase in flexibility was achieved. One of

the most notable advances stemmed from a suggestion by the mathematician H. G. Grassmann (in the middle of the nineteenth century) that there was no necessity to confine geometric thinking to the three familiar dimensions of length, breadth, and height. He pointed out that the patterns of relations found in common three-dimensional geometry could be extended to imaginary domains of four, five, six, or as many dimensions as one wished. At first his ideas were almost completely ignored by the other mathematicians of his time, so he gave up mathematics and proceeded to work out a second career as a distinguished philologist. Fifty years later, his multidimensional algebra and geometry had become one of the principal cornerstones of the magnificent edifice of twentieth-century mathematics.

This remarkable development of Grassmann's theories is a good example of the way in which both mathematicians and scientists have been questioning with renewed vigor the doctrines that had, for so many years, been accepted as undoubted law. As Whitehead pointed out, the doctrines which best repay critical examination are those that have been longest unquestioned. Speaking especially of the mechanical-geometric concept of nature, he remarked that Newton's cosmology was very easy to understand and very hard to believe. He goes on to say that the doubting of the worth or even the propriety of intellectual inquiry expressed in the question, "Canst thou by searching find out God?" is good Hebrew but bad Greek. Whitehead concludes: "The effort to comprehend the great fact which procures order in the Universe urged Greek thinkers to that culmination when Plato and Aristotle defined the complex of general ideas forming the imperishable origin of Western thought. . . . The world will again sink into the boredom of a drab detail of rational thought unless we retain in the sky some reflection of light from the sun of Hellenism."

One of the glories of this century in which we are living is the Hellenic spirit of free inquiry that has given us these startling new pictures of the nature of matter which I have just been describing. Of course, certain stretches on this path to progress are rather rough. Thus, while all scientists worthy of the name have to accept the new experimental facts of the wave nature of matter, there are many who are reluctant to subscribe to their radical meaning. Take the principle of *indeterminacy,* for example. Is it true that on the atomic scale there is no binding relationship of cause and effect? Does an electron move from one wave-like pattern of vibration to another without any predictable cause? Wouldn't this make the whole universe just one big cosmic Monte Carlo? You may remember Einstein's famous remark to the effect that he did not believe that God played dice with the universe. I have had several highly respected physicists say to me that just given a little time—say five, ten, or maybe even twenty years—physics will be able to look more deeply into the atom and will find that the change from one electron wave pattern to another is just as predictable as the mechanical rebound of two ideal billiard balls when they meet in collision on the perfect billiard table. But isn't this attitude itself evidence of the mechanistic bias in so much of our thinking today?

I can't help but feel that such remarks reflect a subconscious longing for the return to the good old days when the few easily understood principles of mechanics appeared to reign supreme. It was a scientific world of law and order—ideally, at least, a world where nothing ever disobeyed law. And there is a kind of pleasant feeling of security in thinking that this is the kind of world we live in. But as Bertrand Russell says in his book "The Scientific Outlook," "It is not by going backward that we shall find an issue from our troubles." The quest of science is not the quest for security. As Sir James Jeans pointed out, a mechanical model is the only *satisfying* one, but it is not satisfaction that we seek in

science. Hocking remarked in his book "Science and the Idea
of God" that scientists must recognize the dilemma in their
emotional attitudes. Do they wish to dwell in vastness or in
domesticity? Will they choose bold scrutiny or indolent
skepticism? The latter phrase is again from Jeans, who
says that the new physics suggests the unlocked door out of
which we can move to the headland and survey the ocean
of truth beyond our reach.

From these few quotations it is clear that there are many
distinguished scientists who are aware of the necessity of
stopping now and then to ask what science really is. Before
trying myself to answer this question, I want to quote a few
other remarks by other outstanding scientists. No one has
ever discoursed more significantly on the nature of science
than Whitehead. In speaking of the influence of science on
European culture he remarked that "as we move from
Athens to Alexandria we find that the special sciences were
established and learning was stabilized. Literature was replaced by grammar; learning by learned tradition. These
men conventionalized learning but they secured it." Putting
it in another way, Dean Schilling of the Graduate School
of Pennsylvania State University says that as science moves
to conquer new continents of learning, there must be both
pioneers and colonizers. As we try to see the influence of
the slant of scientific thought on the nature of scientific
doctrine, it is essential for us to bear in mind these two
varieties of scientific psychology, that of the pioneers and
that of the colonizers. And to understand the psychology of
scientists, we have to explore their motivation.

What makes scientists tick? Whitehead said that "Belief in exactness is the motivating force in the scientific
method." It is a noble discontent from the sense of criticism
founded on appreciations of beauty, of intellectual distinction, and of duty, the passionate desire for the beautiful result. Again he says, "Science and Art are the consciously de-

termined pursuit of Truth and Beauty." In a little more caustic vein Herman Weyl, an equally great mathematician and philosopher says, "The strict systematical performance of our method consists of a shoving around of men in a chess game—a chess game, indeed, that proves to be rather significant for reality." A less well-known but still distinguished mathematical physicist, Paul Ehrenfest, of the University of Leiden in Holland, once remarked to Professor Hocking that the effort to teach mathematical physics in the present confusion had given him an insight into the Hegelian dialectic, a succession of leaps from one lie to another by way of intermediate falsehood. Norbert Wiener, the applied mathematician of cybernetic fame, reminds us in his book on "The Human Use of Human Beings" that too often scientists are concerned with content, not perfection of form, and that ". . . hash may be very nutritive, but it is not a suitable way to educate the palate of a gourmet."

In this perspective it is clear how deeply one must probe to distinguish truth from prejudice. In our current debate over the significance of the principle of indeterminacy, it is apparent that we are dealing with both factual and emotional components. Is the life process merely physicochemical mechanism? Is a living human being basically just a machine, just a few cogs and wheels in a deterministic universe? Or does determinism truly break down at the atomic level and leave significant room for human free will and a real human spirit? We will examine this question at length later in the book; but we should be aware at this point how closely this question is linked with the meaning of matter. We should also be aware that most of us instinctively view this question with a mind that has been slanted by previous intellectual and emotional conditioning. Of course, we *hope* that the scientific approach to this problem is the least prejudiced. But it is well to scrutinize carefully this so-called scientific method.

The Scientific Method

What is the scientific method? I suppose the shortest definition is comprised in the four words *observation, deduction, generalization, verification.* Putting it in a more expanded way, the scientist makes observations of nature presumably in just as objective a fashion as possible, though admittedly with a certain bias stemming from ideas, conscious or subconscious, about what he is looking for. Then from the raw data of observation, the scientist draws deductions primarily about patterns of relationships that exist within the part of nature he has been studying. Finally, through comparing many such deductions from many observations he arrives at the concept of more generalized patterns of relationships which we call laws. These laws, in turn, suggest ways to make new observations by which the laws can be verified and from which new deductions can be drawn leading to a broader understanding of the old laws or the generalization of new laws.

Dean Schilling has some pertinent comments on all this: "According to prevailing notions, science is an intellectual machine, which, when one turns a crank called 'the scientific method,' inerrantly grinds out final truth with complete accuracy and certainty. This method is alleged to have certain 'steps' which must be followed for success. Its thinking is regarded as exclusively logical and its language is utterly precise and unambiguous. Nothing could be further from the truth. Far from being machinelike, science is a characteristically human enterprise that is intensely personal, as well as social and communal, with all the strengths and weaknesses this implies." Schilling then goes on to repeat the oft-quoted remarks by Professor P. W. Bridgman, the world-renowned authority on high-pressure physics, who taught at Harvard University for many years: "The scientific method as far as it is a method, is nothing more than doing one's damnedest with one's mind, no holds barred. What primarily distinguishes science from other intellectual enterprises in which the right answer has to be obtained is not method but the subject matter."

It is often said that the scientific method is the search for and the verification of hypotheses. Again quoting Schilling: "What is demanded for the hypothesis first of all is that it explain what is known, that it conform to the data in hand. But what this amounts to is the *seeing of a pattern* and this is, in essence, a synthesizing act of the imagination." As Phillip Frank, a noted scholar in the area of the philosophy of science, points out (as quoted again by Schilling): "The main activity of science consists in the invention of symbols from whch our experience can be logically derived. This system is the work of the creative imagination which acts on the basis of our experience. The work of the scientist is probably not fundamentally different from the work of the poet."

The Nature of Knowledge

As you can readily see, there are almost as many definitions of the scientific method as there are scientists. But in all this welter of confusion there are a few points on which everyone agrees. Certainly, one important aspect of scientific activity is the acquisition of knowledge. We observe nature. We ascertain fact. But before we go on to discuss what we do with these facts once we get them, I want to stop for a moment and try to see what a *fact* is. What is knowledge, anyhow?

Sir Julian Huxley has some pertinent comments on the role of knowledge in human affairs. I quote from some pages that he wrote as an introduction to Teilhard de Chardin's "The Phenomenon of Man:" "Knowledge is basic. It is knowledge which enables us to understand the world and ourselves, and to exercise some control or guidance. It sets us in a fruitful and significant relation with the enduring processes of the universe. And, by revealing the possibilities of fulfilment that are still open, it provides an overriding incentive.

"We, mankind, contain the possibilities of the earth's immense future, and can realise more and more of them on condition that we increase our knowledge and our love. That, it seems to me, is the distillation of *The Phenomenon of Man.*"

Now it is clear that by the word *knowledge* we might refer to a great many different kinds of things. Knowledge might mean a newly acquired manual dexterity. Suppose that I take lessons in playing tennis. The teacher gives me certain verbal instructions but reinforces these by a visual demonstration of how to hold the tennis racket and how to hit the ball. I take a lesson once a week for a period of two months, practicing for hours at a time between the lessons. At the end of that time I am a better tennis player. I can beat a number of my opponents who before the lessons were able to beat me. We could say I have acquired a knowledge of tennis that I did not have before, a knowledge that enables me to play the game of tennis better.

To what extent is this knowledge expressible in words? To what extent is it a verbal store of ideas in my mind? To what extent is it only strengthened muscles and new channels of interconnection between muscles that represent instinctive, almost instantaneous response that takes place without any verbalization at all? What is my problem if I try to communicate this knowledge of tennis to someone else?

I think it is clear that the kind of knowledge we are talking about in connection with science is not the knowledge of trained muscles but rather knowledge which can be put into words. Of course, we are using "words" in a very broad sense because so much of scientific knowledge is expressed in numbers, in algebraic symbols, or even in special symbols invented for the specific purpose of forming a pattern that communicates from one scientist to another some particular aspect of knowledge. So the conversion of the fruits of the acts of scientific observation into symbols that can be printed, reproduced, and circulated is a very important aspect of the scientific process.

If the results of scientific observations are to be expressed in words then it is clear that these words must have a previously established meaning. They have to be defined. Thus, in order to have a vocabulary in which to express scientific knowledge we have to start with a series of definitions. But in order to state definitions we again have to have words. How, then, do we build the platform of definitions from which we make our first leap into the ocean of knowledge? The German physicist Max Planck, the father of the quantum theory, puts it this way: Every definition must necessarily rest on some concept that does not call for a definition at all. So there is always this component of the indefinable, the instinctively assumed in all scientific knowledge. An essential part of the kind of inquiry we are making in this book is a continuing return to focus the microscope of our scrutiny again and again on these indefinables.

Another important aspect of scientific knowledge is the component of persistence. If we state a fact about a certain relationship in nature, this fact will have significance only if the relationship in nature continues to be true for a reasonable length of time. Suppose that I am observing a small lizard. I write in my notebook that the lizard is green. If, even before I have finished writing, the lizard has turned yellow, the fact that I have observed a green color loses some significance. Of course, I can then write that I appear to be observing one of those strange living creatures that can change its color to match the environment in which it happens to be located. But if, while I am writing that, the lizard happens to nibble on the leaf of some toxic plant and loses its power to change color, then again my observation is of doubtful significance, unless I am completely aware of all of the things that are going on and significantly extend the scope of my observations and notes. Whitehead remarks that this aspect of knowledge is a part of the positivist doctrine: "An observed persistence of pattern, in the observed succession of natural things, merely description." He goes on to say that it tells us to observe and to describe as simply as we can. This is all we can *know*. Laws are then statements of observed facts. He concludes: "This doctrine dates back to Epicurus, and embodies his appeal to the plain man, away from metaphysics and mathematics. The observed facts of your experience are understandable, and nothing else. *Understanding* means *simplicity of description*."

Meditating on these problems we are, of course, browsing in the philosophical pastures of epistomology, the analysis of the nature of knowledge. Whitehead emphasizes again and again the dichotomy of doctrine that appears both in science and in philosophy—for example, the paradox of the particle and the wave that we discussed in taking our look at the atom and its electrons. Sometimes the electron behaves as if it is a particle, as if it is discrete, a discontinuous part of nature. Sometimes it behaves as if it is a wave, spread out, continuous, even extending throughout the entire universe. The proposal by the Greek philosopher Democritus that our world is constructed of particles was perhaps the first really significant appearance in human thought of this doctrine of discontinuity, the doctrine of the particulate, the doctrine of atomism. Whitehead remarks that when a few centuries ago, scientific thinking really began to mature, "the atomism of Democritus in the Science of Cosmology is replaced by the atomism of Hume in the Science of Epistemology." He warns us that it is just as dangerous to regard knowledge as a structure built of discrete bricks—our *facts*—as it is dangerous to regard matter as merely put together from discrete atoms. Just as we have been forced by the new experiments in physics to recognize that atoms are not discrete objects but rather bundles of waves and that the intermingling of these waves hold the secret of understanding the behavior of corporate matter, so in the structure of knowledge it is in the intermingling of the facts, their effects on the meaning of each other, that knowledge leads to understanding.

Whitehead also warns us that the atomistic way of thinking is deeply imbedded in the traditions of intellect that are almost a physical part of our living. We think of a wall as made of bricks and of each brick as having an identity that has very little to do with the identity of the whole wall. It is common sense to think of the whole as just equal to the sum of its parts. But as Lecomte du Noüy reminds us, common sense is misleading. Whitehead calls it "the deceptive nature of hardheaded clarity." He comes back again and again to the fact that "knowledge is more than sense perception. . . . Perception is consciousness analyzed in respect to those objects selected for emphasis. Consciousness is the acme of emphasis. . . . Direct sense perception depends on the immediate surroundings. Light is the same whether it comes from a nebula or from a lamp. . . . Exclusive reliance on sense perception promotes a false metaphysics . . . the whole body is the true organ of sensing." It is in the whole body of facts, the interconnections of facts, the feedback of facts that we find true knowledge. So keeping in mind these thoughts on the nature of knowledge and maintaining a certain distrust in obvious common-sense conclusions, let us now take a look at the third step in the scientific method which is called the generalization of conclusions drawn from observation, the generalization that is sometimes denoted as scientific law.

a liter, to two liters, or to any other amount. It will still be true that pressure times volume equals a constant when we perform the experiment. The relationship remains invariant under this transformation. We can transform the material from oxygen to nitrogen or to helium, or to a hundred other gases. We still will find wide ranges of values at which our law remains invariant. We can vary the temperature from cold all the way to extreme heat. We still find wide ranges where the law is invariant. We can perform the experiment in New York, London, Cairo, or a million other places. The law still holds. It is invariant under the transformation of latitude and longitude. Presumably it would still be invariant if the experiment were performed on the moon or in the vicinity of the star Alpha Centauri or in the remotest nebular region of the universe. Invariance under transformation establishes the true *reality* of this relationship of pressure and volume.

Scientific law is one of the great concepts of the human intellect. This concept not only forms the backbone of science but illuminates many areas not only of philosophy but of man's thinking and action in all aspects of life. The great philosopher-physicist, Professor Henry Margenau of Yale University, makes a penetrating analysis of scientific law in his classic book "The Nature of Physical Reality." Both there and in his more recent books, he stresses the relationship between law and reality and invariance under transformation.

Let us see where we encounter law and especially the limitation of law in our survey of matter. In the first three chapters we looked particularly at the atom, an example of the infinitesimal aspect of nature. Hermann Weyl has commented that only in the infinitely small may we expect to encounter the elementary and uniform laws. But it is precisely by journeying into the very small that we find limitations of law. Thus, the laws of mechanics apply to the motions of the planets, to the motions of an automobile, to the motions of the very small parts of a watch; but they must be modified if they are to be applied to the almost infinitesimally small parts of the atom. *Also,* they must be modified if they are applied to systems far larger than our planetary system, systems made up of nebulae each containing trillions of stars. At the very small end of the scale we have the modifications embodied in the theories of wave mechanics. At the very large end of the scale we have the modifications embodied in the theory of relativity. So in each of these domains there is an appropriate set of laws, the laws of relativity for the very large, the laws of familiar mechanics for objects of the size that we customarily deal with in engineering, the laws of wave mechanics for the almost infinitesimally small atom. As Whitehead has expressed it, there are layers of order in the universe—the very large superimposed on the familiar size, the familiar size superimposed on the domain of the almost infinitesimally small.

The Limitations of Law

This brings out another important guideline which will be useful to us in our further explorations, namely, that we must seek the *boundaries* of applicability of laws. We must expect that when we move from one domain of size to another, laws may change. And we will see that this applies not only to domains varying in size, actual physical size, but also to domains of observation that vary in length of time. In searching for a better understanding of the place of man in the universe, we want to take a look back toward the beginning of things and a look forward toward the end of things. In looking back as we move from the history of the last few thousand years, back to the times of ancient Greece, back to a million years ago and the dawn of creatures barely recognizable as humans, and back to some billions of years ago where we see the rays of the dawn of creation, we must continually ask the question, "Do our familiar laws and our familiar concepts still apply as we extend this domain of time?" And in asking questions about the future of the human race and the ultimate meaning of the future of time, we are forced into the same perspective. In other words, as we shift from questions about man's place in human history to man's destiny in eternity, we must keep in mind at every moment the limitations on the extension of law.

To put it another way, we are trying to *extrapolate* knowledge into areas where we are at present ignorant. Hermann Weyl reminds us of the thoughts of Nicolaus Cusanus in his discourse on the nature of ignorance, *De Docta Ignorantia:* " . . . if the transcendental is accessible to us only through the medium of images and symbols, let the symbols at least be as distinct and unambiguous as mathematics will permit." Of course, when we begin to talk about clarity and the avoidance of ambiguity, we are again getting into the area where we have to keep asking what really is common sense. We mustn't think that things are true just because they are simple; they may appear to be simple just because they are familiar.

Of course, there is no doubt that the principle of simplicity is a valuable guide. If I assert that the stars as they appear to you on a clear night are really just torches held in the sky by a host of invisible angels, you cannot prove that I am wrong. In reply to every astronomical observation that you quote against my point of view, I can assert that the telescope merely gives a better view of the torch and doesn't show the angel. I can argue that as the planet Venus moves across the sky it is being carried by an angel that prefers to fly on this particular course rather than to remain marching with the rest of the host as the angels carrying the fixed stars do. As opposed to my angelic arguments the explanation of the motions of the planets in terms of Newton's laws and the principle of gravitation is almost overwhelming in its appeal because of its simplicity. This argument for choosing the simple rather than the complex explanation for a phenomenon is called "Occam's parsimony," or "Occam's razor."

There is no question that the principle of simplicity is a most valuable guide as one tries to construct and extend the peninsulas of knowledge farther and farther into the ocean of the unknown. Not only does it make sense to accept the simple explanation as probably closer to the truth than the complicated explanation; what is even more important, the simple explanation is a much more usable tool with which to build the structure of knowledge farther into the unknown. On the other hand, as wave mechanics has demonstrated so forcefully, it is not always easy to ascertain which of two approaches to a problem is the simpler. Solving a problem in the behavior of atoms can seem to be far more complex in terms of wave mechanics than in terms of Newton's particle mechanics at first sight. But it has been demonstrated beyond any shadow of doubt that the laws of wave mechanics bring hundreds of times more facts into a consistent pattern of relationships than the laws of Newton's mechanics are able to do when one is dealing with observations of atomic behavior.

The Nature of Identity

I am afraid that this small excursion we have made into some of the philosophical problems in science may be a little confusing to you at this stage of your familiarity with atomic physics, and I think that we ought to get back to the discussion of some of the experimental facts as soon as possible. However, I want to mention just a few of the other problems we are going to encounter in our thinking, so that you will keep in mind some of the questions we ought to ask in order to be sure that we are keeping our thinking logical and meaningful.

One of the more startling aspects of these new pictures of the atom revolves around the concept of identity. Suppose I am in a poolroom and I walk up to the pool table and there are three billiard balls lying on the table. I see the three balls at once. Or, I can shift my gaze to look at the one on the left first, then at the one in the middle, and finally, at the ball on the right. They may be identical in size, shape, color, and every other respect. But the fact of their location, one on the left, one on the right, and one in the middle, makes it possible for me to talk about them individually and unambiguously, designating and identifying each ball by its location. Now a friend comes up to the table with a cue and starts knocking the balls around. If I have a most acute power of observation and power of memory I may be able to follow the course of motion of each ball and still be able to identify each ball properly; but if the game continues for long it will be extremely difficult to say with certainty which ball is which. Of course, you can say that even though an observer loses track of the identity of the balls, there is no question that the identity in principle is maintained. In fact, one can always imagine a motion picture camera sufficiently fast to record instant by instant the position of each ball, so that in viewing the picture of the motions slowly enough one can always follow the movement of each ball and be sure of its identity.

Let's try another experiment: let's consider two billiard balls, one at the left end of the table and one at the right. I take up the position with my cue behind the left ball and you do the same on the right. We each strike a ball, the two balls roll toward each other, they collide at the middle of the table and each returns, rolling along precisely the same track backward that it followed when it went toward the middle of the table. There is absolutely no question about the identity of the two balls. I have my original ball, you have your original ball.

Now, let's go outside the poolroom to a pond nearby. You stand at one end of the pond and I stand at the other. Each of us drops a large stone in at the same time, creating a wave that moves toward the center of the pond. When my wave and your wave reach the middle they merge momentarily, but then a wave continues back toward me and one continues back toward you. Am I getting back my original wave in the same way that I got back my original billiard ball when the two collided? Are you getting back your original wave in the same way that you got back your original billiard ball? I think you can see that there is a distinct difference between the two experiments. The two billiard balls rebounded but in the case of the waves it is difficult to say whether one wave was reflected from the other or whether one penetrated the other so that at the end you got my wave and I got your wave.

All this points to the fact that with waves, it is much more difficult to establish identity than it is with billiard balls. This becomes particularly true in the case of atomic waves and atomic particles. We shall see later that it just does not make sense to talk about the identity of individual electrons or the identity of individual atoms in many instances. We have to establish identity by different means.

Whitehead has a number of comments to make on the importance of the concept of identity, not only in philosophy but in everyday thinking. For example, when we come to consider the meaning of life in terms of the individual human being, Whitehead points out: "Yet personal unity is an inescapable fact. . . . Any philosophy must provide some doctrine of personal identity." From the atomic point of view an individual with five octillion atoms in his body is one of the miracles of nature. Every time you breathe out you expel some quadrillion atoms from your body; every time you breathe in you add another quadrillion. Your existence is one fantastically colossal flux of matter and it is an almost unbelievable miracle to see personal unity "maintaining it-self amid the welter of circumstance."

Does this personal unity persist beyond the limits of the personal life here on earth? As Reinhold Niebuhr points out, individuality would be destroyed by undifferentiated eternity. If we are to examine the bearing that scientific evidence has on the possibility of an individuality that tran-scends mortality, we must scrutinize carefully the concept of identity in modern science.

This brings us right up against the widely debated question of the relation of the whole to its parts. At one extreme we have the philosopher and the scientist who say that reality resides only in the fundamental particles of which the universe is constructed. To this school of thought it is meaningless to say that man is any more than a little machine made up of these individual bits of reality. When life terminates, dust returns to dust and the particles go on their way in new combinations, but the illusory whole that was the personality has vanished forever. At the other ex-treme of this spectrum there are philosophers who maintain that it is only in the wholes that we have reality. Even with respect to matter it has been asserted that atoms exist only in the laboratory when under very artificial conditions (as in the beam of the molecular mass spectrograph) we break matter up into individual atoms with controllable paths and make atoms really exist. These scientists maintain that the atom's existence in a mass of matter is just as illusory as the human personality is claimed to be by the atomist thinkers.

How one feels about such questions is perhaps deter-mined by the extent to which one emphasizes analysis or synthesis in thinking. There is an amusing scene in Goethe's great drama of the life of Faust where Mephistopheles is seated at Doctor Faust's desk while the latter is presumably packing his bag for their departure from the university on

a trip to explore the world. A student enters to get some
advice on his choice of courses and mistakes the Devil for
the professor. (I have often thought that I would almost be
willing to sell my own soul to the Devil if he would be
willing to take over some of the advising problems with
which I have to cope at the beginning of the academic
term!) In the course of their discussion, the talk gets around
to chemistry, my own field, and Mephistopheles comments:

"Analyze things says Chemistry
Makes an ass of itself and doesn't know why."

Speaking of the whole area of scholarship, Mephistopheles' meditations run like this:

"Truly the fabric of mental fleece
Resembles a weaver's masterpiece,
Where a thousand threads one treadle throws,
Where fly the shuttles hither and thither,
Unseen the threads are knit together,
And an infinite combination grows.
Then, the philosopher steps in
And shows, no otherwise it could have been:
The first was so, the second so
Therefore the third and fourth are so;
Were not the first and second, then
The third and fourth had never been.
The scholars are everywhere believers
But never succeed in being weavers.
He who would study organic existence,
First drives out the soul with rigid persistence;
Then the parts in his hand he may hold and class,
But the spiritual link is lost, alas!"

Does science point toward and not away from the existence of "spiritual links"? As we shall see in delving more
and more deeply into the nature of matter, the new wave
perspective shifts the emphasis strongly from parts to

wholes, an emphasis of links. It is sad that Goethe did not live to see this. I quoted Hermann Weyl earlier, pointing out that we must recognize in atomic physics that the whole is more than the sum of the parts. Whitehead also emphasizes this: "But in all analysis there is one supreme factor which is apt to be omitted, namely, the mode of togetherness." In a sense it is the old problem of reconciling unity and diversity, as the distinguished theologian W. T. Stace points out in his discussion of the doctrine of the Trinity in his book called "Time and Eternity."

Of course, it is all very well to talk of reality residing in the wholes, but is this a perspective in which we can do constructive reasoning? When we talk about parts instead of wholes we have the advantage of being able to count the parts and set up quantitative laws in terms of numbers. Assemblages of parts can be combined with the help of the laws of arithmetic. For the study of wholes we need an algebra of form rather than an arithmetic of numbers. So we have to study the relations that restrict putting things together and turn to *combinatorial analysis.*

Coming back to the atom, we are more and more aware that we are dealing here with dynamic forms and that we have to study the relations of forms to one another. We have to see how these forms combine. Because we are dealing with vibrating wave patterns, these forms are dynamic, and this means that we are involved in a kind of combinatorial analysis far different from that involved in combining static geometric forms (though the relations in the latter process do have a most significant bearing on the combination of dynamic forms.)

As you can well imagine, the mathematical representation of these dynamic forms gets us into some very complicated and obscure areas of algebra. I certainly do not want to bombard you with pages of intricate differential equations. But there are certain aspects of this mathematical ap-

proach that can be put rather simply into words. At this
point I want to mention a few of these that we will discuss
particularly in terms of musical analogies.

First of all, we will want to strike right at one of the
most revered of our mental concepts, our existence in three-
dimensional space. Do we have to maintain that reality is
embodied only in three-dimensional forms? Is space *really*
just three-dimensional? And is time *really* one-dimensional?
I like to recall the remark of the Spanish philosopher Ortega y Gasset, who said that conventional space and time are
the stupid aspects of existence. We actually find in dealing
with many of these problems of dynamic form that it is far
simpler to represent them mathematically by employing
spaces of *more* than three dimensions. Physicists and chemists accept the use of many dimensions in space in their
analyses without a qualm. But raise the question of whether
we really *exist* in three-dimensional space or in these highly
useful multidimensional spaces, and you will find many a
head shaking in skepticism. It is an unbelievable departure
from common sense, they say, even to hint that we really
may have not three but perhaps more than three octillion
dimensions. Well, I agree that this is a pretty revolutionary
suggestion but I still maintain that it should not be rejected
until we have summed up the total score, based on the most
objective approach we can make to the problem of existence
with the help of every bit of knowledge available from
science today.

So to me this is the meaning of matter. Our new discoveries reveal these unexpected aspects of the nature of
matter and point emphatically to the need for revising our
basic concepts of what is real. They tell us that reality lies
not in the tangible but in the intangible, in the unseen and
the unheard. We have to think about the behavior of atoms
in terms of *dynamic form.*

The dynamic aspect of these forms consists largely of

vibration with harmonic relations that are in many ways similar to the harmonic relations found in music. It is for this reason that I want to turn now in the next major section of the book to a discussion of music and see how our ideas derived from music can help us in understanding the music of the atom and of the symphony of life.

Part II
The Nature of Music

FIGURE I

BOWSTRING
vibrating up and down from
convex to concave positions

5

The Music of the String

W HAT IS the historical origin of music? We do not know. Perhaps, back in the dawn of human existence, some caveman fashioned a hunter's bow from a willow branch and a deer thong; and one day as he put an arrow on the bow and let it fly, suddenly he became aware of the "twang" from the bowstring. Perhaps one afternoon when he went fishing, he left the bow back at the cave and his children played with it and plucked it as they chanted primitive doggerel. We do not know how man first started making music; but we do know that the meager historical evidence points to the *string* as the first instrument in man's earliest exploration of the structure of music; and we know that the name of Pythagoras, early philosopher of Greece, is associated with the first clear historical statement of the foundations of musical theory, based on experiments with strings. It is a matter of record that the Greeks of Pythagoras' time carried out a systematic study of the relations between the pitch of the tone and the length of the string producing it.

The hunter's bow and Pythagoras' simple lyre are both examples of a class of musical instruments having a single stretched string or monochord. When plucked, such a string gives out a tone of definite pitch. This pitch depends primarily on the length of the string, its heaviness, and the tension under which it is stretched. The longer the string, the lower the tone sinks into the bass range; and, of course, the shorter the string, the higher the tone rises into the soprano. Similarly, lightening the weight of the string makes the tone more shrill, and stretching the string tighter moves the tone toward the upper ranges also.

Twenty-five hundred years ago there were no instruments for accurate measurement of the tension or even of the heaviness of a string; but *length* could be determined precisely with a graduated stick or ruler. So it was in the study of the relation of the pitch of the tone to the length of the string that the first advance was made in discovering the laws of music. In order to get a clear picture of these laws, we need a slow-motion view of the twanging string just as we used imaginary slow-motion to study the vibrating atom. We want to see the pattern of the string's vibration just as we observed the patterns of the atom's vibration.

The string has the simplest forms of vibration to be found associated with any kind of rhythmic motion. Once we are familiar with these forms, we can study the vibrating patterns in the atom in detail and it will be easy to recognize, figuratively speaking, when the atom is singing *do, re, mi, fa,* or *sol*; and we can see how atoms can sing a quartet blending their vibrations together in close chemical harmony, which might sound a lot like the "barbershop" variety if we could actually listen to it.

String Harmonic Motion

Let's imagine that we have a hunter's bow like that pictured in Figure 1. The string is stretched at constant tension and is uniform throughout its length with respect to thickness and weight. Now hold the bow horizontal and pluck the string exactly at the midpoint; listen carefully to the tone given out. After the first sharp twang as the string snaps back from your finger, you hear a humming tone. This is fairly loud at first but then gradually dies away, lapsing after a few seconds into silence. Notice that this tone has a constant pitch; as it hums it does not go up the scale like a fire siren shrieking higher and higher. And, as the string gives out this tone of constant pitch, you can look at the string and see it as a blurred image, especially indistinct near the center, because it is moving most rapidly at this point.

Now let's make a bow with a string exactly one yard long and tuned to the pitch of middle C. We go into a darkened laboratory room where we can illuminate the string by the light from a lamp that is flashing rapidly, with a steady rhythm controlled electronically so that it is just a little faster than the vibration of the bowstring. Under these conditions you see the movements of the bowstring in "slow motion." The action looks exactly like that in a moving picture when the film is run through the projector very slowly and, for example, one sees a girl take a high dive and glide gently down through the air and gradually disappear into the water.

Observing the vibrating bow with this pulsating light, we notice that the string rises and falls in a steady rhythm. From the horizontal position where it is a straight line from one tip of the bow to the other, it rises forming an arch, moving more and more slowly until it pauses momentarily in the position where it makes an arch. Then the center sinks more and more rapidly, passing through the straight-line position until it makes an *inverted* arch like the trough of a wave. When the plucked string is surrounded by air, its motion continues up and down, up and down, for several seconds but with diminishing amplitude, until finally it settles down to the motionless horizontal position.

We can eliminate this rapid cessation of motion by putting the bow in a large glass vacuum jar where the air no longer absorbs the energy of its motion. Under these conditions it will remain vibrating for a much longer period and we have more time to study it carefully. Since our bow is tuned to middle C (scientific pitch) we find that the string vibrates up and down exactly 256 times per second. In

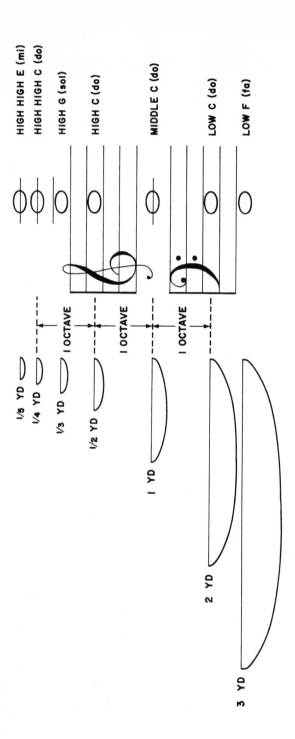

FIGURE 2

SHORT and LONG BOW TONES

Figure 2 this bow is shown at the center along with the note of middle C on a musical staff.

Now let's make a bow two yards long, twice as long as the one we have just been studying. We use a string of precisely the same weight per unit length and stretch it to precisely the same tension that we had in our one-yard bow. Now we pluck this two-yard bow and find that it sounds a note exactly one octave lower than the original bow; that is, it sounds the note of low C as shown on the bass staff. We count the number of vibrations per second and find that it is moving 128 vibrations per second, or just half the number we had with our original bow. So we draw our first quantitative conclusion: *Doubling the length of the string cuts the frequency of vibration in half.*

If we repeat this experiment with a string three yards long, we find that this relationship of inverse proportionality continues to hold. Trebling the length of the string cuts the frequency to a third of its original value. The same relationship is true if we use strings 1/2, 1/3, 1/4, and 1/5 of a yard long. Halving the length of the string doubles the frequency of vibration; quartering the length of the string quadruples the frequency of vibration, and so on. What is even more important, in these experiments we establish notes of a musical scale, the tones which seem to bear the closest "family" relation to our original tone of middle C. The illustration shows the notes of the scale that are given out by these different bowstrings. They cover a wide range of pitch from low bass to high soprano.

The early experimenters with music felt as we do that among all these notes, those having the octave ratios to the original note are its closest relatives, its brothers. Some genius then thought of the possibility of dropping the note of high G by an octave and high-high E by two octaves, producing the major triad *chord,* as shown in Figure 3. These three tones have the simplest and most closely related

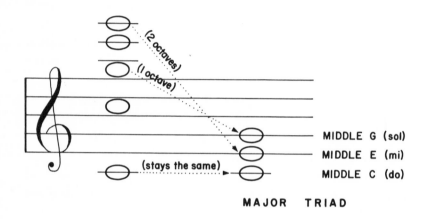

MAJOR TRIAD

FIGURE 3

ORIGIN of the MAJOR TRIAD

harmony. They are the first cousins of middle C. If we call our original note of middle C by the name *do,* we now have the chord *do-mi-sol.*

It was a great day in the development of man's sense of tonal beauty when he first heard these harmonious sounds.

Now it takes only a short leap of logic to pass from the lowering of the high tones to the raising of the low tones to produce another major triad, *fa-la-do,* as shown in Figure 4. We build a major triad on *fa,* raise the F and the A by an octave, and we have a scale of *do-mi-fa-sol-la-do. Fa* and *la* are the second cousins of *do.*

If we sing this scale, we are struck immediately by the presence of two gaps, one between *do* and *mi,* and one between *la* and *do.* Since our progress has been made so far by selecting related tones, we can argue that we should take the notes of the other major triad that is most closely related to our original *do-mi-sol.* This is, of course, the major triad constructed with *sol* as its lowest note, the triad *sol-ti-re.* Accepting these notes into our scale, as a second set of second cousins, we now have our complete familiar major scale: *do-re-mi-fa-sol-la-ti-do,* as shown in Figure 4.

In Figure 5 these notes are shown with the ratio of the frequency to that of middle C written above each note. Recall that we have derived all these notes by altering our string lengths in the ratio of simple integral numbers. We can show just how we have shifted the frequency to get each note by writing the whole numbers in to form a fraction. When we go up an octave we put a 2 in the numerator; when we go down an octave we put a 2 in the denominator. When we shift *up* to the note of the string that has one third the length of the original, we put a 3 in the numerator; when we drop a note to the tone produced by a string three times as long, we put a 3 in the denominator, and so on. The line of fractions below the notes thus shows how the notes are derived from the simple prime number ratios of 1, 2, 3, and 5. (A prime number is, of course, a number that can only be divided by itself and 1 without leaving a remainder.) In forming the notes of the scale in this way we have exhausted every possible combination that we can write with 1, 2, 3, and 5 in the numerator, and with 1, 2, and 3 in the denominator to give a note lying between *do* and high *do*. It is this mathematical fact that makes these notes and only these notes members of this closeknit family of "numerical brothers and cousins." When you think of the complex mechanical-neuro-psychic chain by which we perceive music, it is amazing that we recognize and find such beauty in the tones and combinations of tones that represent these prime-number ratios. I hope to show you how this fact suggests a completely new basis for the reality of beauty, the reality of the intangible.

It was only after centuries of musical experimentation that this particular prime-number scale was worked out in its entirety. It is called the scale of *just-intonation.* Many other scales constructed on other principles were tried; some are still in use in various parts of the world. However, in the music of our western culture this scale of just-intonation appears to embody the relationships that guide those musicians like singers and violinists who have complete control over the frequency of the tones that they produce.

In instruments like the piano and pipe organ other scale problems are encountered. In order to transpose from key to key without producing discordant off-pitch tones, it is necessary to adopt a scale of tuning that differs slightly from that of just-intonation. This other scale is commonly constructed by dividing the interval from *do* to high *do* into twelve equal parts. This yields the notes that are sounded by both the white keys and the black keys of the piano or pipe-organ keyboard. The great composer and organist Johann Sebastian Bach was one of the early advocates of this *well-tempered* scale and wrote the famous

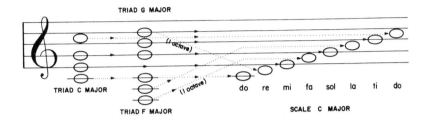

TRIAD G MAJOR

(1 octave)

TRIAD C MAJOR

(1 octave)

TRIAD F MAJOR

do   re   mi   fa   sol   la   ti   do

SCALE C MAJOR

FIGURE 4

ORIGIN of the C MAJOR SCALE

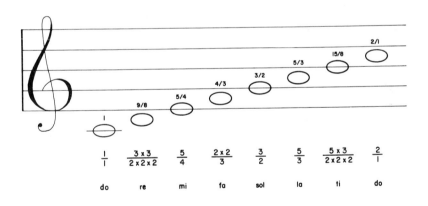

2/1

15/8

5/3

3/2

4/3

5/4

9/8

I

$\dfrac{1}{1}$ $\dfrac{3 \times 3}{2 \times 2 \times 2}$ $\dfrac{5}{4}$ $\dfrac{2 \times 2}{3}$ $\dfrac{3}{2}$ $\dfrac{5}{3}$ $\dfrac{5 \times 3}{2 \times 2 \times 2}$ $\dfrac{2}{1}$

do   re   mi   fa   sol   la   ti   do

FIGURE 5

TONE RATIO to MIDDLE C

Forty-eight Preludes and Fugues to promote its use. Without exploring other parts of this fascinating scale aspect of music, I want to go on to show you how many of these notes of the scale can be produced from a single string merely by plucking it carefully at various points. The tones made in this way are called the overtones of the string.

String Overtones

At some time after curious individuals started playing with stretched strings and made music with them, someone discovered that it is possible to get different tones from a single string even though the string keeps a constant length and is maintained at a constant tension. This is done by plucking this string lightly at different points along its length. Let's try this with the bowstring in the darkened room equipped with the flashing light. Actually, this is not an easy experiment; I want to emphasize here the result that one gets under ideal conditions, without taking time to discuss the difficulties inherent in the procedure.

As a start you take the bowstring one yard in length and pluck it at the center, as shown in Figure 6. As you saw previously, under these conditions the string gives out the note of middle C and rises, forming a single arch, and then falls to form a single trough. This is called the *fundamental.*

After the string has quieted down, pluck it, not at the center, but halfway between the center and the peg at the end of the strings, as shown in the second line from the bottom in Figure 6. Now you hear a tone that matches high C on the piano keyboard. You look at the string with the flashing light and find that there is a new pattern of vibration. The point at the center of the string does not rise or fall but stays essentially motionless. The left half of the string, where you plucked it, is bowed upward to form an arch, while the right half is bowed downward to form a trough. As you watch, the arch falls while the trough rises.

The string goes through the straight position and then the pattern is reversed; there is a trough on the left and an arch on the right. Thus the two halves of the string go up and down like the opposite ends of a seesaw, the left rising while the right falls, then the left falling while the right rises. Since the string is one yard long, the left half obviously must be half a yard long. It is the same length as the bowstring in our first series of experiments that gave out the note of high C; so it is not surprising to find that in this seesaw pattern the one-yard string gives out the note of high C. In other words, without altering its length, its tension, or its heaviness, we can make this one-yard string give out a different tone merely by setting it in a different pattern of motion.

This new tone (high C) is called an overtone of the original fundamental tone of middle C. It is only one of an overtone series, a large collection of tones which the string can be made to sound by plucking it at various points. The drawings in Figure 4 show the modes of motion that sound the fundamental and the first four overtones of the one-yard string. You will find that these tones are those we obtained by taking strings 1/2, 1/3, 1/4, and 1/5 yard long. So the overtones provide us with the cornerstone of the musical scale.

In an actual experiment the string always sounds all of its overtones to a certain extent. By plucking the string at various points we can give a certain tone a greater intensity, but we never can produce an absolutely pure single tone; these overtones present in varying amounts give the tone its timbre or quality. It is also interesting to remember that because of its thermal energy, the string is continually sounding all its overtones all the time, though we never hear these because of their low intensity. Thus a violin, lying apparently still on the table, is in truth always humming its overtones.

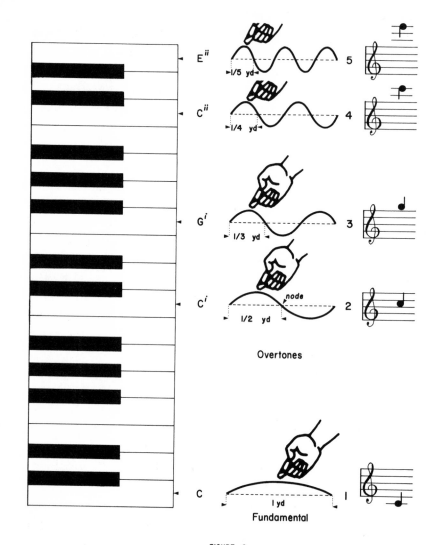

FIGURE 6

THE SHAPE of a STRING vibrating in its Fundamental and Overtones

The arches and troughs in the motion of the string are called collectively *loops*. In the *fundamental* motion at middle C, there is one loop, in the seesaw motion at high C there are two loops, in the motion at high G there are three loops, and so on. The number of loops is called the *quantum* number of the string's vibration. Through these numbers we can relate the motions of the string and the associated notes of the scale directly with the vibrations of the atom. The points of no motion between the loops are called *nodes*.

Quantization

The string illustrates in its simplest form the process of *quantization*. By this I mean that the *natural* ways in which the string can vibrate are limited; the frequencies of the overtones form a limited series of numbers. All other frequencies of vibration for the stretched string are impossible as steady, sustained, unforced vibrations. When out of a total continuous series of numbers only certain specific numbers are associated with a process, we say that this process is *quantized*. The quantized behavior of the atom was discussed in Chapters II and III.

To illustrate the meaning of quantization, we ask the question, "Can the string vibrate with *one and a half loops in its pattern?*" Recalling the illustration that shows the modes of vibration associated with the overtones, we remember that, in the fundamental vibration which sounds middle C, the string vibrates up and down with *one* loop, forming *one* arch when it moves up and *one* trough when it moves down. In the first overtone, that of the octave, the string vibrates with *two* loops, an arch up and a trough down, which keep changing places in a seesaw motion. But why can we not have a vibration with one and a half loops? The answer lies in the conditions we impose in order to make the string vibrate. We peg the string down at each end. This is done in the case of the bow by fastening the string at each end to the bent bow, which put it under tension. In the violin it is done by having the string attached at each end to pegs that are fastened firmly in the main body of the violin. The same is true of the piano string. The string forms these loops as it vibrates, because it is *in motion*. At every point in the loop, we see the blur because the string is *moving*. To get one and a half loops we would have to have the *end* of the string moving; but that is exactly where it is pegged and cannot move. We thus see that a motion involving a fractional number of loops is by the very nature of our arrangement impossible. We cannot have the end of the string fixed to give it tension, and moving at the same time. We cannot eat our cake and have it too. Of course, we could imagine a very intricate apparatus where one end of the string was attached to a moving arm that both kept the string under tension and also went back and forth at exactly the frequency we wanted that end of the string to move—but mechanically, this would be like having the string pegged further along; it would be the equivalent of two loops and not a true *independent* vibration with one and a half loops.

These conditions of having the ends of the string pegged and motionless are called *boundary* conditions, an aspect of motion that we have mentioned before. We shall see that boundary conditions are one of the most important ingredients in the whole picture of dynamic form. Music is really dynamic form; it arises from and is composed of forms that vary regularly in time. Whether we regard music as the actual motions of the string or the motions of the molecules of the air as they convey the sounds to our ears, it is clear that we are dealing with forms that are rhythmic. Since atoms now appear to have wave characteristics that are rhythmic, a knowledge of the dynamic forms of music can help us in understanding the dynamic forms of the atom.

6

The Music of the Drum

IKE THE origin of stringed instruments, the origin of the drum is concealed in the mists of prehistory. Just as man's first awareness of the music of the string may have come from the twang of the bow when an arrow sped on its way, the first awareness of the music of the drum may have come from the "bong" when that same arrow hit a membrane of skin stretched on a hoop to form a primitive shield. We can understand why the "bong" tone produced under these circumstances might arouse emotion in the breast of the man holding the shield. At any rate, at some time back in the Stone Age or even earlier, man discovered that emotions could be stimulated by beating on a stretched skin, especially if it lay over a resonating cavity. Ever since that time drums have played an important role in the production of music.

Probably the earliest systematic study of the vibrations of drumheads was carried out by the German physicist Ernst Florens Friedrich Chladni (1756-1827). An early student of law, he left this profession to become a pioneer in the experimental investigation of sound. He made some of the earliest measurements of the speed of sound in various media; but he is best known for his study of vibrating plates that in their modes of motion resemble the vibration of drums. At that time there were no instruments like stroboscopes for studying these vibrations in slow motion; but Chladni found that by scattering finely divided sand on the plate or drumhead, various patterns were formed indicating various modes of motion when the vibration was induced by rubbing a violin bow along the edge.

If a musical tone is sounded with sufficient intensity, such a drumhead also may be made to vibrate by sympathetic resonance. Suppose that we have a large square drumhead stretched to vibrate in its fundamental mode when the note of middle C is sounded. We cover it with a light coating of sand. If now a soprano sings high D slightly off pitch, the sand forms a pattern of three broad vertical stripes, the pattern of the flag of France. (This might be a dramatic way to end a rendition of the *Marseillaise*.)

Whether Chladni ever performed this feat, history does not record; but the most substantial recognition of his work did come from France. In 1809 he was invited to give a demonstration of his vibration figures at the French Institute and, soon after, for the Emperor Napoleon himself. Napoleon was so impressed that he gave Chladni a grant of six thousand francs, one of the earliest examples of government aid for research.

Two-Dimensional Music

As I mentioned previously, the music of the drum differs from the music of the string essentially because the drum is two-dimensional while the string is one-dimensional. The string has only the significant dimension of *length*. Geometrically it is a line. On the other hand, the vibrating element of the drum, its membrane, is a surface; it has two dimensions, *length* and *breadth*. This difference in dimensionality is reflected also in the shapes that the vibrator can have.

The string can have only one shape when it is stretched from end to end, the shape of a straight line. By way of contrast, the drum membrane can have an infinite number of shapes depending on the shape of the rim over which it is stretched. This may be a circular rim, as in the case with al-

MIDDLE C

FIGURE I

THE SQUARE DRUM

sounding its fundamental tone

(I,I)

most all the drums that we see in a band or orchestra; or it may be a square rim giving a square vibrating membrane; or the edge can be triangular, oval-shaped, or any strange shape chosen at random.

Undoubtedly, most drums have circular rims because it is easier thus to attain uniform stretching of the membrane. In order to get the most resounding tone from the membrane it is important to have the tension evenly distributed. With a circular membrane there are no preferred directions and uniform tension is automatically achieved. If, however, the rim of the drum is square, then there is trouble getting uniform tension at the corners. I think this is why square drums are seldom if ever seen in an orchestra. It is a pity, because a square drum has a far more beautiful tone, blending far more harmoniously with tones from the other instruments of the orchestra, than is the case with drums constructed with circular drumheads. The reason is that the square drum possesses a set of overtones that contains all the overtones of the violin string plus some others that produce a tone of even richer texture than that of the violin.

Of course, before one can use the square drum to the fullest extent of its musical capabilities, one must understand the nature of these overtones. In fact, to write music for the square drum, one should employ a scale based on its "square" overtones. This construction of a *square scale* is one of the problems that we will solve in this chapter. I have a friend in New York who is a distinguished concert violinist, Mr. Robert Gerle. He has told me that if I will give him the notes of the square scale, then a composer friend of his will write a sonata for violin and square drum and they will perform this at one of their concerts in Town Hall. Then for the first time, an audience will have an opportunity to hear really "square" music!

It is difficult to predict how people will react to polydimensional music. There have been so many pioneering explorations of various new forms of percussion ensembles, such as the compositions of Cage, that an audience should not be shocked by anything, no matter how unusual. I do hope that the experiment can be tried.

In order to see the overtones that are associated with the vibrating square membrane let us consider a series of experiments similar to those that we performed with a set of bows of varying string lengths. Let us suppose that we have a square drum that is made by stretching a membrane over the top of a box which is exactly one yard long and one yard wide, as shown in Figure 1. The membrane has a uniform thickness and is stretched to a uniform tension so that the fundamental tone of its vibration has the pitch of middle C with 256 vibrations per second. We also have a series of larger boxes that are square and have the length of each side exactly two feet, three feet, and four feet. We have a set of smaller boxes that have the length of each side one half foot, one third foot, one quarter foot, and one fifth foot. In each case the box is covered by a membrane with the same thickness and stretched at the same tension as that in the first box which gives us the fundamental tone of middle C.

As you might guess, if we tap the membrane that has the side half a yard long, it sounds the note of high C in just the same way that our bowstring half a yard long sounded the note of high C, or high *do*. Like the string one third of a yard long, the drum one third of a yard long sounds high *sol*. The one-quarter-yard drum sounds high-high *do* and the one-fifth-yard drum sounds high-high *mi*.

Turning now to the larger drums, the drum that is two yards on a side sounds low *do*. The drum that is three yards on a side sounds low-low *fa*. The drum that is four yards on a side sounds low-low *do*. Thus with drums where the length of the side has an integral-number ratio to the length of the side of the fundamental drum, we can establish the notes of our scale in just the same way that we did with the

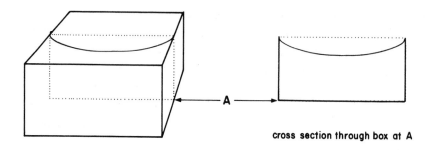

cross section through box at A

FIGURE I·A

THE SQUARE DRUM

sounding its fundamental tone

(I,I)

shown also in cross section

bowstring. But, you may say, there is nothing very new about all this; and you are correct. To see the truly new tones of the square drum we must investigate the *overtones*.

The Overtones of the Square Drum

To examine the overtones of the square drum we proceed exactly as we did in investigating the overtones of the string. Imagine that the room is equipped with a flashing light so that we can observe the vibration of the drum in slow motion. When we tap the drum at its precise center very gently, we see the drum vibrate up and down very much like the fundamental motion of the string as shown in Figure 1a. The center of the drum moves with the largest amplitude. It arches up forming a convex bowl and then falls rapidly, passing through the plane position, sinking to form a concave bowl. If the drum is tuned to middle C, this rising and falling takes place 256 times during each second. This is the *fundamental* mode of vibration of the drum.

To get the overtone of the drum corresponding to the first overtone of the string, we now tap the drum lightly exactly half way between the center of the drum and one of the corners. We now observe the drum rising and falling in a checkerboard pattern as shown in Figure 2 at the top; and the tone corresponds to high *do* or high C, with 512 vibrations per second. In this motion there are four points of maximum vibration, each lying on a diagonal drawn from the center of the drum to each of the four corners. The lower left and the upper right quarter-squares rise to form convex domes while the upper left and lower right quarter-squares fall to form concave bowls. In the first string overtone we had the convex arch and the concave trough with a *node* or motionless point on the string between them. Here in the drum we have two convex domes and two concave bowls with *nodal lines* between them. Draw the line from the front to the back of the box passing through the exact

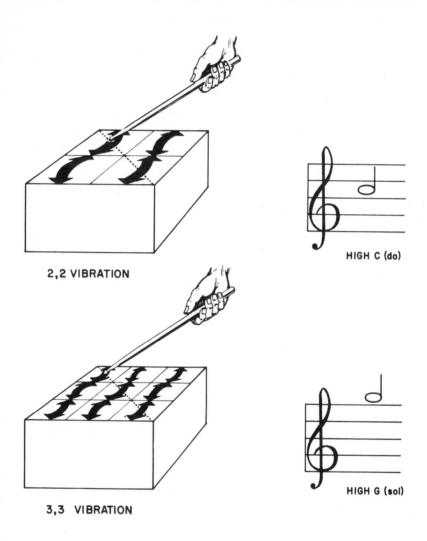

2,2 VIBRATION

HIGH C (do)

3,3 VIBRATION

HIGH G (sol)

FIGURE 2

center of the membrane and you will observe that along this line there is no motion of the membrane when the drum vibrates in this mode. The same is true if you draw a line from the left edge of the drum to the right edge of the drum, perpendicular to the edge and passing through the center. Along this line on the membrane there is no motion as the drum vibrates in this first overtone mode.

We now continue the game just as we did with the bowstring. To get the second overtone of the string we plucked the bowstring one third of the distance between the end and the center. This gave us the motion of the string with three loops, an arch at each side while the center of the string bowed down in a trough. You may have guessed the pattern that we get with the square drum when we tap it one third of the way on the diagonal line from the edge to the center: it is a pattern of nine domes and bowls, four of these rising while the other five fall, as shown in the lower part of Figure 2. Like the violin string, the drumhead sounds high-high *sol* in this vibration characterized by three loops. In this mode of vibration the nodal lines form a checkerboard pattern exactly like that which children use when they play tic-tac-toe.

Continuing in the same way, we can make the drum sound all the other notes of the bowstring overtones. If we pat the drum one quarter of the way from a corner to the center, we get the tone of high-high *do* having sixteen domes and bowls of vibration, eight rising while the other eight fall. If we tap the drum one fifth of the way from the corner to the center we get twenty-five domes and bowls, and the drum sounds the note of high-high *mi*.

But why tap the drum just along the line from the center to the corner, the diagonal line? Why not tap it on the line from the center to the middle of an edge? In the string we had only the possibility of plucking the string at various distances along the bow; here in the drum there are an end-

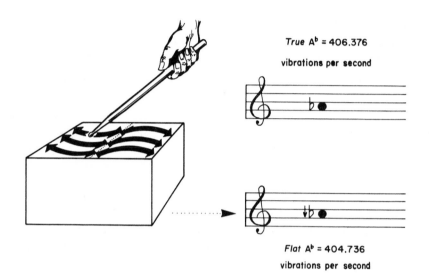

True A♭ = 406.376

vibrations per second

Flat A♭ = 404.736

vibrations per second

FIGURE 3

THE SQUARE DRUM

Overtone (2,1)

less number of different spots where we can strike it. Let's tap halfway between the center of the drum and the middle of the lefthand edge, as shown in Figure 3. Now we get a tone that is completely different from any that we can produce with the bowstring. At first hearing, the tone sounds a little out of tune; it lies a little below the note that in music we normally call A-flat. If we count the vibrations, we find that the drum is vibrating at 404.736 vibrations per second. Obviously, this is not an integral number of vibrations per second. In fact, it is a number that cannot be expressed precisely in ordinary decimal notation; it would take an infinite number of digits to express this number! Where our familiar note of *sol* had a vibration that was 3/2 times the vibration of the base tone, *do,* this strange new tone has a vibration that in ratio to the fundamental tone of middle C has the value $\sqrt{5}\sqrt{2}$. We might call this note A-flat-flat, since it is A-flat flatted slightly more.

Let's turn on our flickering light and see in slow motion what this pattern of vibration looks like. As we observe the drum with our stroboscope we find that the right half of the drum rises while the left half falls, and that the nodal line separating these two halves is a straight line passing from the middle of the front edge of the drum to the middle of the back edge of the drum, as shown in Figure 3. The right half of the drumhead in its risen position looks like the top of a loaf of bread while the left half in its fallen position is a long trough. We shall call this the 2, 1 pattern.

But if tapping the drum halfway between the center and the *left* edge gives us this new tone, what happens if we tap it halfway between the center and the *top* edge? If we try it, we get a tone of the same *pitch;* but if we look at it, we see a different *pattern* of movement. Now the membrane vibrates as shown in Figure 4b, the bottom half rising while the top half falls.

This is our first example of two types of vibration that

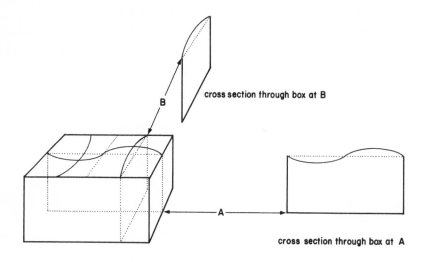

cross section through box at B

cross section through box at A

FIGURE 3·A

THE SQUARE DRUM

vibrating in overtone

(2,1)

showing cross sections

have exactly the same frequency, patterns of vibration that are the same type but differently oriented. In one case the nodal line runs from left to right; in the other case, the nodal line runs from top to bottom. Such a pair of vibrations is called a *degenerate* set of vibrations. In such a set, nodal lines are always at right angles to each other; in more mathematical language we say that the vibrations are *orthogonal.*

Whenever we have such a set of vibrations, we can always start them going *simultaneously* and in this way produce still other patterns of vibration. For example, we can have a vibration in which the nodal line runs from the left back corner of the box to the front right corner, as shown in Figure 3c. Here we have a triangular shape of vibration, the southwest corner rising while the northeast corner falls. Equally well we can have the southeast corner rising while the northwest corner falls, as shown in Figure 3d. All of these vibrations have the same frequency; they give out tones of the same pitch.

Now let's silence the drum and strike it *one third* of the way from the center to the left edge. Now we find the pattern of the flag of France, three vertical stripes as shown in Figure 5, part e. This is the pattern that was produced when the soprano sang the last note in the *Marseillaise* off-key. If we observe this motion with the flickering light, we see that the left third and the right third of the drum rise while the central third falls; and the left third and right third fall when the center is rising. If we take a slice across the drum from left to right we find that in such a slice there are two arches and one bow or, in other words, three loops. Slicing the drum from front to back we get only one loop. Like the 2, 1 motion that sounded A-flat-flat, this 3, 1 motion is *degenerate* and can be oriented in a number of ways. It can be made to produce the pattern of the flag of Belgium, three horizontal stripes shown in part f of the same Figure; or it can even produce a pattern closely resembling that of

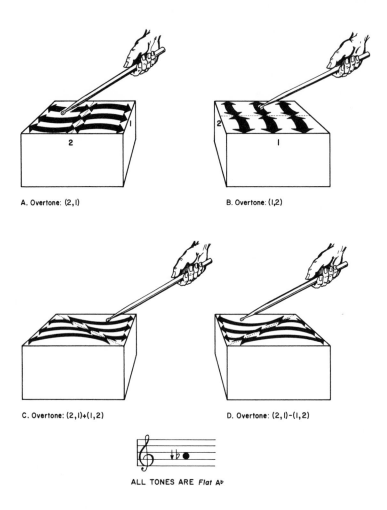

A. Overtone: (2,1)

B. Overtone: (1,2)

C. Overtone: (2,1)+(1,2)

D. Overtone: (2,1)-(1,2)

ALL TONES ARE *Flat* A♭

FIGURE 4

Equivalent Overtones from the Square Drum

the flag of Japan, as shown in part g. I am not arguing that there is any subtle similarity of culture between these three nations associated with their flag symbols of the same dynamic symmetry; but who knows all the secrets of the cultural subconscious?

The frequency of this 3, 1 motion is such that its tone lies just slightly below the pitch of high D. We will call it D-half-flat since it is not quite as low as a normal D-flat.

In Figure 5, there are drawn the patterns of motion associated with the fundamental tone and the first three overtones of the square drum, together with their frequencies and the notes of the scale to which they correspond. We thus see that the extension of our vibrating medium from the one-dimensional string to the two-dimensional square drumhead gives us one additional overtone just above *sol* in the first octave of middle C and an additional overtone in the octave above high C. In establishing our string scale of *do, re, mi, fa, sol, la, ti, do,* we used the ratios of the overtones up to that overtone which was five times the original fundamental frequency. It seems logical, then, in making a square scale to add notes that correspond to these two additional unsymmetrical overtones. On this basis the square scale has been worked out as shown in Figure 6. This is the scale that we must use if we wish to write "square" music.

To maintain the *do-re-mi* notation in this extended square scale, we need names for the two additional notes. I modestly suggest for the D-half-flat the syllable *fra,* as it is this note that produces the pattern of the flag of France; of course it also produces the pattern of the flag of Belgium and one could argue that *bla* would be equally appropriate but I personally prefer the French prefix. For the note A-flat-flat I suggest the syllable *sqa* since this is the overtone that is most characteristic of the square. But it may be a long time before singers abandon *do-re-mi* and begin to sing *do-fra-re-mi-fa-sol-sqa-la-ti-do.*

Square Harmony

Someday I hope to build a square drum and record some of these strange square tones. I have produced a few of them with the help of electronic oscillators, where the tone can be adjusted to approximate quite closely any frequency desired. Thus I have made the major tetrad of *do-mi-sol-sqa* that plays a role in the square scale comparable to the major triad *do-mi-sol* in the harmony of our conventional string music.

There are also electronic organs which are built so that all the different notes can be tuned by electrical means to any desired frequency. My ambition is to devise someday an electronic organ on which I can play "square" music. I propose to cut the black notes in half, the front half sounding conventional notes and the back half sounding the extra notes of the square scale. By pulling other "stops" I may be able to transform the scale to some of the other geometric possibilities such as a rectangular, triangular, or even circular scale. But this is a long way in the future.

Allow me "one more word" on the vibrations of the square drum. Just as the vibrations of the string are quantized by the boundary conditions, the two pegs that fasten the string at each end, similarly the vibrations of the square drum are quantized by the shape of the rim. The quantum numbers of the vibrations of the string are the numbers of the loops: 1, 2, 3, 4, 5, and so on; the quantum numbers of the vibrations of the drum are the numbers of loops along *each* edge. Thus the fundamental has the set of quantum numbers 1, 1. The A-flat-flat vibration has the quantum numbers 2, 1; high *do* has the set 2, 2; D-half-flat has 3, 1; high *sol* has the set 3, 3, and so on.

The pitch of the tone is determined by an equation analogous to the famous formula of Pythagoras, stating that the sum of the squares of the lengths of the two sides

g. Overtone, type 3, 1

f.

$D^{i\sharp} = \dfrac{\sqrt{10}}{\sqrt{2}} \times 256 = 573.235$ vps

$(D^i = 574.702$ vps$)$

$3^2 + 1^2 = 9 + 1 = 10$

e.

Overtone, type 2, 2

d.

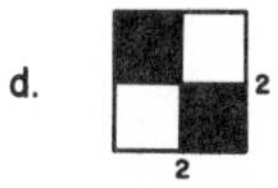

$C^i = \dfrac{\sqrt{8}}{\sqrt{2}} \times 256 = 2 \times 256 = 512$ vps

$2^2 + 2^2 = 4 + 4 = 8$

Overtone, type 2, 1

c.

$A^{\sharp\flat} = \dfrac{\sqrt{5}}{\sqrt{2}} \times 256 = 404.736$ vps

b.

$(A^\flat = 406.376$ vps$)$

$2^2 + 1^2 = 4 + 1 = 5$

Fundamental tone, type 1, 1

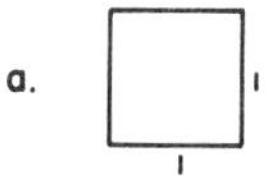

a.

$C = 1 \times 256 = 256$ vps

$1^2 + 1^2 = 1 + 1 = 2$

FIGURE 5

SUMMARY: Overtones of the Square Drum   (vps = vibrations per second) of a right triangle is equal to the square of the length of the hypotenuse.

Thus the ratio of the frequency of the overtone to the frequency of the fundamental tone is the square root of the ratio of the sums of the number of loops along each edge of the drum squared. Thus for the note *fra:*

$$\frac{\text{Frequency of } fra}{\text{Frequency of } do} = \sqrt{\frac{3^2 + 1^2}{1^2 + 1^2}} = 404.736$$

Is it just a coincidence that the pitches of the square tones are given by a formula first proposed in an entirely different context by the founder of the analytical theory of musical tone?

The Music of the Circle

You may think it strange that I have devoted so many pages to the discussion of the music of the square drum, a type of drum that today exists only in my imagination. At least, I have never heard of square drums in an orchestra, or even in a jazz combo. Probably one could search all the way from the stage of Lincoln Center in New York to the witch doctor's hut in the African jungle without finding anything but drums with circular rims. So we certainly ought to have a look at the music of the more familiar round drum.

In contrast to the square drum, the overtones of the round drum have no integral-number ratios to one another; and for this reason the sound of such a drum strikes us at first as being far more noise than music. But if our ears were sufficiently keen and our perception trained to appreciate the nuances of simultaneous frequencies corresponding to the irrational numbers in mathematics, we might find the tones of the circular drum esthetically far more pleasing and interesting than the simpler tones we get from string and reed instruments. And there is another reason for having a look at the overtones of the round drum. These over-

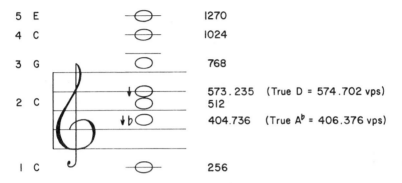

vibrations per second

5	E		1270
4	C		1024
3	G		768
2	C		573.235 (True D = 574.702 vps)
			512
			404.736 (True A♭ = 406.376 vps)
1	C		256

The Square Scale:

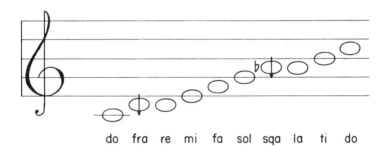

do   fra   re   mi   fa   sol   sqa   la   ti   do

FIGURE 6

SQUARE HARMONY

tones bear a much closer relation to the overtones of the atom. As we shall see in the next chapter, the overtones of the atom are closely related to the overtones of a vibrating sphere; and since the sphere is round its overtones are again related to those of the round drum.

In Figure 7 I have shown the overtone patterns of vibration in both the square drum and the round drum. They are closely related to one another as you can see, but the frequencies have a different pattern.

What are the quantum numbers of the overtone vibrations of the round drum? As you may recall, we have a fairly simple system for identifying the modes of the square drum. We merely count the number of loops up the left edge and the number of loops across the bottom edge, and then give the mode of motion a label with two numbers. Thus the label for the fundamental mode of motion of the square drum is 1, 1.

The first overtone of the square drum in the horizontal position looks like the signal flag for E; and in the vertical position it is like the signal flag for K. We give this motion the quantum number 1, 2 since we arbitrarily choose the vertical position of the stripes and put the lowest number first.

It is a little more difficult to assign quantum numbers to the circular vibrations and the system used is, perhaps, a little more arbitrary. We call the fundamental vibration 0, 1. The zero indicates that there is no interior nodal line; the 1 following the comma stands for the nodal circle that is the actual *rim* of the drum.

For the mode of motion that lies three places above the fundamental, the circle with the big black dot in the center, we use the quantum number 0, 2. The zero tells us that there are no nodal lines crossing the drum while the 2 tells us that there are two circular nodal lines, one of these being the rim itself and the other the rim of the black dot.

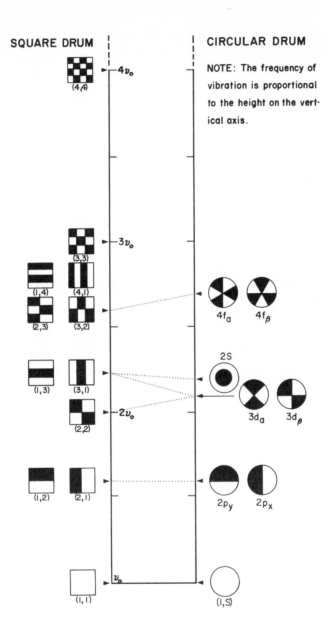

SQUARE DRUM

CIRCULAR DRUM

NOTE: The frequency of vibration is proportional to the height on the vertical axis.

FIGURE 7

Correspondance between Square and Circular Drum vibrations

Because the circular drum closely resembles a simplified atom, an atom reduced from three to two dimensions, an alternate system is frequently used to designate the modes of vibration. This system is shown in Figure 7 and emphasizes the analogies between drum vibration and atom vibration.

It would be interesting to go on and discuss overtones in triangular drums, oval drums, and drums of many other strange shapes; but for our present purposes it is more important to move on from the two-dimensional drum vibrations and examine the three-dimensional vibrations that we get in objects such as a bell or a rubber ball. These are the vibrations that are most closely related to the atom and, therefore, most closely related to the "music" of life.

7

The Music of the Bell

JUST FOR a little recreation, imagine that you take a stroll to the city art museum and visit the gallery of sculpture. As you walk in the door, you see before you a beautiful marble statue of a young woman with upraised arms, poised in a pirouette from a ballet. You step closer and with your magic eyesight you observe that the statue is breathing. The woman's bosom rises and falls gently in a slow rhythm. There are rippling motions along her arms. Her face quivers. Her whole body appears to be alive.

You bend over and listen. With your magic hearing, you are suddenly aware that the woman is singing, a clear bell-like soprano tone accompanied by a muted chorus of exquisite harmony, trilling flute-like notes, rising higher and higher in a gossamer web of chromatic overtones extending octave upon octave into the ultra-ultra-ultra-high soprano, beyond the range of human ears, beyond the range of canine perception, beyond the range even where insects sing their inaudible songs of entomologic love. You hear the music that was in the sculptor's brain even before this graceful shape was created. You hear the song of the marble that first resounded when its shining crystals appeared from the flux of calcium and carbon aeons ago during the birth-pangs of our earth.

No, this is not science fiction. These are the imperceptible rhythms of the atoms. This is the mysterious music of the electron bells, music that peals unheard around us in every form of matter, whispers of sound too infinitesimal ever to be perceived, but conclusively proved present by hundreds of incontrovertible scientific experiments. The experiments date back many decades, but their interpretation in terms of these ultraharmonics is new. So let us explore this arcane atom-bell music and try to understand something of its meaning.

Like the origins of the music of the string and the music of the drum, the origin of the familiar music of the bell lies obscured in prehistory. Early man may have become aware of the musical tones of bell-shaped objects like hollow pebbles even before he twanged his first bowstring or built his first drum from animal hide. It is well known that in elongated form, like the hanging stalactites in a cave, stone will give out a beautiful bell-like tone when struck. Perhaps some caveman banged his head by accident on a stalactite when exploring some dark, underground tunnel. Perhaps it was part of the curiosity of early cave dwellers to hit various objects just to see what kinds of sound they gave out. At any rate, from our earliest recorded history, it is clear that primitive man was aware that solid objects emitted sounds and that he used these sounds as part of his earliest musical ensembles to accompany religious ceremonies, war dances, marriage rites, and also to make many hours of enforced inactivity less boring.

Countless early historical records refer to sounds from solid objects. They mention rods of stone and metal, squares and discs of wood, and other objects of varied shapes made from various materials. In fact, it is difficult to trace the path of evolution from this motley collection of sound-makers to the rather specialized quasi-hemispherical resonators that today we call *bells*. The tone goes from "dink-donk" to "ding-dong" as the shape changes from a rod to a bell; but just at what point is the real bell-shape and bell-tone reached? Just when do we have a bell? For our purposes the exact dividing line between such tone makers as xylophone slabs and cymbals on the one hand and bells on the other is not particularly significant. Our objective is to consider the essential differences between the vibrations of the string with its one dimension of *length,* the drumhead with its two dimensions of *length* and *breadth,* and the bell with its three dimensions of *length, breadth,* and *height;* and to see how this leads us to an understanding of the vibrations of the atom.

Considering the number of dimensions involved in the vibration, we may regard all solid objects—whether shaped like rods, slabs, cubes, spheres, or true bells—as constituting a class of "bells," a class of three-dimensional vibrators. This class of vibrators has been studied far less than the vibrators that make one-dimensional music, like the string, or two-dimensional music, like the drum. For it is only recently that scientists have become aware of the fundamental importance of three-dimensional vibrations; and this awareness dates primarily from the discovery of the vibratory nature of the atom. The atom is essentially three-dimensional in nature. In its simplest form it vibrates in a manner very similar to that of a spherical bell. As we shall see, there are certain aspects of the atom that suggest at least another, "fourth" dimension; but for the moment we will consider only the many similarities of form between atomic vibration and bell vibration. Since all real objects are made of atoms, all real objects also have certain patterns of vibration that must be analyzed in three dimensions. In particular we shall see that the thermal vibrations in statues, due to the presence of heat in the marble or metal from which the statue is formed, constitute an especially intriguing class of vibrations.

As a first step let us consider some of the analogies between the simpler vibrations of the string and the drumhead and the vibrations of solids. In the case of drumheads we found that the *square* drum bears the closest relation to the vibrations of the string and, therefore, produces tones most like the tones we hear in familiar music. In the same way, in studying vibrators that have the three dimensions of length, breadth, and height we find that the vibrating *cube* has the greatest similarity to the vibrating string. So let us take a look at the way a cube of metal will vibrate when struck, observing it in the same way that we observed the vibrations of the string and the square drum.

The Music of the Cube

When you strike a metal cube with a hammer you do not hear anything nearly as suggestive of musical tone as when you strike the drumhead of a kettle drum or pluck the string of a violin. The cube merely gives out an extremely high-pitched and not very loud "ping." Nevertheless, it is vibrating with a fundamental tone and a set of overtones, in exactly the same way as a drumhead or a string does. This cube tone can be amplified and analyzed and, in theory at least, can be reproduced by tape recorders so that, when played back, it sounds like a particularly rich violin tone.

The *fundamental* tone of the cube is produced by a total expansion and contraction analogous to the fundamental mode of vibration of the string (where it rises making a single arch and falls making a single trough), and the fundamental vibration of the drumhead (where it rises forming a single dome and falls forming a single bowl). You remember that for purposes of classification the fundamental vibration of the string is given the symbol 1 because it has the single loop. And the fundamental vibration of the drum is given the symbol 1, 1 because viewed either from the front edge or from the side edge it appears also as a single loop. So we give the label 1, 1, 1 to the fundamental vibration of the cube because it shows a single loop when viewed along its length, its breadth, or its height.

Let us suppose that we have a cube that is made of material of the right density and natural tension so that it vibrates with the tone corresponding to our old familiar friend middle C, with its 256 vibrations per second. We now play just the same game with the cube that we played with the string and the drum, striking it at different places and setting up different overtones. Because the larger part of these vibrations are taking place in the interior of the cube it is virtually impossible to draw any diagram of the cube showing the nature of these overtone vibrations. In the string, you will remember, the overtones consisted of an integral number of loops, sections of the string that were vibrating with more or less intensity, and separated by points on the string called nodes where the string remained stationary. In patterns of motion on a drumhead we had areas of more or less intense vibration separated by lines where the drumhead remained stationary, called nodal lines. In an analogous way, the cube, with its three dimensions of length, breadth, and height, has nodal *surfaces* with the dimensions of length and breadth. These surfaces are the planes that divide the interior of the cube into smaller portions of volume in which the motions of the atoms take place that constitute the vibrations.

We find the label or *quantum number* for the octave vibration in the cube in a manner strictly analogous to the octave for the string and the octave for the square drum. In the case of the string the octave vibration has two loops. It is designated by the single number 2. In the case of the drum the octave has two loops along the front edge and the side edge and is designated by the multiple number 2, 2. In the cube the octave is a pattern of eight little vibrating cubes and is designated by the multiple number 2, 2, 2. The cube vibrates at exactly the same frequency as the octave in the string and the octave in the drumhead if the fundamental tone for string, drumhead, and cube is the same; for our study, we have selected this tone in each of these three cases as the tone of middle C with 256 vibrations per second.

In the case of the string there was no way to make it

vibrate with any *overtone* frequency between its fundamental tone and the tone one octave above that. In the case
of the square we found that we could make the upper half
of the square drum rise while the lower half fell, and this
gave us the overtone mode of motion that we call 1, 2 motion. This tone lies almost exactly midway between *sol* and
la on our string scale. We also included in the scale the overtone derived from D-half-flat sounded when the square
drum formed the pattern of the flag of France, and we called
this note *fra.* This gave us the square scale.

In the case of the cube we have three new overtones in
this first octave of the scale. The first of these is the 1, 1, 2
tone and coincides almost exactly with F-sharp if the cube
has its fundamental at middle C. It is a type of motion with
one loop along the axis of length, one loop along the axis
of depth, but two loops along the axis of height. The second
overtone corresponds to the mode of motion designated by
1, 2, 2. This, of course, indicates that there is one loop of
vibration along the axis of length, two loops of vibration
along the axis of breadth, and two along the axis of height.
Finally, the third overtone of the cube has the label 1, 1, 3.
This mode of motion has one loop along the axis of length,
one loop along the axis of breadth, and three loops along
the axis of height.

If I am ever able to build my organ for polydimensional
music, I will have a stop that I can pull which will introduce
these cubic overtones into the scale. I plan to have the black
keys split in half so that by pressing the back part of the
black key I can sound these cubic notes. Following the same
pattern that we used in naming the square notes, we might
call the three new overtones of the cubic scale respectively
cu, lu, and *tu;* then we find *cu* inserted between *fa* and *sol*
at almost exactly the same frequency as F-sharp, if we are in
the key of C. We find *lu* lying just above *la*, not quite as
high as A-sharp; we find *tu* lying halfway between *ti* and *do.*

Thus our cubic scale becomes *do, re, mi, fa, cu, sol, la, lu, ti, tu, do.*

The pitch of these new cubic notes is given by an extension of the Pythagorean formula; for example, for the 1, 1, 3 overtone called *cu:*

$$\frac{\text{Frequency of overtone}}{\text{Frequency of fundamental tone}} = \sqrt{\frac{1^2 + 1^2 + 3^2}{1^2 + 1^2 + 1^2}}$$

The Music of the Sphere

Just as we can make two-dimensional drums in an infinite variety of shapes like the square, the circle, the triangle, and the other variations, we can make three-dimensional "bells" in as many shapes as we wish. While the cubic "bell" has tones that have the most direct relation to the set of overtones we derived by going from the string to the square drum, we find also that the spherical "bell" has tones, strangely enough, related closely to the overtones of the string and the square drum. This is one of the mysterious surprises of mathematics. Why should the drum with the circular rim have overtones with no direct matching to the overtones of the string, while the extension of the concept of the circle to the sphere in three dimensions gives us a "bell" that *does* match all the overtones of the string? This is an example of the fascinating tapestry of relationships that we find among various dynamic forms; and since these dynamic forms are the essence of the atom, and we are made of atoms, this is an area of mathematics that applies directly to us.

You may feel that I am stretching the meaning of the word *bell* quite a bit in using this term for the set of resonators I am about to describe. But this is the kind of linguistic choice that we are forced so many times to make in exploring domains of mathematical relationships. We say that *four times four times four* is *four cubed,* and feel that we have not distorted the meaning of *cube* very much. Then we go on to talk about a *cubic* equation in algebra if, for example, we find a term where the variable x is raised to the third power and written x^3. So rather than try to invent one single new short word to describe the whole class of three-dimensional vibrators, I will refer to them as "bells."

The particular three-dimensional vibrator or "bell" that I want to describe now consists of a thin-skinned rubber balloon blown up to moderate pressure with air. If I tap such a balloon lightly I can hear a slight humming vibration; I am making the balloon vibrate with overtones in exactly the way that we vibrated the bowstring and the various drums that we have studied. It is a little more difficult to draw a picture that conveys the nature of these bell overtones but I shall use the type of illustration that Professor Walter Kanzmann of Princeton University employs in his book "Quantum Chemistry." We represent the balloon by a circle. We then show the various nodal surfaces associated with the overtones but only in cross-section. In describing these vibrations I shall use terms that are visual rather than mathematical, hoping to achieve a little more clarity, even at the expense of logical precision. In this vein, we can say that the fundamental vibration consists essentially of the expansion and contraction of the air inside the balloon. In a sustained vibration the air alternately expands and contracts just as the bowstring or the drum membrane alternately rises and falls. We indicate this in the diagram by putting a plus sign at the center of the balloon, a symbolism comparable to that used in designating the motions of the drumhead where we put a plus sign to indicate that the whole membrane rises and falls as a unit.

We find that it is possible to set up an overtone in this spherical "bell" with the frequency just one octave above the fundamental; and as you might guess, this is where the outer half of the air contracts while the inner half expands.

FIGURE I

THE TONES of THE SPHERE

1 s
256 C

2 s
512 c

3 s
768 g

2 p
367 F#

3 p
630 e

4 p
887 a

3 d
470 B

4 d
742 f#

5 d
1011 c'

There is a spherical nodal surface (at which the air is not moving) that separates the part of the air expanding and the part of the air contracting. This is a somewhat stylized description of what goes on but I think for our purposes we should concentrate on the shape of the pattern and not concern ourselves with the exact details of expansion and contraction. We can produce the note *sol* with a frequency three times that of the original frequency if we have three of these expansion-contraction zones; and we get high-high *do,* a note two octaves above the fundamental, if we have four of these. So you see how analogous this series of overtones of the spherical "bell" is to the overtones of the bowstring. But as you might suspect, we also have a series of overtones that are inserted in the interstices of this simple set of string overtones.

The description of the overtones of the sphere is somewhat more complicated than the description of the overtones of the cube. In the latter case we could designate these overtones by the quantum numbers that stood for the number of loops along each edge of the cube. Since the sphere has no edges, we obviously cannot use this system to get labels for the different overtones. I shall follow the notation of Professor Kauzmann and use the same labels that we employ to describe the overtones of the atom. Since the atom is also a three-dimensional "bell," there is a close resemblance between the overtones of the spherical bell and the atom-bell.

In the music of the square drum we find the scale *do, fra, re, mi, fa, sol, squa, la, ti, do* (where the note *fra* produces the pattern of the flag of France and the note *squa* is sounded when the pattern of vibration has the back half of the drum rising and the forward half falling, a pattern of vibration like the signal flag "E." In the spherical bell we have an analogous overtone that we can call *spha,* where the back half of the air in the sphere expands while the front half contracts. If the spherical bell has its fundamental at middle

C then this tone, *spha,* will lie just a little above F-sharp.

There is another overtone where there are two nodal surfaces at right angles to each other as shown in the illustration. This overtone occurs about halfway between A-sharp and B if our fundamental tone lies at middle C. We give this note the name of *sphi.* Thus the scale for the music of the sphere is *do, re, mi, fa, spha, sol, la, sphi, ti, do.*

In the notation commonly used in chemistry and physics we denote the simplest series of overtones corresponding to the overtones of the string by the labels *1s, 2s, 3s, 4s,* and so on. The *mode* of motion *(1s)* is the fundamental where there is just one expansion-contraction zone. In the mode of motion designated *2s,* there are two expansion-contraction zones, and so on. Actually, the symbol *s* was chosen because atoms in moving between these modes of motion gave out visible light under the conditions which in a spectrograph resulted in sharp lines; so *s* was chosen to designate *sharp.* It is perhaps more useful to think of *s* as associated with the word *sphere* because in these modes of motion the nodal surfaces separating the expansion-contraction zones have actually spherical symmetry. We shall see later that this is also true in the wave-picture of the atom.

Proceeding up the ladder of complexity, the next series of overtones are those where there is a nodal surface that can be called equatorial, since in cross-section it is represented as a line around the sphere that corresponds to the equator on our own global earth. These are designated as *2p, 3p, 4p, 5p,* and so on. The letter *p* also was selected originally in the study of spectra to denote the word *principal* since the lines associated with these modes of motion were regarded as the principal lines. The third set of overtones are given the labels *3d, 4d, 5d, 6d,* and so on. The letter *d* comes from the word *diffuse* and again has its origin in spectroscopy since the lines associated with these modes of motion in atoms are somewhat diffuse.

You may wonder why we start with the number *2* in labeling the *p* series, and the number *3* in labeling the *d* series. This comes from the number of nodal or quasinodal surfaces involved. If we think of the outer circle in the diagram of the balloon as a quasinodal surface, we note that for the simple *1s* motion there is only one surface, the actual surface of the balloon. There is one circle above the label *1s* in the diagram. In the same way there are two circles in the diagram labeled *2s;* these correspond to two surfaces, the outer being the balloon itself and the inner the nodal surface between the two zones of expansion-contraction that are labeled *minus* and *plus*. In the same way there are three surfaces in the *3s* and four surfaces in the *4s* mode.

Turning now to the modes of motion that we have called *2p, 3p, 4p,* and *5p,* we find that in the *2p* mode there are two surfaces. These are, first, the quasinodal surface (the balloon itself) and, second, the nodal surface that is the equatorial plane designated in the picture by a line. In the mode of motion that we designate *3p* we have two circles and a line, or three surfaces altogether. In *4p* we have four surfaces, and in *5p* we have five surfaces.

In the series that we designate *3d, 4d, 5d, 6d* we follow the same plan. In the *3d* mode we have two lines and a circle; this is two plus one, or three surfaces altogether. You can see that this same rule applies to the higher modes of motion that are the *d* series.

You remember that in setting up the scale of the string we obtained the note *sol* from the overtone with three loops that had a frequency three times that of the fundamental. We dropped this high *sol* by an octave and thus got the note *sol* down in the range where we were setting up the scale. In the same way we could introduce many more notes in the scale of the sphere. We could take the frequencies of these higher *s, p,* and *d* modes and drop them down and get a very rich and complex scale. When the day comes that I build an electronic organ and play the music of the sphere on it, I may include many of these extra notes in the scale. It will be interesting to see whether with sufficient training we can correlate esthetically the subtle intervals of sphere harmony and find that it has a special beauty all of its own. My prediction is that sustained chords of sphere harmony will be quite dissonant; but if played as a running series of notes, I believe that these spherical overtones and the scale notes derived from them will have a unique chromatic beauty. The day may come, a hundred or a thousand years hence, when a new breed of musicians will possess a kind of musical perception far more sophisticated than ours today. These neo-musicians may derive exquisite pleasure in hearing tones that correspond to the spherical ratio numbers 1.43, 2.46, 3.47, 4.49, 4.95, and so on, just as we derive pleasure from tones that have the ratios corresponding to the simple integers 1, 2, 3, 4, and 5. If this is true, there will be new worlds of harmony for composers to explore for many centuries to come, because the possibilities of scales constructed from the overtones of various geometric forms is unlimited. Not only can these neo-composers compose in the scales of the cube, the parallelepiped, the tetrahedron, the dodecahedron, the sphere, the oblate spheroid, and so on; they can also set up scales constructed from the overtones of the *Venus de Milo,* the *David* of Donatello, the *Moses* of Michelangelo, the *Thinker* of Rodin, or for a more modern tonality, a *Thing* by Epstein. For each statue has its own set of overtones which can serve as the basis for its own unique scale, and provide its own unique harmony. And if a million years hence, composers have exhausted all the possible patterns of harmony from all conceivable statues, they can start composing in the fourth dimension. We know how to compute the overtones of forms like the *tesserac,* which is the analogue in four dimensions of the cube in three dimensions. So why worry about stagnation in musical art!

The Music of Venus

Just to understand these startling relations in a little more detail, let's examine the metamorphosis of the harmony of the cube into the harmony of Venus. Suppose that you are transported back in time two thousand years to the Golden Age of Greece and that you are standing in the courtyard that served as the studio of the artist who produced the *Venus de Milo*. A great cube of marble rests on a sturdy bench in the center of the court. With your magic eyes you see this cube quivering with its thermal atomic motion; and with your magic ears you hear the cubic harmony of Pythagoras resounding all around.

The sculptor enters, gazes at the cube, picks up his hammer and chisel, and the chips begin to fall. With each blow the harmony of the cube is altered. As each fragment is severed from the mother matrix, there is a transposition of the chords, a subtle metamorphosis of the overtonal texture. Hour after hour, day after day, as the sculptor labors you look and listen. The head of the statue emerges as the chips fall; then you see the outlines of the shoulders, the arms, and the body. And now your ears perceive that the chaos of tone is evolving into a pattern of incredibly beautiful chromatic harmony. Finally, when the statue stands complete in all its sculptural perfection of form, you hear the music of the *Venus de Milo* sounding for the first time its immortal song.

Or is it really for the first time? If you had listened to the atomic music within the artist's brain weeks or months before the statue took shape, would you have perceived in his cerebral symphony these same Venusian chromatic intervals that are now an immortal part of our esthetic heritage? In our later exploration of the dynamics of beauty we want to consider this aspect of artistic creativity.

Iconoclastic Adventure

In Baltimore the Municipal Museum of Art is located on a tract of land adjoining the campus of The John Hopkins University, where I served as Professor of Chemistry for thirty-six years. One day, as I was seated in my laboratory meditating on the theory that predicted these strange harmonies in statues, I said to myself, "Why not go over to the museum with a tape recorder and try to get a recording of some of these sounds?" It was Monday, the day when the museum was closed to the public. So I called the museum office and asked permission to come over that afternoon and do a few experiments in the sculpture gallery. The curator assured me that I would be most welcome, and promptly at two o'clock I appeared at the door of the sculpture gallery carrying a tape recorder and a hammer. The curator of the gallery glanced at the hammer and looked a little apprehensive, but I assured her that I would tap the statues very gently and she finally, with some reluctance, told me to go ahead with my experiments. (One of my students remarked later that she thought I was an iconoclast.)

My plan was to give a statue a light tap with the hammer at various points and record the slight "ping" that resulted with the tape moving at maximum speed. In this way the vibrations from the statue would be spread out over as long a stretch of tape as possible. Tapping a statue with a hammer is like plucking the violin string with a finger. You recall that we plucked the string at the center in order to set up the fundamental vibration. If the violin string were plucked at some point chosen at random, then we might find quite a few of the overtones all being sounded at once. You also recall that the violin string actually is sounding all these overtones even when to the naked eye it appears to be motionless. The presence of thermal energy in the string causes these various types of vibration to take place continuously at very small amplitudes so that even though the

string is apparently motionless and silent, actually it is
sounding all its overtones with a very slight and inaudible
vibration. In the same way the statue as it sits apparently
motionless and silent on its pedestal actually is resounding
with slight vibrations that represent its fundamental mode
of motion and a number of its overtones. Just as plucking
the string activates a number of the overtone motions so that
they give off *audible* sounds, so tapping the statue activates
a number of its overtones and their sounds are heard as the
small "ping."

By recording this "ping" on a fast-moving tape, it is
spread out over six or eight feet of the tape. This same tape
can then be run through the recorder with the mechanism
set at the "play" position so that one gets the "ping" coming out of the loudspeaker several octaves lower than it
sounded when originally produced by the statue. If this
recreated "ping" is then recorded once more on another fast-
moving tape it can be spread out over as much as twenty or
thirty feet of tape. Then you can take scissors and cut out
about two feet of this part of the tape and glue the ends
together. Over this short section of tape the amplitude of
the sound decreases only slightly in contrast with the original "ping" from the statue, when the sound died away in
less than a second. By transferring the vibrations from this
loop of tape back to another tape and reversing the speed
ratio, you obtain a long stretch of tape with the continuous
sound that is the sort of sound that you would hear with
your magic hearing if you listened to the actual thermal
vibrations of the statue.

I made recordings of this sort by tapping an individual
statue at different places. For example, there was a statue of
a woman by Matisse, which I tapped on the head, the arms,
the front of the torso, the back, and the thighs, obtaining
different qualities of sound in each case. Just as plucking the
string at different points excites different ratios of amplitude

in the different overtones, so tapping the statue at different points likewise sets up different ratios of overtones and gives the final blended "ping" different timbres. In the course of the afternoon I made recordings from about a dozen different statues. Some were marble, some bronze, some wood. Thus I obtained a very interesting collection of ensembles of overtones.

As I have discussed these experiments subsequently before many audiences, certain questions are frequently asked. Suppose we have two statues identical in shape but different in size, will this size ratio make a difference in the statue's music? I reply that *size* in the case of the statue has an effect strictly analogous to *length* in the case of the bowstring. If we make a new bow just half the size of the original bow, so that the new string is half a yard long whereas the original string was one yard long, then all the notes in the new bow will sound an octave higher. The second, third, and fifth overtones give us the three notes of the major triad chord. Making the bow smaller still leaves us with the major triad, but it now sounds one octave higher than it did with the original bow.

Exactly the same relation holds for the statue. Suppose that we have a lifesize statue of a man. Suppose that precise measurements are taken of the various parts of the statue and a new statue is cast which is exactly half lifesize. In the original lifesize statue there will be a fundamental tone and a series of overtones running up into the millions. In the statue that is half lifesize the fundamental tone will be one octave higher than in the original statue and each of the million-odd overtones will also be one octave higher. However, the harmony will remain essentially the same; the chord of the statue is merely transposed an octave higher but is unaltered in its harmonic quality, just as the major triad in the case of the bowstring is transposed unaltered to a pitch one octave higher when the bowstring is cut in half.

I am also asked frequently whether the *material* out of which the statue is made has an effect on the harmonic content of the statue. I reply that the material affects primarily the higher overtones of the statue. The lowest overtones, by and large, depend only on the shape of the statue.

I think that the easiest way to understand this relationship is to recall the relation in the case of the bowstring between the number of the overtone and the length of each loop that is found in its vibration. In the case of the bow, the third type of vibration had three loops so that each one of the loops was one third of the length of the bowstring. If the whole bowstring was one yard long, then each of the three loops would be one foot long. Suppose we have a bowstring that is one meter long: then the one hundredth mode of motion will have one hundred loops and each of these will be one hundredth of a meter long, or one centimeter long. Now let's take an enormous leap up the series of overtones and consider the billionth overtone of the string. If the string is one meter long, according to the simple theory of overtones, each loop in this mode of motion will be one billionth of a meter in length.

Now a billionth of a meter is just about the diameter of an atom. If we had a bowstring that consisted of a chain of atoms strung together like beads on a string, then in this billionth overtone each atom would be moving away from the neighboring atoms on each side and stretching the electron bonds that tie the atoms together. If the composition of the material composing the string were changed this would change the kinds of atoms involved. This, in turn, would change the weight of the atoms and the strength of the bonds tying them together. This would mean that, in these *very high* overtones, we would have types of vibration different from those found in the original material.

Thus, speaking in broad generalizations, we can say that it is these very *highest* overtones, in the case of the string approaching the billionth, where the material out of which the string is made affects the *ratio* of the overtones to one another. On the other hand, the string will sound the same *lowest* overtone ratios, giving us the *do, re, mi, fa, sol, la, ti, do* of our scale, whether it is made of metal, of plastic, or of linen thread. By the same token the *lowest* overtones of the statue will occur in ratios that are dependent only on the shape of the statue. The *highest* overtones will occur in ratios that depend on the chemical nature of the material out of which the statue is made.

Chemical Music

The musical tones connected with the chemical bonds provide some of the most interesting examples of three-dimensional music, or broadly speaking, the music of the bell. Let's consider one of our most familiar combinations of atoms, water. As you undoubtedly know, the chemical formula for water is H_2O. This formula tells us that the water molecule the smallest unit of water containing all the ingredients of its properties, is composed of two atoms of hydrogen and one atom of oxygen.

Extensive research on the structure of this molecule has made it clear that the oxygen atom is in the center and the two hydrogen atoms are on each side inclined at an angle, so that the correct picture of the water molecule is something like this:

This water molecule is much like a very tiny bell. As the water vapor in the air around you circulates, each of its water molecules sounds a very high-pitched tinkle of three tones. Actually, of course, this "tone" energy is given out not as sound but as radiation in the infrared part of the spectrum that we discussed in the first chapter. Let's go back to the magic piano and I can give you an idea what the tones of the water "bell" sound like. If you happen to have a piano of your own you can pretend that it is a magic piano and actually strike these notes. Naturally you will not see the infrared radiation coming out of the keys but it won't be too difficult to visualize the colors.

First, drop down two octaves below middle C and then strike the note C-sharp that is just above this note of C. This is the lowest tone that the water molecule gives out and the deep red color on this key, which you would see with your magic vision, would match the color that the water molecule radiates. Now go up a little over one octave higher and strike E-flat and E. The water molecule also give out tones corresponding to these tones on the magic piano. E-flat gives out a flame-red color and E gives out light of an orange color. If you strike these three notes on your own piano, you are hearing harmony very much like that which your magic ears would perceive coming from the moisture in the air all around you. As the water molecules dart past at incredibly rapid speeds (running into thousands of feet per second), they are giving out these flaming colors very much like little rockets, and "sounding" this tinkling chord. To reproduce the harmony of the water molecule precisely one needs to have three electronic oscillators that can be set or tuned to give out notes precisely in the ratio of 1615/3674/3796. These numbers are the "wave numbers" that are proportional to the actual frequency of the tones of the water molecule.

It is rather interesting that we can tell exactly how the water molecule moves as it emits these shrill cries. The oxygen atom is in the center and we can think of this as resembling the body of a small bird, with a hydrogen atom on each side like a wing. As this little water-bird flies through the air around you, it actually moves these hydrogen wings up and down; and when it changes from a more violent flapping, where the wings move further up and down, to a more peaceful flapping with the wings just moving a little bit, it emits the radiation corresponding in frequency to C-sharp on the magic piano.

But the water-bird executes other motions that I have never seen a real bird perform. As it flies, it sometimes extends and retracts its wings; in other words, both of the hydrogen atoms move out away from the oxygen and then move back in toward the oxygen. The note of E-flat thus is associated with this motion. Finally, the water-bird sometimes stretches one wing while it contracts the other wing, and vice versa; this type of motion has the note E associated with it.

Strike the chord on your piano and you find that it is somewhat dissonant; it has a somewhat melancholy quality. If you had magic ears that could be tuned to these high frequencies of radiation, you would hear these shrill, melancholy cries coming from the water molecules as they continually circle around your head. I think that you will agree that it is fortunate that nature has restricted our range of hearing!

A Chemical Ballet

I first tried the experiment of playing chemical chords on the piano about thirty years ago. It was rather fun to take the frequencies of radiation from various familiar molecules, convert these to the musical scale, and then play the notes on the piano in order to find out what different molecules are singing to us. I have transcribed a few of these chords as shown in the accompanying drawing. To me the water chord is somewhat melancholy; the chord of benzene is a bit like modern jazz; the chord of methyl alcohol is extremely harsh; and the chord of ethyl alcohol is suggestive of some of the music of Debussy. In the more complicated molecules I have omitted some of the overtones that are so close to other overtones that they cannot be reproduced completely on the piano.

As I have mentioned, one needs a series of electronic oscillators to produce these chemical harmonies acurately. In the electronic organ that I propose to build, I will have oscillators tuned to match these tones exactly; and by pulling the right stops, I will be able to play real "water music" or a real "alcoholic rag." I am sure that my water music will not sound much like Handel's. It is hard to say just how intoxicating the music of alcohol may be.

In the mid-1930s the directors of the American Chemical Society decided to have the national meeting of this organization in Baltimore in the spring of 1939. As local plans were made for the meeting, I was requested to arrange for an evening of entertainment for the two thousand-odd chemists who would be coming to town, so that there would be a break in the monotony of the long series of scientific lectures.

The thought occurred to me that it would be fun to have a ballet based on the music of some of the more familiar chemical compounds. I had already transcribed the vibrations of water, benzene, methyl alcohol, ethyl alcohol, methane, and a few other compounds in musical notation. So I set out to compose a series of twelve ballet numbers each based on a familiar molecule. One of my more musically inclined students also helped me, Mr. Lyman Mauk. When I had the piano score written, I enlisted the aid of the arranger for the Baltimore Symphony Orchestra and he transcribed and orchestrated the ballet.

Fortunately, the previous year had been a prosperous one for the local chemical companies and they contributed such a large fund toward the cost of the meeting that I was able to engage sixty members of the Baltimore Symphony, rent the large concert hall in Baltimore, and persuade the girls in a local ballet school to perform the actual ballet.

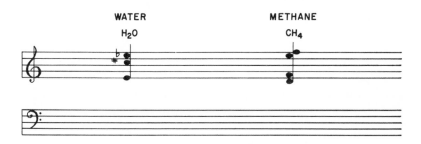

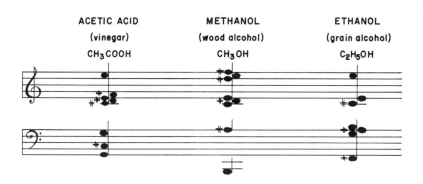

FIGURE I

CHEMICAL CHORDS

One of my graduate students worked out the choreography. We had girls dressed in red to represent hydrogen atoms, girls in blue for oxygen, girls in black for carbon, and girls in metallic costumes for the metals.

In each dance the girls executed the motions that the molecules actually perform in their vibration. For example, in the water dance, the girls were in groups of threes. In each group there was a girl dressed in blue in the middle, representing the oxygen atom, with girls dressed in red (for hydrogen) holding a hand with her on either side. The girls moved backward and forward, in and out, as music was played based on the actual chord of the water molecule. Thus the audience saw the motions of the atoms, heard the harmonies that the atoms were emitting, and got a rough idea of what it would be like to watch real atoms dancing through magic glasses. It would be a wonderful way to teach chemistry and I wish I could use this ballet in my own chemistry classes at the University.

Each girl had the chemical symbol for her atom sewn on the back of her dress in transparent cellophane. This cellophane was made of material that fluoresced in ultraviolet light. At the end of each dance, the girls turned their backs to the audience, the house lights were extinguished, the stage was flooded with ultraviolet light, and the chemical symbols appeared glowing on the girls' backs.

The story of the ballet was concerned with the efforts of a chemist to synthesize benzene with radioactive carbon. At the rear of the stage there was an enormous "Rube Goldberg" machine that contained nearly all the discarded apparatus which had collected in the attic of the chemistry laboratory for over fifty years. One of the components of this machine was an electrostatic device that when operated gave out great blue sparks several feet long, with very loud snapping. The students in the Chemistry Department took such an interest in this project that there was little work done that spring, and they constructed a most impressive machine. In fact, when the curtain rose to disclose the setting of the ballet, the audience gave a loud round of applause just for the machine even before any of the ballet dancers appeared on the stage. At the back of the stage there was a row of king-size cylinders of the kind used to hold compressed gas. Girls came on stage from back of these cylinders, slipping through the spaces in between them.

In the opening scene, the chemist is trying to synthesize the radioactive benzene. He tries several times and fails, and then in despair sits down at his desk, puts his head in his hands, and falls asleep. The clock strikes twelve and, in his dream, he sees the atoms appearing and dancing before him.

The first dance was based on the frequencies found in the hydrogen atom. These are frequencies that have familiar integral ratios, and the music was somewhat in the manner of a Viennese waltz. Then there was music based on the tones of the chemical molecule called methane, one of the principal constituents of illuminating gas. This has the formula CH_4, and was portrayed by a girl dressed in black representing the carbon atom surrounded by four girls in red representing the hydrogen atoms. This music was a little more chromatic than that of hydrogen; once when I played it on the piano for some of my friends, one of them remarked that it sounded like "watery" Chopin, whatever that means. We went on from there to do a dance based on the vibrations in two other compounds composed of carbon and hydrogen atoms, ethylene and acetylene. This was a lively dance. The ballet then went on with the water music, the music of benzene which is quite dissonant, the music of methyl alcohol, also filled with harsh harmony, and finally ended with the ethyl alcohol number. As I remarked earlier, the chord of ethyl alcohol sounds a bit like that of Debussy. I managed to use this chord as the basis for a rather snappy chromatic dance number with quick rhythm to which the girls did a tap dance. This made a fine climax for the whole ballet. (If you are interested in seeing some of the pictures of the ballet, go to the public library and look up the issue of Life magazine for April 17, 1939. On pages 22 and 23 you will find eight pictures showing the girls doing some of the different dances.)

The Mingled Chime

As you stand in the museum and gaze at the *Venus de Milo* it may be hard to accept the fact of the dynamism in the apparently cold, lifeless stone. You do not see the marble quivering. You cannot hear the tones that express in musical harmony the perfection of the curving surfaces. You cannot detect the electronic rhythm of the atoms, the dynamism of their chemistry. But it is all there, unheard melodies woven into a symphony of integral beauty, that moves in silence beyond time into the eternal. Once more quoting T. S. Eliot:

"Words move, music moves
 Only in time; but that which is only living
 Can only die. Words, after speech, reach
 Into the silence. Only by the form, the pattern,
 Can words or music reach
 The stillness, as a Chinese jar still
 Moves perpetually in its stillness.
 Not the stillness of the violin, while the note lasts,
 Not that only, but the co-existence,
 Or say that the end precedes the beginning,
 And the end and the beginning were always there
 Before the beginning and after the end.
 And all is always now."

8

The Meaning of Music

I
T IS THE year 2001. After finishing your evening meal, you and your wife have just left the dining room of your home to go into the library and enjoy some after-dinner music. You settle comfortably into your special music chairs, facing the hearth where a cheerful fire is crackling with little flames and glowing embers. "What will it be tonight?" you ask. "Something romantic? Rubinstein's *Rachmaninoff's Second?*" She smiles and nods. You both relax, settling back on the cushions, your hands resting on the metallicized fabric of the arms of the chairs. There is not a whisper in the air of the room but you "hear" the first low, mysterious minor chords of this great piano concerto sounding in your mind with a clarity and purity never attained in the concert hall. For the electronic ears of your own home music center heard your words, obeyed your command, sensed your wife's acquiescence, and is already feeding the waves of proper frequency into your brain so that you are "hearing" the performance of the concerto without the intermediary of sound or of vibrations of your ear drums.

Of course, this is all science fiction and very unlikely ever to happen. And I confess that the idea came to me after reading Aldous Huxley's "Brave New World" wherein he describes how the movies evolve into the "feelies" during the late twentieth century. You may remember his description of the hero of the novel, sitting in the feelie house and grasping the metallic arms of the theater seat through which feelie currents are fed to his brain as he revels in the sensation of lying on a bearskin rug.

Perhaps someday we will be able to enjoy a "brave-new-world" way of hearing music without ears, but a careful examination of the actual physiological mechanism of hearing makes me feel that it will never be quite as simple as the method Huxley suggests. In fact, the process by which we really do perceive music is so complex that I often wonder how it possibly can give us pleasure.

In terms of physicochemical mechanism, music comes to our brain as a series of electrochemical impulses transmitted by hundreds of nerve fibers, impulses that would sound like a chaotic series of little pops if they were amplified electronically and reproduced by a loudspeaker. And yet undeniably, from this series of pulses delivered to various cells in the brain, there is synthesized cerebrally that wholeness of incredible beauty that we call music.

Why is music meaningful? Why should a succession of complex vibrations of the eardrum produce effects in the mind that convey to us so much beauty? Why should thousands of human beings make it their main purpose in life either to compose new combinations of these complex vibrations or to play them? Considering the sheer greatness of personality of so many of the composers and the performers of the past, we cannot brush music aside as one of the trivial aspects of human life here on earth. Even though we may never find an answer, we must continue to ask the question, "Why is music so meaningful?" We must examine the possibility that in music we are in touch directly with one of the deepest aspects of reality.

The recent evidence from science implying that our universe is composed not of matter but of music makes this question most significant. Years ago Whitehead wondered: "Does Nature contain within itself a tendency to be in tune?" Let us now take a look at our music of song and symphony in the light of this new perspective that music itself is the very stuff of reality.

The Sensation of Music

Music as it normally comes to us is in the form of sound. Sound consists of series of waves in the air around us. These waves strike the eardrum and make it vibrate. These vibrations act through a complex mechanism of bone and cartilage, stimulating impulses in the fibers of the auditory nerve. When the nerve impulses reach the brain we get the sensation of music. At this time I do not want to discuss in detail the physiological mechanism of hearing. Rather, let us first examine the physical aspects of sound.

The simplest sound consists of a series of waves that move through the air with a velocity just a little over one thousand feet per second. Sound waves are different from waves traveling on the surface of water. Sound waves have alternate zones of compression and rarifaction while water waves have alternate crests and troughs; but both are true wave series in the sense that they repeat both in space and in time. As you ride in an airplane across the ocean you see a regular series of wave crests passing beneath you. You observe that the surface of the water is first up, then down, then up, then down, then up, then down, as you travel by in *space.* But if you stay in one place—for example, sitting on the beach—and watch the surface of the water close to your feet, there is a repetitive pattern in *time.* The water moves up, then down, then up, then down, then up, then down, and so on as *time* goes by. It is this repetition that is the most characteristic quality of a wave series. Of course, there are non-repetitive waves, such as tidal waves when one enormous "mountain" of water moves across and breaks over the land. So, in one sense, a wave may be thought of as a kind of single pulse of energy, whether conveyed by water or by air. A shock wave from an explosion is another example of a single wave pulse.

In music we are concerned both with the successive series of waves producing regular repetition and also with the pulse-type wave which we get especially from percussion instruments; both kinds of waves play an important role in producing different qualities of musical tone. For example, the percussion wave formed when the hammer hits the string of a piano is essential to give piano music its full esthetic and emotional impact. The *chuff,* when the air first starts coming out of an organ pipe as its note is sounded, is also an essential ingredient of the esthetic and emotional content of the organ music. However, for the purposes of our discussion, I want to focus on the *regularly spaced* impulses that give to musical tone its *pitch.*

As you will recall, the string corresponding to the note of middle C on the piano gives out as its fundamental tone a series of regularly spaced air waves that strike the ear at 256 times per second (on the scientific pitch).

When a simple wave with no overtones is produced by an electronic oscillator, the tone is peculiarly boring. Such a wave is called a *sine* wave. Apparently, the music center of our brain does not respond favorably to such purity in tone. We much prefer to have the fundamental tone coupled with overtones of varying degrees of amplitude to give the total tone a richer quality. We even like to hear a singer introduce *vibrato* into the tone, making the pitch of the tone rise and fall slightly in regular rhythm perhaps four or five times per second. Thus, during a good part of the time when the tone is sounded, it is actually off pitch. Nevertheless, we find an esthetic and an emotional appeal in *vibrato.*

Of course, it is practically impossible to separate the esthetic from the emotional side of music. There are a few instances where one can say that the involvement is almost entirely emotional, however.

Some years ago, a friend of mine was asked to help with the sound effects in the production of a mystery play at a theater in New York. According to the story he told me (possibly with a few extra trimmings added, as he loved a good story), he was told to create a sound that would heighten the effect of horror when, at the end of the second act, a corpse fell out of the closet on the stage. He had heard that organ tones of very low frequency sometimes produced a psychological reaction of fear so he constructed two large organ pipes with tones so low that they sounded like a deep rumble rather than true musical tones. He tuned the pipes so that the pitch of one differed slightly from the pitch of the other and when sounded together they produced a "beat." This is the effect where the tone from one pipe will alternately reinforce and nullify the note from the other pipe so that one gets a slow "shake" in the combined tone. The theory is that these low tones are perceived less by the ear and more by the chest cavity, and that the shaking of the chest cavity produces a kind of instinctive fear.

It turned out that there was some delay in getting the pipes operating; the effect of their tone was not tried out until the dress rehearsal during the very afternoon before the show opened. Then, just before the end of the second act, the pipes were sounded, the corpse fell out of the closet, and five of the actors fainted! As the result of this, such fear was also produced in the hearts of the management that they decided never to try the device with an audience. Whether or not this story is completely true, most of us will agree that there is an emotional component in music that sometimes can be physiological in its impact.

The Intellectual Component of Music

As contrasted with the sensation produced by a single tone like that of the low organ pipe, it seems fair to conclude that the greater part of music has more of an intellectual than a physiological-emotional appeal. I grant that one can derive such intellectual satisfaction from a Bach fugue that by this very fact emotion is aroused. What I want to explore, however, are the components in the appreciation of music that can be called *intellectual* because they depend primarily on the *recognition of form* and not on direct physiological response.

Consider a melody, for example. As the succession of notes in the melody is played, we subconsciously associate these notes with the familiar notes of the scale. As I pointed out in the analysis of the music of the string, the notes of the scale are in turn associated with combinations of simple, integral numbers. When the eardrum is vibrated successively with frequencies that are related to each other by these simple integral ratios, the effect is intellectually satisfying.

There is very much the same dynamic pattern when related notes are played *simultaneously* to produce a musical chord. In the chord of the major triad, we have ratios that involve the simplest prime numbers, 2, 3, and 5. Of course, the number 1 is a prime number also but it is only present implicitly in such a chord. When the chord is sounded, the eardrum is vibrated by a complex wave, made up of different waves superimposed and having frequencies in the ratios of these prime numbers, numbers that are called *prime* because each is divisible only by itself and by the number *one*.

Of course, with melody and harmony, we have scarcely begun to explore the domain of the *form* of music. Another of the simple ingredients of form comes from the transposition of chords to other keys related to the key of the musical scale on which the composition is primarily based. I think that everyone will agree that for the appreciation of music, it is essential to be able to recognize that the triad of the chord of C major when transposed to the key of G major is the *same* chord but with all the frequencies raised by a factor of 3/2. Here we have a most important example of *Gestalt* psychology, the recognition of form as a whole. I doubt whether anyone will ever argue that, in recognizing a chord as a major triad transposed by a fifth, you stop to count the notes and identify the fact that each tone has had its frequency increased by 3/2. On the contrary, you recognize instantly the character of the major triad, whether it is played in any one of a dozen keys or transposed up three octaves or down three octaves from its original position. Of course a major triad played with its lowest tone at about sixteen vibrations per second might be a little more difficult to recognize, just as one played with its tones in the range above five thousand vibrations per second might also be difficult to recognize. But apart from these extremes, the triad has a unique character which is instantly identified even by persons with only rudimentary musical training.

Thus, in any musical composition, even of the most elementary sort, there is a whole tapestry of interrelations of dynamic form. Our intellectual perception and appreciation of the qualities of this pattern of dynamic form rests upon our ability to recognize almost instantly related *similarities* and *differences* of form.

Recognition of Audible Form

The cerebral mechanism by which we are able to identify patterns of dynamic form in a split second is still almost a complete mystery. It is logical to argue that we must have had experience with these forms, that by hearing them repeatedly we somehow acquire centers of identification so that, when these forms are presented to us, the total act of appreciation is made possible by interplay between these recognition centers.

Of course, it is trivial to say that a center of *recognition* or of *memory* is established by the repetition of the sensation to be remembered. I suppose this is true not only of waves perceived by the ear or by the eye but also of physical sensations. For instance, a hammer blow on the head: I am not sure how much repetition would be necessary in order to have the blow establish some kind of recognition center in the memory; in fact, it is conceivable that the blow might wipe out such a memory center instead of establishing it.

The repeated mental *recall* of the memory of a sensation also helps to anchor this point of recognition more firmly in the mind without the need of having the primary event repeated over and over again. There is a constant interplay of stimuli between centers of memory so that the whole process of memory takes place to a considerable degree by association, as is well known to psychologists.

A physical analogy of this cross-stimulation is provided by the piano itself. First depress the righthand foot pedal on the piano, sometimes called the "loud" pedal, thus taking the dampers off the strings. Then strike the note of middle C. You can prove easily that the tone coming from the C string will also set in vibration the other strings that are related to the overtones of this string. If you listen closely after you have struck the original note, you can hear the other strings giving out their tones. This is an example of a resonance transfer of energy. Of course, the energy from these other strings also will be passed back by sound waves to the original C string, so that there is a constant exchange of energy by a process analogous to "feedback" in cybernetics or control engineering.

This "feedback" interplay is important in a number of the areas of dynamic form which we want to explore later in the book, when we examine the life process in general and the nature of human beings in particular. For this reason I want to take the time here to explain feedback in some detail.

One of the simpler examples of feedback is the relation between the furnace and the thermostat that turns the furnace on when the house is too cold or turns the furnace off when the house gets too hot. The thermostat senses when the temperature falls below the desired level, and sends a signal down to the furnace that turns on the fire and produces heat. The heat comes up by way of ducts into the room where the thermostat is located and raises the temperature of the thermostat, until the mechanism senses that the room is too hot and turns the furnace off. Then the temperature in the room falls until the thermostat again senses that the room is too cold and turns the furnace back on. There is thus a kind of circular action: air to thermostat to furnace to air, round and round, cycle after cycle as long as the mechanism continues to operate. The ultimate result, the maintenance of the temperature of the house at the desired comfortable level, is achieved by the action of the mechanism in its cyclic *whole* and cannot be ascribed to any particular part. The result is achieved by cyclic interplay and not by part A moving part B moving part C and part C producing the result. In feedback there is a kind of intimate togetherness never found in a linear chain of cause and effect.

The furnace-thermostat mechanism is an example of a most important kind of relationship that plays a profound role not only in our mental processes but throughout the whole process of life. We shall explore this in much more detail in some of the later chapters. At the moment I only want to point out that it is the feedback or mutual exchange of signals between our recognition centers that is the core of our appreciation of music, of our ability to remember the music once we hear it, and of our ability to reproduce the music again. The point to emphasize is that we are dealing here with a pattern of *interrelations* of dynamic forms. Whitehead comments on our ability to identify patterns, saying that: "Some partial identity of pattern in the various characters of natural things issues in some partial identity of pattern in the mutual relations of those things. . . . It is evident that the doctrine involves the negation of absolute being. It presupposes the essential interdependence of things."

I am arguing that we must renounce the concept of *ab-*

solute being implicit in the argument that the universe is merely a *whole* composed of *parts,* a *whole* put together from particles which are the fundamental, indestructible building blocks possessing *absolute being.* I am arguing that the universe is a *whole* of dynamic form, a symphony woven with essential interdependence, and that *being* resides in its aspects of *wholeness,* in its cosmic *chords,* rather than in its individual *notes.*

Invariance in Transformation

As we look further into the nature of musical form, I think we are bound to get the feeling that these forms, these wholes, have an identity of their own far beyond the sum of the identities of their parts. I am trying to explore the question, "Where is ultimate reality?" But before getting entangled in abstruse, philosophical arguments, let's look over a few simple examples from another domain of music.

Let's consider what happens just before the performance when a symphony is broadcast. The musicians assemble on the stage of the auditorium. Then the conductor raises his baton and the symphony is on its way. We can think of the physical origin of the symphony at this point as in the *minds* of the conductor and the musicians. Impulses come from minds and activate muscles. From muscles energy passes to the bows of the violinists, and from bows to strings. Energy passes from air expelled from lungs to the reeds of the oboe and clarinet, from the muscles of the tympanist to the vibrating membrane of the kettledrum. Thus by these and a dozen other processes, the complex symphonic pattern of sound waves is produced in the air and travels to the microphone.

At the microphone this complex wave changes into an electrical wave and is carried by wires to the broadcasting station. After going through a number of further electronic transformations, it becomes a radio wave going out from

the tall antenna at the broadcasting station and may travel
one hundred miles before being picked up by another antenna at the point of reception. There the radio wave is
transformed back into an electrical wave, goes to the loudspeaker and by magnetic action sets another membrane in
motion that, in turn, produces air waves. If you are seated
before the loudspeaker, these air waves come to your eardrum, set it in motion, and thereby stimulate impulses in the
fibers of your auditory nerve. These impulses then travel
to your brain and set in motion the complex process of
cranial cybernetic feedback that enables you to "hear" the
symphony and enjoy its beauty.

What is the "reality" of the symphony? Can you say
that the *real* symphony is the sound waves, any more than it
is the electrical waves or the radio waves or the mysterious
brain waves by which you ultimately perceive it?

Here we have an example of *invariance under transformation*. We have a complex pattern of dynamic form stemming from the brain waves of one hundred musicians, fused
under the direction of the conductor's baton into a complex, flowing pattern of sound, transformed into a dynamic
pattern of electrical impulses, then into radio waves, back to
electrical impulses, back to sound, and finally, back to brain
waves in the audience one hundred miles away. It is an
incredible series of metamorphoses; but after passing
through these drastic transformations, the pattern still
emerges so unaltered that if a recording were made of the
radio broadcast in your home, it might be almost impossible
to distinguish it from a recording made in the studio.

In fact, it is interesting to ask the further question,
"What has happened to the dynamism of the symphony
when it is frozen into the grooves of a plastic record disk
or magnetized into the orientation of atoms on a magnetic
tape?" We must recognize that in either case the loss of the
dynamism is illusory. Both the plastic disk and the magnetic

tape are composed of atoms. In the disk and in the tape we have merely substituted the dimension of length for the dimension of time. The mingled chime of these sextillions of atoms in the disk or in the tape is quietly sounding the symphony in the silent record just as truly as the molecules of air sound the symphony in the auditorium where the broadcast took place. If you slip the disk with the record into its paper jacket and place it on the shelf of your record cabinet, the symphony continues to "sound" even though you do not hear it. In the coils of recording tape the music of the symphony is resounding continuously, although we have to feed the tape through a reproducer in order to make this atomic music audible again.

Both in mathematics and in mathematical physics it has been recognized for many years that such an *invariance under transformation* is one of the deepest tests of significant reality. In order to explain in a little more detail the meaning of this important concept of invariance, I want to discuss briefly an example or two.

In mathematics, one of the most useful symbolic expressions of dynamic form is the algebraic matrix. This consists of a square array of symbols which may be letters or numbers. Thus, we may have four rows of symbols with four symbols in each row, known as a four-times-four matrix. Frequently, these symbols refer to values related to coordinates, which may be coordinates of position like latitude and longitude; or the values may be velocities in the different coordinate directions. There are many possible choices of coordinates to describe any specific situation. When one changes from one set of reference coordinates to another, the values in the matrix are transformed according to certain recognized mathematical laws. But if the coordinates are a significant frame of reference for the situation involved, then the essential meaning of the matrix remains unaltered; the significant reality of its expression is unchanged by the coordinate transformation. That is why one can say that if there is a significant reality expressed which remains unaltered when the matrix undergoes transformation, then we have in this unaltered, underlying reality something that is far more significant, something that has a better claim to the word *real* than the particular coordinate values in one or the other of the expressions that depend upon the coordinates selected.

I am sure this all sounds horribly complicated. Let me give a simpler example. Suppose that in the course of spending the evening with an extraordinarily beautiful and attractive woman you suddenly feel that you are falling in love with her. You want to tell her that you love her. Now you can say, "I love you," or you can say, "Ich liebe dich," or, "Te amo," or, "Koham cic," or, "Mina raka stan snoia," or, "Jeg elsker dig." You can say the same thing in a hundred or more other languages.

As you switch from one language to another you are using different word symbols; but the message, the meaning, remains invariant under the transformation of words. Of course, you had better make sure that the girl knows the language you are speaking or there will be a break in the chain of invariance as you try to get the message through from your mind to hers.

If there is an emotion identifiable as love, is it not obvious that the true reality lies in the emotion, rather than in the particular words selected for its expression? If there is a harmony as recognizable as a major triad chord, is it not logical to say that the reality lies in the mingled chime of the chord and not in its individual notes, whether in C major or F-sharp major? Is it not reasonable to conclude that this reality is present whether this mingled chime is sounded by air waves, radio waves, electrical waves, or brain waves? Will you agree that true reality resides not in the *parts* but in the *whole?*

Reality and Unity

I believe that the meaning of music teaches us that reality is to be found in unity. The meaning of music shows us that the deepest reality is not in the millions of little pulses on the eardrum but in the unities of the forms whose interplay constitutes the living, dynamic song. In music we find overwhelming evidence that *the whole is more than the sum of the parts*. If this *whole* is really more than an additive aggregation of the *parts,* then it must have a reality of its own.

We cannot deny that *in the laboratory* when matter is broken down into its individualized structural parts—the electrons, the protons, the neutrons, and their cousins—then, under these highly special conditions, the fundamental particles do have reality. But I want to show you why I believe that the overwhelming preponderance of *significant* reality is to be found not in the reality of these extracted fundamental particles, but in the unities of the *wholes* from which these particles are formed when the *wholes* are broken down.

If you are willing to focus your mind in this new perspective, the realities of wholes rather than the realities of parts, then I can show you the amazing new patterns of significance that emerge when the phenomena of life, the phenomena of humanity, and the phenomena of the universe are viewed in this focus of unity. But before exploring this aspect of the meaning of music, I want to quote for you some passages from distinguished scientists and philosophers that point toward the validity of this new perspective that I am proposing.

My first quotation is from the volume entitled "Philosophy of Mathematics and Natural Science," by Hermann Weyl, who was as I mentioned before a member of the faculty for many years at the Institute for Advanced Study in Princeton, New Jersey. His interests ranged widely from the foundations of mathematics to the philosophy of art. I want to express my deepest gratitude for the inspiration that I have derived from his writings and from personal conversation with him at the Institute. In this passage that I am quoting, he is discussing the concept of wholeness as it has arisen in mathematical physics, as it has been discussed by biologists and psychologists, and as it may be extended in the future far more widely. He writes as follows:

"The wholeness conception in biology has been represented with a variety of nuances by Bertalanffy, Haldane, A. Meyer, Alverdes, v. Uexküll, Woltereck and others. Within psychology, gestalt psychology exhibits a similar tendency. . . . Even the atomic physical processes have very little similarity with the gross macroscopic action of a machine. Every atom is already a *whole* of quite definite structure; its organization is the foundation for possible organizations and structures of the utmost complexity. . . . There is no reason to see why the theoretical symbolic construction should come to a halt before the facts of life and of psyche. It may well be that the sciences concerned have not yet reached the required level. But that this limitation is neither fundamental nor permanent is already shown by psychoanalysis, in my opinion. The fact that in Nature 'all is woven into one whole,' that space, matter, gravitation, the forces arising from the electro-magnetic field, the animate and inanimate are all indissolubly connected, strongly supports the belief in the unity of nature and hence in the unity of the scientific method. There are no reasons to distrust it."

This statement of Hermann Weyl's must be given considerable weight because of his eminence both as a mathematician and a mathematical physicist. He is one of less than half a dozen men who have earned the right to speak authoritatively in this area because of their intimate familiarity both with the physical facts and with the structure of the mathematical laws and symbolism by which we are attempting to express the relationships of these facts.

Alfred North Whitehead also speaks with authority though his contributions as a mathematician have been less directly related to the areas of mathematical physics most intimately involved with this problem of wholeness. In his book on the "Adventures of Ideas." Whitehead remarks that in all analysis there is one supreme factor which is apt to be omitted, namely, the mode of togetherness. In his discussion of the relations of law to the occasions whose regularities suggest law, he writes as follows: "But there is no reason to doubt, that the laws are the outcome of the environment of electromagnetic occasions. This whole process of regression suggests an inversion of ideas. The laws are the outcome of the character of the behaving things: they are the communal customs of which Clement spoke. This conception should replace the older idea of given things with mutual behavior conditioned by imposed laws. What we know of external nature is wholly in terms of how the various occasions in Nature contribute to each other's natures. The whole environment participates in the nature of each of its occasions. Thus, each occasion takes its initial form from the character of its environment. Also, the laws which condition each environment merely express the general character of the occasions composing that environment. This is the doctrine of the definition of things in terms of their modes of functioning." In other words, Whitehead is saying that we must always keep in mind the togetherness expressed in the fact that the *whole* environment participates in the nature of each of its occasions. These dynamic forms of vibration that are the origin of musical tones have this essential character of wholeness, the whole string vibrating together, the whole drumhead vibrating together to produce the tone that is the ultimate expression of the wholeness, the unity.

Teilhard de Chardin in his writings also emphasized the aspect of the whole. In speaking of the variety of living forms he asked: "In these multiple combinations, is there really one which can be said to be *truer* than the others? Is there one, that is to say, which gives to the whole of living things a more satisfying coherence, either in relation to itself, or in relation to the world to which life finds itself committed?" In reply, he says: "I think we had better go back to what I said about the mutual relations between the *without* and the *within* of things. The essence of the real, I said, could well be represented by the 'interiority' contained by the universe at a given moment." It is in the interiority of the violin string, in the surge of vibrational energy back and forth in the form of waves, that we find the origin of the special quality of tone that comes from the string acting as a whole.

Finally, I want to quote the words of the distinguished philosopher, Professor Irwin Edman, of Columbia University. In his foreword to the Modern Library Edition of Henri Bergson's classic book on "Creative Evolution," he writes: "One of the most characteristically contagious passages of Bergson's works is in his little introduction to metaphysics, where he makes one feel and realize, almost as a poet might, the tension and the fluency of time, the urgency and poignancy of duration. Bergson was rebelling against the fixities and rigidities which both logicians and materialists had ascribed to reality. Bergson found reailty in movement and change themselves, an aperçu not uncongenial to the dynamic changing society in which he lived. If change was real, novelty was real; if novelty was real, freedom was real."

This is exactly the chain of logic that I want to forge from this discussion of the meaning of music. Music is change; it is *dynamic* form; and in this domain of dynamic, changing form, reality is to be found in the dynamic wholes rather than in static parts. Scientific experiments have established that atoms are likewise dynamic form. Therefore, I assert that reality is to be found in the unity of the wholeness of these dynamic forms, not in the parts obtained from them when they are artificially broken down. Finally, I want to show why it is logical to believe that in this dynamism of matter, of life and of humanity we find that the ultimate reality is freedom. This is the freedom that is the essence of the human spirit. This is the freedom of which Kierkegaard speaks when he writes: "What is this I myself? It is freedom."

I close this section with a quotation from the profound book on the "Nature and Destiny of Man," by Reinhold Niebuhr: "The problem of meaning, which is the basic problem of religion, transcends the ordinary rational problem of tracing the relationship of things to each other as the freedom of man's spirit transcends his rational faculties."

Part III

The Nature of Life

9

The Structure of Life

AMONG THE lighter traditions of academic life at The Johns Hopkins University, where I taught for thirty six years, was the custom of asking certain humorous questions in the oral examination taken by all the candidates for the degree of Doctor of Philosophy just before their graduation. In essence, these examinations were serious occasions. The student was displaying to the faculty his knowledge of his chosen field of study and his intellectual skill. Very few students failed the examination, but there was always present the spectre of a mental blackout and, as a rule, the students were under considerable tension. Whenever there was a feeling that tension was building up almost to the breaking point in an examination in Chemistry or the Life Sciences, some member of the faculty usually managed to ask the student to name the chemical elements most necessary to sustain life. The student always replied by writing on the board: "C HOPKINS CaFe." This always brought a smile and usually some relaxing of the tension. It was an old joke, going back so far into the early days of the University, almost a hundred years ago, that no one knew how it started. The phrase, of course, consisted of the chemical symbols for carbon (C), hydrogen (H), oxygen (O), phosphorus (P), potassium (K), iodine (I), nitrogen (N), sulfur (S), calcium (Ca), and iron (Fe). This list omits certain important chemical elements like sodium and chlorine; but it is a joke that many times served a useful purpose.

When we stop to think about the structure of living matter, it is amazing to realize that the near infinite complexity of life, found all the way from bacteria to man, is achieved almost completely with the help of only a dozen kinds of these building blocks, the chemical elements. Think of the five octillion atoms in your own body. Remember that five octillion peas would make a layer four feet deep over the entire surface of 1,250,000 planets, each the size of the Earth. Yet practically all of this inconceivably vast collection of atoms in your body consists of only about a dozen different kinds. It is extraordinary parsimony on nature's part.

In the perspective of our new knowledge of the musical structure of the atom, we can think of these twelve most important kinds of atoms as the notes of the musical scale in which nature writes the symphony of life. In order to understand the nature of the life process from the point of view of our new concept of the basic nature of matter, I want to show you how these twelve tones of the scale of the symphony of life are related to each other. Thinking of atoms as resembling little bells, we will refer to these twelve different bell-atoms as the chemical carillon of life.

The Chemical Carillon

Just as nature exhibits a certain parsimony in using so few notes for the scale of the music of life, she also is most economical in the way she constructs these twelve scale notes. They arise from astonishingly simple relations, strictly analogous to the relations we observed in the scale of the violin string, the scale of the drum, and the scale of the spherical bell.

First of all, to be meaningful, to contribute something new and different to the scale, a note must have a dynamic form differing from all the other members of its musical family that comprise the scale. In the language of physics, it must have its own unique set of quantum numbers. The easiest way to see how nature carries out this plan is to take a look at a few of the simpler kinds of atoms in the order of their increasing complexity.

The simplest kind of atom is hydrogen; and, as you know, hydrogen is one of our most familiar chemical friends. Water has the formula H_2O and, of course, H stands for hydrogen; it is the symbol used in the chemist's shorthand to denote this chemical element. Since our bodies contain so much water, there is a great deal of hydrogen present in us; and it is also a constituent of many other components of the body like fat, sugar, and protein.

Today the name *hydrogen* has an ominous overtone since this substance also plays a prominent role in the thermonuclear or hydrogen bomb. The nuclei of heavy hydrogen atoms can be made to combine or *fuse* together with the release of enormous amounts of energy. It is possible that someday conditions may be found under which it will be not too difficult to get all our body hydrogen to undergo nuclear fusion. Actually, if you could snap your fingers and in one instant release the nuclear energy in your body, you would explode with the force of more than a hundred bombs of the sort that fell on Hiroshima. It is startling to think of the latent energy that each of us possesses.

This powerful little hydrogen atom has an extraordinarily simple structure. Rutherford and Bohr portrayed it as a tiny solar system with one planetary electron. The nuclear "sun" at the center consists of nothing but a single proton, which is the elementary mass particle and carries a single elementary unit charge of positive electricity. Around this proton-sun there circulates just one electron, the elementary unit charge of negative electricity.

According to the modern wave-picture of the atom, we think of this electron not as a little planet moving in orbit around the nuclear sun but rather as a ball of fog enveloping this sun and thinning out indefinitely into space. This ball of fog has a spherical symmetry. It behaves as if it were vibrating in a single spherical wave form like the spherical bell, expanding and contracting as a whole. Of course, we must not take this picture too literally; as I have remarked so many times, we cannot hope to draw real *pictures* of nature at this most basic level. Still, the idea of vibration like that of a spherical bell gives us a more vivid feeling of the morphology of the relationships; it enables us to get the feel of the dynamic forms that are the essence of the atom.

You recall that the spherical bell expanding and contracting—everything out and everything in together—sounds the fundamental tone, the *do* of our scale. So we may think of the hydrogen atom as the bell of our chemical carillon that sounds *do*.

You recall that in the vibrations of the violin string you can have one loop or zone of vibration, or two loops, or three loops, but you cannot have a loop and a half. You have to have an *integral* number of loops. It is the same way with atoms. As we proceed from the simplest atom of hydrogen to the more complex bells of our carillon, we have to build up using integral units. Thus, after hydrogen we find the next element, *helium,* with two positive charges on its nuclear sun and two planetary electrons with negative charges. This change from *one*ness to *two*ness produces a profound change in the chemical properties of the atom. Hydrogen atoms are gregarious. They combine readily with each other and with almost every other kind of atom. Unless you raise the temperature of hydrogen gas up to 1,000 degrees centigrade or more, you will find nearly all the atoms going together around in pairs, H_2 molecules. You do not find a hermit hydrogen, H, except on rare occasions. Hydrogen is also very plentiful in nature. There are far more hydrogen atoms in the universe than there are atoms of any other kind. By way of contrast, helium is quite rare. There is no helium to speak of in our bodies, almost none in the solid and liquid world around us, only a trace of helium in the air, but some helium in the sun, whence its name (from the Greek *helios,* meaning sun). And the helium atom is a hermit; it almost never combines with any other atom, not even with itself.

The helium atom's inertness or unwillingness to combine with other atoms originates in the "satisfaction" that its two electrons seem to find in each other's company. While the one electron of the hydrogen atom is extremely lonesome and is ready to pair with another electron at almost any time, the two electrons of helium are a happily married couple, quite content to go their own way and having no interest at all in any other members of the chemical family.

(Again, do not take my personalizing of the electrons too seriously; I do not think that the electrons have sex!)

The two Dutch physicists Uhlenbeck and Goudsmit suggested that this phenomenon is due to the possession of *positive and negative spin.* Many scientists today wonder whether *spin* is just the right concept. At any rate, it is clear that here at this most basic level in the structure of the Universe we have an example of *two*ness, the *yin* and *yang* of the Oriental philosophers.

It seems, by and large, that sex is also an example of twoness in the structure of nature. My former colleague Adolph Meyer, psychiatrist-in-chief at The Johns Hopkins Medical School, once remarked to me somewhat facetiously that if sex could only be introduced into mathematics we would all be Einsteins. So I am going to talk about the electrons as having *yin* and *yang,* and sometimes think of them as being feminine and masculine. I hope that this conferring of gender on the electrons does not irritate my scientific colleagues.

You can see that this personalized perspective does give us a little feel for the pattern of behavior of the helium atom. There we have the boy and the girl electrons happily singing a duet together, so content, so engrossed in their mutual activity that they refuse to play games with any other atoms except on the most rare occasions. And remember that it is the *exclusion principle* of Wolfgang Pauli that guarantees that we will have electrons of the opposite sex singing together in the helium atom.

While there is no general agreement about nature's reason for adopting the exclusion principle as a fundamental component of the structure of nature, it seems to be closely related to the problem of establishing identity. If the violin string sings its fundamental tone and vibrates with one loop—one arch up followed by one trough down, back and forth—there is no way to have two waves, each with a single arch spanning the string from one end to the other, and still maintain the waves with separate identities. We can, of course, have a wave with an amplitude twice that of our original wave; and if you want to say this is two waves superimposed one on the other, you have a right to use this phraseology. But there is absolutely no way to tell which wave is which; and it is far more logical to say that we have only *one* wave present whether the amplitude is small or large. By way of contrast, if we have a wave with *one* loop and another wave with *two* loops superimposed on it, then it is possible to see clearly with the help of slow-motion vision that there are two distinct waves present. Thinking along these lines it seems clear why, at the basic level of the electron, we must have a male and female electron present if we are to have *two* electrons. At any rate, that is the way nature operates. The comparatively few helium atoms in the universe go on their lonely way, their paired boy-and-girl electrons quite content with each other's company, almost never linking with any other electrons. Thus the helium atom does not play a role in the music of life.

The Eight-Bell Cycle

As we pass to the more complex patterns of dynamic behavior beyond helium in the periodic table of the chemical elements, it becomes increasingly difficult to devise any kind of drawing that even suggests the essential features of the vibration. In trying to think of a better way to give you an idea of these dynamic relationships, I suddenly remembered a story about a trip that my friend, Professor Alexander Goetz, made in China years ago.

This all happened back in the 1920s when the government of China was endeavoring to improve the instructional quality in the various Chinese universities. My friend was invited to spend some months at a university in the heart of China, seldom visited by western people. On arrival at his post, he asked that he be permitted to live in the Oriental manner; so he was offered a house near a Buddhist temple on the outskirts of the university. In return for this privilege, he was told by the abbot that he must spend a certain amount of time meditating about the principles of life.

The abbot explained that it was customary for the priest of this temple to accept a meditation problem, spend some time each day pondering on it, and then return to the abbot when he was satisfied that he had found the correct answer. My friend agreed to this proposition and was given a small folded slip of paper which he was to examine on his return to his temple. A few days later he unfolded the paper and found drawn upon it a circle with a dot in the center. He spent some time every day for a couple of weeks looking at this esoteric symbol and finally decided that the dot represented man and the circle represented the horizon of his capacity to understand his *raison d'etre*. No matter how far man traveled, he was still always at the center of the circle formed by this horizon. So one day Goetz went back to the monastery and was granted an audience with the abbot. He told the abbot his solution to the problem and the abbot replied; "My son, your answer is typically western. So return to your temple and meditate at greater length." Unfortunately, my friend's visit to the university terminated before he solved the problem.

Twenty years later, I went to visit my friend at the university in the United States where he was teaching at that time. When I came into his secretary's office, she explained that the professor had visitors and asked me to sit down and wait for a few minutes. About ten minutes later, the door to his office opened and three Chinese walked out and silently left the building. When my friend learned from his secretary that I was waiting to see him, he rushed out, shook hands and said excitedly: "You remember the story I told you about my experiences in the Buddhist temple in China? I have just been visited by three emissaries from the abbot who came to inquire if I had advanced my understanding by my meditation on the dot and the circle!"

Now another twenty years have passed, China has changed profoundly, and I fear that my friend will never learn the abbot's solution to his problem. However, I have been meditating on it myself and want to propose my own solution. I believe that the dot and the circle stand for the *yang* and the *yin,* the positive and negative principles of the universe, much discussed in Oriental philosophy. And I believe that this doctrine of *yang* and *yin* is just one example of the widespread recognition of twoness in the universe. We encounter twoness in many aspects of our universe both inanimate and animate. There are the positive and negative charges of electricity; there are the two poles of magnetism; there are the aspects of *within* and *without;* we can *have* and we can *have not;* and there is the *male* and *female* dichotomy that appears in so much of living matter.

The dynamic forms of electron waves are certainly among the most basic aspects of our universe. Therefore, it is not surprising to find the electron exhibiting a twoness in a way that is even more fundamental than its twofold wave which corresponds to the tone of the octave. Whether the twoness of the electron is truly a spin as suggested by Uhlenbeck and Goudsmit does not matter as much to us as the basic fact that here at the simplest level of dynamic form we find twoness. So I propose to use in my diagrams a dot to denote the charge cloud of the "masculine" electron having *Yang* and a circle to represent the "feminine" electron having *Yin*. The density of the dots or of the circles represents the density of charge, the fog. When a dot is shown within the circle, then the *two* electrons thus represented are paired like the two electrons in helium, which are so satisfied with each other that they refuse to link up with the electrons in any other atoms.

When we proceed from *hydrogen* with its one positive charge on the nucleus, through *helium* with two, to the next kind of atom, *lithium,* with three positive charges, the pattern of threeness gives us a completely new kind of behavior. What form of vibration will this third electron have? We have exhausted the possibilities of spin, of "sex difference" with the male and female electrons of the helium atom. We have no other possibilities for one-loop vibrations. Because the Pauli exclusion principle necessitates a different pattern of behavior for the third electron, we turn back to observe the dynamic form of the string and the drum to find a suggestion for the next simplest pattern.

This pattern is obviously going to be one with two loops of vibration if the principle of maximum simplicity is followed, which it is. You remember that, in the string, this overtone had the pattern where the left half of the string moved up while the right half moved down; and the two halves alternated up and down in "seesaw" fashion. In the spherical drum it was the pattern where the inner half of the drum moves up while the outer half moves down. In the spherical bell it is a pattern where the zones of vibration look like the skins of an onion, an inner zone contracting while an outer zone expands. We believe that this is the kind of dynamic form associated with this third electron in the lithium atom.

Thus, the inner two electrons behave just like the pair in helium and stay very much to themselves in the core of the lithium atom; but the outer electron has this two-loop pattern of vibration and is extremely active in joining with electrons on other atoms. As a result of this, instead of existing as a gas like hydrogen and helium (which have to be cooled to over two hundred and fifty degrees below zero centigrade before they can be made to solidify even under considerable pressure), lithium is found as a metal that has to be heated to about one thousand four hundred degrees centigrade before it will vaporize at normal atmospheric pressure.

Proceeding up the atomic chime, we now add still another positive charge to the nucleus and thus have four electrons surrounding it; this gives us the element *beryllium*. As you might guess, this fourth electron could "pair up" with the third in another positive-negative-spin combination or, in our more vivid and less scientific language, male-and-female combination, with both electrons having the dynamic form with two loops of vibration. You might say; "Well, then, beryllium must be a gas." This is an example of how dangerous it is to jump to conclusions. It turns out that with the dynamic pattern of two loops the beryllium boy-and-girl electrons are not nearly as content with each other's company as the electrons in helium; and beryllium is found as a metal with an even higher boiling point than lithium; it has to be heated to about two thousand five hundred degrees centigrade to make it vaporize under atmospheric conditions.

This unexpected behavior is largely the result of the

energy conditions of these dynamic forms. If the beryllium atoms are aligned in regular order in a crystal, the influence of regularity somehow "persuades" the outer boy-girl pair of electrons to break up and go jump into the crowd and dance with the other trillion or so electrons in neighboring atoms. This example of conflicting tendencies is a most interesting phenomenon. There is the tendency for the pairing-up, the hermit-like existence that one finds in helium; and there is also the tendency for communal living that one finds in the metallic beryllium. The pattern of behavior is determined largely by the amount of energy associated with it. As a rule, nature seeks the lowest energy level.

The element with a shell of five electrons is called *boron.* When the fifth electron is added to form this element, we get for the first time an example of an unsymmetrical type of vibratory wave. You remember that our first pair of electrons used up all the possibilities for a one-loop wave. There are two possibilities of positive and negative spin, or male or female as we have facetiously called them. The next two electrons used up this same pair of possibilities for two-loop waves.

"Well," you may say, "isn't it obvious? This fifth electron will just be a three-loop electron." But think what happens in the case of the drumhead. As you can see in Figure 1, just as soon as we go to two loops, there is both the possibility of having concentric loops with one inside the other *and* the possibility of having the two loops side by side, one on the left and one on the right. This is an unsymmetrical vibration in the sense that the line separating the two loops points in a certain direction. We can have it pointing up and down or we can have it pointing sidewise.

When we go over to the vibration of the spherical bell, there is a precisely similar situation. We can have the two loops concentric, one inside the other, as we did for the electrons in lithium and beryllium; but we also have the

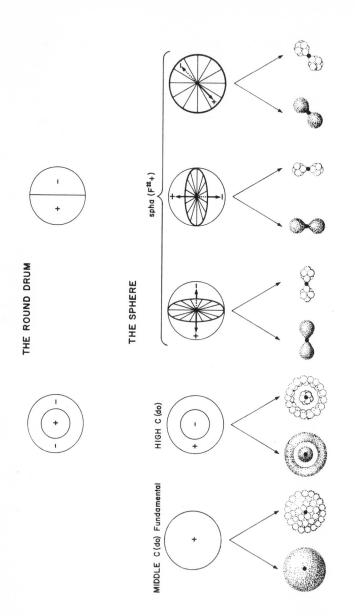

FIGURE I

Vibrations in Drum, Sphere and Atom

possibility of having the upper half of the bell expand while the lower half contracts. And this is exactly what happens in the case of the fifth electron in *boron*.

As you can see in the case of the spherical bell, there is a plane which cuts across the sphere separating the upper half from the lower half, a kind of equatorial plane. Think of an arrow sticking up in the center of this plane, in the manner that the mathematicians call *perpendicular* to, or *normal* to the plane. We can have this arrow pointing up; we can have it pointing to the right; or we can have it pointing out of the paper toward us. There are these three possibilities because of the three dimensions of our space in which we live: *length, breadth,* and *height.* You may ask; "Aren't there all kinds of possibilities in between?" I reply that mathematics shows us that there are only three *independent* orientations, that the other orientations can always be constructed from these three, and that we need only consider the possibilities of the arrow pointing in each of these three directions which the mathematicians normally denote by the symbol $x, y,$ and z. In terms of dynamic form, the electron density or the electron "fog" will look like that shown in the illustration for boron. There are these two pearshaped arms of fog protruding from the little ball in the center formed by the two electrons in the helium pattern and the two electrons in the two-shelled onion pattern of beryllium.

It is completely arbitrary whether we say that in the case of boron we choose to have these pear-shaped arms pointing upward and pointing downward; but let us select this for purposes of convenience. We now have an electron dynamic form which is different from those of the preceding electrons; it has quantum numbers differing from those of the preceding electrons that were added in forming the preceding four elements. Following the convention of quantum chemistry, I will refer to these fog patterns as *orbitals* to imply that they are associated with the older orbit ideas from the Rutherford-Bohr model but that they convey a basically different meaning.

This particular dynamic form indicated in the picture for boron is called a *p-orbital.* The selection of the symbol *p* was made when physicists were studying the spectra of atoms; and as I mentioned before, *p* actually stands for principal. However, for purposes of memory, it is convenient to think of this as also the initial letter of *pear,* which helps us to remember the pear-shaped arms associated with this particular dynamic form.

Boron is again somewhat metallic in character when found as a pure chemical element, though it differs sufficiently from familiar metallic behavior so that it is called a metalloid. Like beryllium it must be heated to two thousand five hundred degrees centigrade to make it vaporize under normal atmospheric conditions. Like helium, lithium, and beryllium, boron does not play any significant role in the life process.

When we add the sixth electron, however, we get the element that is the most important of all in making life possible, the element *carbon.* If we could observe a single carbon atom floating alone in space the chances are that we would see a pattern of its electron fog looking like the picture in Figure 2; though we might find that with the presence of the four electrons, the fog cloud would point toward the corners of the tetrahedron circumscribed around the atom with the nucleus at its center. In other words, there is interaction between the different patterns of vibration in the atom. This interaction plays a most important part in the ultimate determination of the atom's behavior. At this point, however, I want to stress the different *types* of dynamic form and the way in which their frequencies are related to the notes of the spherical scale; and I will not digress into a discussion of the effects of interaction. We will survey this later when we talk about the unity of the life process.

1 HYDROGEN

2 HELIUM

3 LITHIUM

4 BERYLLIUM

5 BORON

6 CARBON

7 NITROGEN

8 OXYGEN

9 FLUORINE

10 NEON

FIGURE 2

PERIODIC TABLE of CHEMICAL ELEMENTS

Thinking in an imaginative way about the relationships of these dynamic forms, we can regard hydrogen as the fundamental tone in this carillon of life and think of carbon as providing the next most important note. On the spherical scale we have the usual notes of our violin string scale—*do, re, mi, fa, sol, la, ti, do*—but we also have the note that is introduced by the unsymmetrical type of vibration where the upper half of the sphere expands while the lower half contracts. Somewhat facetiously and with the idea of making this extra note easy to remember, I suggested that we call it *spha*. Since the last electron added to form the carbon atom had this unsymmetrical type of vibration and since I suggested that we think of this as pointing in the vertical direction generally labelled by mathematicians with the symbol y, I suggest that we call the tone that carbon contributes to our chemical carillon by the name *sphay*. This name then implies the relationship with the vibration of the spherical bell, the fact that this tone lies near *la* in the violin string scale and that the last electron added was thought of as having an orientation in the y direction.

Without taking too much time at this point to go into details of the construction, I want to go on to portray the patterns of vibration in the other four chemical elements that together with carbon and hydrogen make up the half dozen most important kinds of atoms for the life process. These are *nitrogen* (N), *oxygen* (O), *phosphorus* (P), and *sulfur* (S). If you look in a chemistry textbook you will see that these four together with *carbon* (C) make a compact group lying near the center of the first two rows of the diagram of chemical elements that is generally called the *Periodic Table*.

The nucleus with seven positive charges is the basis of the atom of nitrogen. This also is an extremely active kind of atom and its linkage with other atoms plays a most important role in the structure of living matter. It has three pairs of pear-shaped arms forming a kind of triple cross in space.

When we go on to eight positive charges on the nucleus, we now find that the added electron must share one of these three unsymmetrical types of vibration and, therefore, must have a spin opposite to the electron already occupying that position. This leaves the oxygen atom with only two electrons that do not have partners. This is why oxygen in so many compounds does unite with just two other atoms. This is why the formula for water is H_2O or, written out more fully, H-O-H. The oxygen atom is sharing its two unpaired electrons with hydrogen atoms.

If you have followed the argument so far, you may guess that when we go on to nine positive charges on the nucleus, adding still another electron, this will pair up with one of the electrons already present and vibrating in the unsymmetrical wave pattern, thus leaving us only one unpaired electron. This is why this atom, *fluorine,* has a tendency to form compounds where just one fluorine atom unites with one other atom. Finally, when we go on to ten positive charges and add still another electron we now have all the electrons in the unsymmetrical types of vibration present in pairs. Call them negative and positive spins, or call them male and female, if you prefer. At any rate, this atom, *neon*—where all the possible vibration states with one and two loops are occupied by a pair of electrons—has such an extremely stable structure that it is a gas much like helium. We have here an example of the periodicity encountered as we go up the carillon of atoms with electrons sounding tones of higher and higher pitch.

I do not want to take the time at this point to extend this survey further since this is not a book on chemistry but rather a survey of certain philosophical principles. However, I do want to point out that we have here a beautiful example of the way in which the structure of reality mirrors the structure of mathematics. With one and two loops of vibration we have the possibility of ten different forms as may be seen by counting the ten different types in the bottom line of Figure 1. So the combination of the basic twoness, the *Yang* and the *Yin,* combined with the basic forms of one-loop and two-loop vibrations, give us a pattern of dynamic forms that determine the first ten chemical elements or kinds of atoms.

As we proceed further in the periodic table of chemical elements, we find that the corresponding three-loop possibilities give us eight more chemical elements, each of which is closely related in chemical properties to the element just above it in the table. In other words, the pattern of dynamic form that we observed in the two-loop vibrations of the spherical bell (Figure 1) is repeated exactly in the atoms where the added electron has three loops in the vibration. It is this kind of repetition that justifies the application of the adjective *periodic* to this table of elements.

Without going into the details I want to point out that just as the addition of two loops provided vibrations of more complex symmetry, three loops provide still more complex patterns of symmetry. These can be determined directly from the wave-mathematics; they match precisely and explain exactly the appearance of the additional chemical elements beyond argon. Thus, we get these families: the first short family of hydrogen and helium (2); the next family where we have the numbers $2 + 2x3$; then the family of the numbers $2 + 2x3 + 2x5$; and finally, the family of the numbers $2 + 2x3 + 2x5 + 2x7$.

Remember that we worked out the simple musical scale of the violin string with the use of the prime numbers 2, 3, and 5. Although it seemed logical to go on and try a note formed with the help of the number 7, such a note has not been accepted as part of conventional music. Nature in playing tunes with three-dimensional dynamic forms constructs the atom-bell to sound the notes of the chemical scale in much the same way, using 2, 3, and 5 but also adding a few very heavy kinds of atoms that do involve 7. However, it is interesting that in building the structure of *life,* nature selects the bells for this carillon that are related only to the lower prime numbers 2, 3, and 5, like the notes of our conventional musical scale. In fact, it is extraordinary that with such large chemical resources at her command—ninety-two naturally occurring kinds of atoms—nature selects only about a dozen to play the vast majority of the "notes" in the symphony of life. It is these few kinds of atoms, essential to all living matter, these bells in the chemical carillon, that we now wish to examine in more detail.

The Chime of Life

Suppose that some biochemist invents a kind of hypodermic needle with a point so fine that it can be inserted into any part of your body without pain or injury. Suppose that you take this instrument and extract one hundred atoms from your body, selecting them by blind chance, completely at random. You then sort these atoms out under the magic microscope, identify the kinds of atoms you have found, and count to see how many of each kind there are.

According to the best information that chemists have compiled, out of these one hundred atoms, the chances are that sixty-three will be hydrogen atoms. Sixty-three per cent of your body, atomically speaking, is made up of this simplest kind of atom—a single proton surrounded by the little ball of fog made up of a single electron. If we think of the hydrogen atom as representing the oneness principle of Nature, you are highly endowed with this special kind of unity.

If you have sorted out the atoms in piles you will find that after the pile of hydrogen atoms, the next largest collection is composed of oxygen atoms. Out of the one hundred atoms that you selected, you will find that twenty-six

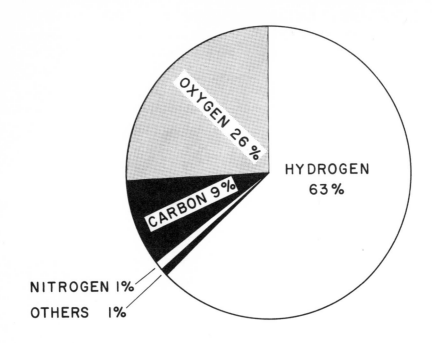

HYDROGEN	_____	63 %
OXYGEN	_____	26 %
CARBON	_____	9 %
NITROGEN	_____	1 %
OTHERS	_____	1 %
		100 %

FIGURE 3

ATOMIC COMPOSITION of the HUMAN BODY

are oxygen. These fractions are shown graphically in the anatomic-atom pie in Figure 3. Recall that oxygen is the kind of atom that has four out of the six possible threeness modes of vibration represented in its dynamic structure.

In descending order of numbers, the next pile of atoms will be made up of carbon, a pile representing only nine out of the total of one hundred atoms that you have selected. Remember that carbon is the kind of atom that has two of the three-loop vibrations in its outer shell. If you have kept count, you will find that there are only two remaining atoms on the plate under your microscope lens. If you tried this experiment of selecting atoms just once, then these two remaining atoms might be almost anything. The residue of two in the selection of a hundred objects from a collection of five octillion represents a poor statistical average. On the other hand, if you repeated this selection of one hundred atoms from your body about ten thousand times (a rather boring procedure), then on the average you would find that one of the two remaining atoms would be nitrogen. In the total count of atoms, your body contains about one per cent of these nitrogen atoms which have three of the six possible modes of three-loop vibrations filled.

The one remaining atom could be any of the other ninety-two naturally occurring varieties, since a collection of five octillion atoms is almost certain to have at least one of each of the ninety-two varieties represented. However, the chances of this one atom being either calcium or phosphorus are pretty good (though there is a fair chance that it might be potassium, sulfur, sodium, chlorine, magnesium, or even iron manganese and iodine). In the table in Figure 3, the percentage of these atoms present is also given and you can see that it is extremely low. Of course, we must remember that even these chemical elements occurring in small amounts can still be essential for the life process.

Still thinking of the enormous complexity of the pattern

of life in a human body, we are bound to be puzzled as to why nature plays ninety-eight per cent of the notes in the symphony of life with only three kinds of atom-bells. Of course, we must keep in mind that, when these atom-bells are linked together by sharing their electrons, the notes of the tune that they play are greatly altered. If we think of each of these clusters of atoms, the molecules, as an instrument of the orchestra that plays the symphony of life, then we find that nature does play on a variety of instruments comparable to that of a real symphony orchestra, with quite a few rare and special types of horns, flutes, and drums introduced now and then when there is a particularly difficult or dramatic passage to be rendered. We now turn to examine the nature of some of these molecular instruments.

The Instruments of Life's Orchestra

Just as a violin may be regarded as the basic instrument of a symphony orchestra, the water molecule is certainly the basic instrument of the orchestra of life. Not only is water the fundamental constituent of most of the body fluids like blood, lymph and spinal fluid, it plays an even more basic role as the fundamental constituent in cytoplasm, the fluid comprising the medium inside every one of the living cells of the body where metabolism response and growth take place at the most fundamental level. Water may certainly claim not only to be "the trilling wire in the blood" of T. S. Eliot, but the beating heart at the core of life.

Of all the fluids that nature might have selected as carrier and solvent for life, why water? I should think science-fiction writers might have a lot of fun speculating about strange beasts on planets circulating around other suns in other constellations where the life fluid was not water but ammonia or hydrogen sulfide. Undoubtedly, the temperature that nature selected for the life process, just under one hundred degrees Fahrenheit for man, must have been a governing factor in the selection of the life fluid.

Is it conceivable that on some remote planet in the Andromeda nebula there are creatures with hydrogen sulfide in their veins? Of all the million-odd chemical compounds, this substance with the formula H_2S is the most closely related to water (H_2O), since sulfur lies just below oxygen in the periodic table of chemical elements. If there really are such sulfurous beings, the planet which they inhabit must have a relatively cold temperature, because hydrogen sulfide boils at a little over sixty degrees *below* zero centigrade (as contrasted with water which boils at one hundred degrees *above* zero centigrade). From this point of view, in spite of the sulfurous atmosphere generally attributed to Hell, it is extremely unlikely that the Devil has hydrogen sulfide flowing in his veins, if the temperature of the Infernal Region is as high as we are led to believe.

When we discuss the dynamics of the life process in the next chapter, other reasons will appear for the choice of water as the fluid of life. At this point I merely want to call your attention to one of the most remarkable properties of water molecules (discovered fairly recently), namely, that they can swap partners with the greatest of ease. This is the phenomenon known as *hydrogen bonding*. To see the nature of this swapping, let's take a look at the structure of the water molecule. At the bottom of Figure 4 there is a picture of the water molecule as it is frequently represented in a freshman chemistry class using balls joined together with sticks. As you can see the oxygen atom is in the middle, with a hydrogen atom on each side so placed that the angle between is just a little over ninety degrees. The reason for this arrangement in the water molecule lies in the structure of the oxygen and the hydrogen atoms.

At the top of Figure 4 you see the diagrams that give a rough idea of the density of the electron-wave "fog" cloud for hydrogen and for oxygen. You recall that in the hydro-

Electron-wave Fog Clouds

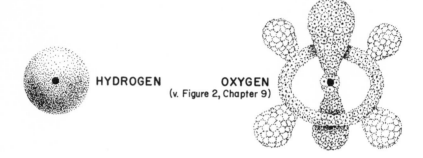

HYDROGEN

OXYGEN
(v. Figure 2, Chapter 9)

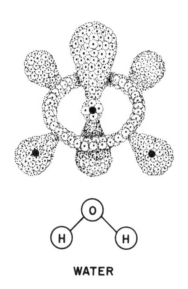

WATER

FIGURE 4

ELECTRON DENSITY DIAGRAMS

gen atom there is the nucleus in the center (shown by the black dot) surrounded by the electron fog that is densest at the center and thins out as the distance from the nucleus becomes greater. This fog cloud has spherical symmetry, that is, it is shaped like a sphere although it does not have any distinct surface. The oxygen atom is far more complicated. There are ten positive charges on the nucleus (shown again as a heavy black dot at the center). In the normal electrically neutral atom of oxygen there are consequently ten electrons making up the fog cloud.

It is important to realize that one cannot speak of electrons maintaining their identity when there are ten of them surrounding a nucleus as in the oxygen atom. What Whitehead calls the "togetherness" is so dominant that, in effect, we have just a single complex wave pattern. In the course of time this complex wave may split off part of itself and we say that the atom has lost an electron. This splitting takes place according to quantum rules. The oxygen cannot lose half an electron or one and a half electrons. Whenever the ball of fog splits and part of it is lost, this must always take place in distinct integral units of electrical charge; the same is true when some "fog" is adsorbed from a neighboring atom or from a small unit fog droplet (an electron) that happens to be passing by. This *particle* aspect of the exchange of charge has given scientists a mental habit of thinking of the total atom as *made up* of particles; but we are becoming more and more aware of the fact that the behavior pattern emphasizes almost exclusively the *togetherness* aspect and that it scarcely makes sense or conveys truth to speak of individual electrons as being present in the complex fog of the atom.

Tracing the evolving complexity as we pass from hydrogen with its one charge on the nucleus through helium with two, lithium with three, and so on up to oxygen with ten, we can associate different features of the oxygen cloud with the dynamic forms that we found in the simpler atoms. We believe that there is a denser region of fog immediately surrounding the nucleus at the center of the atom. As I mentioned earlier, I have tried to convey some sense of this with the dot and circle notation, the dots indicating the *Yang* component and the circles representing the *Yin* component of this one-loop or *fundamental tone* aspect of the complex vibrations in the wave cloud. In the same way, there is an outer ring of *Yang* and *Yin* due to the two-loop or high-*do* component in the vibration. The part of the fog which is the equivalent of the last four electrons added has the threefold or three-loop vibration that would produce the protruberances along the *x* axis, the *y* axis, and the *z* axis, more or less of equal size if we forget the interaction of the different parts of the cloud. Since we must have the equivalent of four electrons in three of these sets of pear-shaped knobs, it means that one pair has both the *Yang* and the *Yin*, leaving us two pairs where there is only the equivalent of one electron in each and spins do not cancel out. The result of this is the tendency of the oxygen atom to share these two pairs with other atoms giving it a *valency* of two, chemically speaking.

In the fog-pattern drawing for water, we show how a hydrogen atom attaches itself to each of these two unsatisfied knobs of the fog cloud. When this happens, then every part of the oxygen cloud has its *yang* and *yin*, or complementary spins; and each of the two hydrogen atoms also is now surrounded by a fog cloud of *yang* and *yin*. Thus, with the principle of twoness satisfied throughout the entire fog cloud, we have this stable cluster of H-O-H, the water molecule.

But it turns out that when H-O-H molecules are massed together, they are not as stable as one might expect. Put a large number of them next to each other, as we have them in a drop of water, and some of the hydrogen nuclei show a tendency to wander away from home. You note that each water molecule consists of an oxygen atom in the center, yet has three pairs of knobs, the result of the threeness of the unsymmetrical vibration that can take place in either one of the three dimensions of space. Three pairs of knobs add up to three sets of two each, or six knobs protruding from the oxygen atom altogether. In the water molecule, two of these knobs have hydrogen nuclei imbedded in them out toward the tip but the other four are unoccupied by any such visitors. When a knob having a hydrogen nucleus imbedded in it gets near an empty knob on the oxygen atom of an adjoining water molecule, then the hydrogen atom has a tendency to stray over to the neighbor's knob. The result of this is that a large number of hydrogen atoms spend their time effectively hovering between two knobs on adjoining oxygen atoms. The result is a kind of special interaction between water molecules that is called *hydrogen bonding* because it is a kind of bridge of fog established between neighboring molecules due to the presence of a hydrogen atom that, so to speak, cannot decide whether to hop one way or the other and so lies in between two adjacent knobs. As a result, not only each individual water molecule has this high degree of togetherness but the whole collection of molecules that make up liquid water are all bridged together so that there is an overall collective togetherness also.

Adding together all the factors that tend to push the electron cloud around, it is found that the central oxygen atom is more strongly enveloped in the fog than the two positively charged hydrogen nuclei out in the knobs. The result is that there is a kind of residual negative charge around the oxygen atom and residual positive charges around the hydrogen atoms. This uneven distribution of charge creates an electric *dipole*. If there is a negative charge in the neighborhood, the molecule twists around, pointing its positively charged knobs with the hydrogen nuclei toward the neighboring negative charges because opposites attract in the world of electricity. This means that atoms or clusters of atoms with charges tend to surround themselves with oriented water molecules when they get into water. In other words, substances which are made up of clusters of atoms with dipole charges are highly soluble in water. The high solubility in water of such charged atoms and clusters of atoms (called *ions*) is one of the factors that make water an ideal fluid for the life process.

We now want to examine a very special and important class of atom clusters or molecules that ionize and become electrically charged in a very special way. These are the amino acids, which along with water may be classed as among the most important ingredients in the structure of life.

The Chords of Life

The analysis of the atomic composition of the human body shows that there are about a dozen kinds of atoms that are the most important in the life process. We can think of these dozen atoms as the twelve tones that constitute the musical scale in which the symphony of life is written. Extending this point of view a little farther, we can think of the special combinations of these atoms in clusters, the molecules, as the musical chords that are the principal ingredients of the harmony of life. We have just examined the nature of that important molecule with three atoms, the molecule of water, that can be regarded as the major triad chord in this scale. We now survey briefly a group of two dozen molecules, called the *amino acids,* all of which have a common structural pattern and constitute the chords which, next to water, play by far the most important part in the composition of life's harmony. Structurally these molecules are considerably more complex than water. They range from the simplest, *glycine,* with ten atoms to the most complex, *thyroxine,* with thirty atoms.

All the members of this amino-acid family have a chain-like structure. The links in the chain are mostly carbon atoms, though occasionally there is a nitrogen, an oxygen, or a sulfur link. The chain can be stretched out in a single straight line; there may be side chains; or there may be occasional rings. All these molecules possess a special characteristic feature. Attached to the carbon atom at one end we find a quadruplet made up of a nitrogen atom and three hydrogen atoms; also attached at the same point is a triplet made up of another carbon atom and two oxygen atoms. In the grouping that I have just described, both the triplet and the quadruplet are charged, the former having a negative and the latter a positive electrical charge. It is easy, however, for one of the hydrogen atoms to hop occasionally from the quadruplet to the triplet, making both groups electrically neutral. The presence of this triplet-quadruplet pattern makes possible the bridging between the amino acids and surrounding water molecules, which we have called "hydrogen bonding." The result is that the amino acids are moderately soluble in water and they can be transported by the life dynamics not only in the cytoplasm, the fluid inside the body's cells, but also in many of the other body fluids.

Perhaps the most important property of these triplet-quadruplet structures is their ability to link with each other. When two hydrogen atoms from the quadruplet join with an oxygen atom from the triplet, a molecule of water, H_2O, is formed, thus bonding together the carbon atom on one amino acid to the nitrogen atom on another. In this way dozens of amino acids may be linked together to form a giant molecule. Frequently the amino acids are linked to form one long chain; at other times they can form a branched structure; or there may be combinations of the two. In terms of our musical analogy the atoms may be thought of as tones or musical notes; groups of the tones (atoms) may be thought of as chords (molecules); and the sequence of chords may be thought of as resembling the *movement* of a symphony. There are literally thousands of different combinations of these twenty-odd amino-acid chords found in the different "movements" of the life symphony. These super-large or macromolecules are called *proteins*. An example of such a macromolecule is beef insulin. The backbone of this molecule is a chain of thirty amino acids linked carbon-to-nitrogen, carbon-to-nitrogen, carbon-to-nitrogen, right down the line. Attached to the seventh and the nineteenth links we find a bridge consisting of a pair of sulfur atoms holding a shorter chain that lies parallel to the original one. This shorter chain has twenty-one links. This particular duplex chain, insulin, plays the key role in controlling the chemical processes involving body sugar.

You can see that our analogy between the tones of the scale and chords on the one hand, and vibrating atoms and molecules on the other, must be viewed in a very broad perspective. For example, as this duplex chain of fifty-odd links moves through the body fluids, the sequence of the amino-acid chords is present all the time. It is not being played in sequence as when the movement of a symphony is played by an orchestra. The nearest thing to the actual playing of the movement of the symphony occurs when this chain of amino-acid chords is synthesized. Then the notes of the various atom-bells are sounded in sequence and the chords are played in sequence as they are synthesized into the final movement. Once the synthesis is complete, then the vibrations merge together into a very complex whole that in some ways resembles the pattern of vibrations recorded on the plastic disk that we use on a phonograph when we want to reproduce music.

As we noted in the chapter on three-dimensional music, a record of a symphony actually is vibrating and "playing" the symphony even when it sits silent in its jacket in the record storage cabinet. Because this plastic record is made of atoms, because these atoms are grouped together in a pattern that in essence contains the dynamic form of the symphony, because these atoms themselves are dynamic patterns of thermal energy and electron waves, the symphony is actually "sounding" day in and day out, vibrating within the substance of the plastic record. It is only by spinning the record against the needle of the record player that we transform the silent symphony of the record through the electronic circuits and the loudspeaker into the audible symphony on a time sequence.

Thus, the insulin molecule, this assembly of the fifty chemical amino-acid chords, sounds its own particular movement of the symphony of life as one single but complex dynamic form. We turn now to survey the way in which movements of this symphony of life are played in sequence during the process of biosynthesis, the topic of the next chapter.

10

The Dynamism of Life

IT IS A night in June. You and I are standing on the patio of my home in Florida on the bank of the Spanish River. Just across the dunes that separate the river from the sea, we can hear the pounding of the Atlantic surf on the beach. It is midnight. Only a few distant lights are reflected on the surface of the lagoon, but overhead the stars are shining in tropic brilliance.

I turn to you and nod toward the patio gate, quietly quoting T. S. Eliot's beautiful lines:

"Footfalls echo in the memory
Down the passage which we did not take
Towards the door we never opened
Into the rose-garden. My words echo
Thus, in your mind.
                          But to what purpose
Disturbing the dust on a bowl of rose-leaves
I do not know.
                          Other echoes
Inhabit the garden. Shall we follow?"

As we walk into the rose garden, I continue:
"And the bird called, in response to
The unheard music hidden in the shrubbery,
And the unseen eyebeam crossed, for the roses
Had the look of flowers that are looked at."

We sit down on the garden bench. A few feet away we see a rosebush with one white rose barely visible in the starlight. We are about to hear the unheard music hidden in the shrubbery. We are about to take another journey, this

213

time into the heart of life, this time into a living, growing cell where a rosebud is about to be born.

This time we will not enlarge the cell as we enlarged the atom in order to see it. We will reduce ourselves, become smaller and smaller in size until we are one ten-millionth of our normal stature. Now each of us is the size of the smallest speck of dust that can be seen by the eye with the aid of the most powerful microscope. We are each two tenths of a micron tall, two one-hundred-thousandths of a centimeter in height. We can float like pollen in the air, supported by the molecules of oxygen and nitrogen.

We drift slowly toward the tendril of the rose that is forming a bud, cling for a moment to the outer wall of the stem, and then step inside through one of the passages leading into the interior. Now we are swimming in the sap that flows like an underground river through this labyrinth. We glide forward through passage after passage, over a distance of miles as measured in our new hyper-Lilliputian scale. And then, suddenly, we pass through an archway and find ourselves in a great vaulted cavern, the interior of a living cell in the heart of the rose.

But it takes only one look to see that this cell interior is far more than a cavern. It is a cathedral. We are in a *"cathedrale engloutie,"* like the engulfed cathedral that inspired the somber and mysterious orchestral tone-poem of Debussy. We look upward and see dimly through the cytoplasmic fluid the vaulted ceiling rising over one hundred feet above our heads. On either side the walls are lined with tall fluted columns, their surfaces covered with involuted carved helices that spiral upward into the shadows of the recesses of the vaulting far above us. Looking down the vast nave we see at the end, over three hundred feet away, a towering structure of an intricate network pattern some forty feet high, rising like a tall altar and glowing in its own radiance behind a gossamer veil.

The whole nave is bathed in the dim light of a thousand different rainbow shades. The brightest colors are the quinary red, orange, yellow, green, blue, and violet that we recognize as matching the colors five octaves below the familiar visible rainbow colors, the invisible quinary colors of subvisible radiation lying beyond the limit of visible red. But these are only a small part of the multi-rainbow shades that stream in patterns of chromatic complexity from the cathedral floor, from the walls, from the roof, from the altar, and from thousands of mysterious forms that float like strange sea creatures through the fluid vastness of this immense sanctuary.

Now we listen and are aware that this engulfed cathedral is filled with music, as if a great pipe organ were playing melody and harmony, deep bourdon tones resounding from the walls, joined by the notes of a thousand violins, a thousand reeds, and a thousand flutes, trumpeting from above the altar in a pattern of fugal intricacy and merging with a myriad of soprano, alto, tenor, and bass voices from the mysterious glowing forms that glide in complex processions, moving backward and forward in ritual choreography throughout the whole immensity into which we gaze.

We are about to witness the mass of replication. To the accompaniment of a symphony in four movements, the altar will glide to the center of the nave; it will divide; a double wall will be built across the nave; and then the whole cathedral will be rent in twain and there will be two where only one existed before.

At the time we entered the cell-cathedral, the mass was in its first part, the interphase. In this portion of the cell's cycle there is far less apparent movement. There are no major gross changes. But the cell is still far from quiescent. The essential dynamism is all pervasive if one only looks and listens carefully. As we stand and observe this *lento* movement that precedes the *allegro* and *prestissimo* of the

climax of replication, I point out some of the essential features of the quieter dynamism that we are watching. Because
the cell is dynamic, because we are observing a dance and
not a tableau, there must be a constant flow of energy. I
call your attention to the oblong fluorescent forms (on this
scale ten to twenty feet in length and a yard or so in diameter) that float here and there in the space above us. These
are mitochondria. They are the containers of the special
groups of atoms that take energy from the food of the cell
which is constantly seeping in through passages in the walls,
and chemically transform this energy, sending it floating
out again to be distributed to all the portions of the cell
that require it. As we look at a passing mitochondrion, we
see with our X-ray vision that the walls are involuted, that
the interior of this strange form is filled with small tortuous
passages. In its walls we recognize the twenty-odd kinds of
clustered atoms that are called the amino acids. You recall
that these comprise the twenty major symphonic chords that
form the basis of so much of the harmony of life. In the walls
of the mitochondrion, these "chords" are in a sequence of a
special kind that constitute the macromolecule that we call
a *protein*. Within these folds we hear over and over again
the special bell-like tones of the phosphorous atoms that
play a key role in the distribution of the cell's energy. These
bell tones form part of two special chords that are continually repeated as the flow of energy takes place, the chord
of adenosine diphosphate (ADP) and the chord of adenosine triphosphate (ATP). These chords are echoing not
only in the cell of every rose, in the cell of every flower, in
the cells of every kind of plant and tree, but in the cells of
bacteria, of animals, and of every human being. ADP and
ATP are the twin keys to the energy of life, the chords of
the energy of life in every form. Life is not an arrangement
of parts. Life is dynamism. The breath of life is energy. Life
is the intricate, channeled flow of energy.

Even if we think of this flow of energy as being channeled by material barriers, by matter in the form of the walls of the tubes through which the energy flows, we must remember that these barriers are essentially themselves energy, potential energy directing kinetic energy. In the last analysis, all that moves and all that directs motion are in essence pure rhythm, pure waves so fundamental, so basic that we cannot say *what* the waves are. We can only say the waves *are*. So as we stand and gaze into the interior of this cell of the rose, what we see is really melody and harmony made visible and what we hear is the complex unity that extends all the way from the larger waves that envelop in their rhythm the entire organism and its environment, through the sonic waves, the thermal waves, down through the waves of radiation, the waves of chemical vibration, to the waves of the electrons and protons that are the fundamental aspect of all reality.

As we look about us, we see many other strange forms moving through the sea of cytoplasm. There are the golgi bodies. There are the lysosomes. There are the plasmodesmic threads that form a web extending far beyond the cell. There are the ribosomes. We see the smaller forms containing groups of atoms much like the amino acids but even more highly specialized, the five molecular groupings, the chords that play a key role both in the replication of the cell and its evolvement into more specialized cells. These five special nucleic compounds are called adenine, thymine, cytosine, guanine, and uracil. We see them linked together in long threads where they are combined with phosphorus and oxygen atoms and with a kind of cyclic sugar called ribose. These five forms are singing the quintet of generation.

We become aware that this quintal harmony is a basic component of the music coming from that specially intricate structure at the end of the cell which we have referred to as the "altar," technically called the *nucleus* of the cell.

While we have been observing the many forms floating

by in the nave of the cell-cathedral, there has been much
activity in this altar structure. When we first entered there
were two specially-shaped groups of atoms floating just before the altar. On our Lilliputian scale, each of these was
about six feet tall. In fact, it would take but little imagination to think of these as two priests kneeling before the
altar. As we watch we see these two forms move away from
the altar toward the center of the nave of the cathedral, as
the altar itself begins to move as if pulled by invisible cords
in the hands of these vested *centrioles.*

Meanwhile, we find that there have been changes in the
many forms moving behind the veil of the altar, the membrane surrounding the nucleus. Behind this veil we observe
again many long, threadlike forms woven into a fantastically
complicated inner tapestry. We step closer and observe that
these threads, the chromosomes, are in turn woven from the
groups that we called the quintal chords of generation. We
hear the special harmonies of four of these chords coming
from the twin strands of the threads that are called DNA
(deoxyribosenucleic acid). The overall pattern of the harmony is something like a quartet sung by these four special
molecules. The bass tones are provided by guanine, which is
the heaviest of these groups. The tenor comes from adenine,
thymine is the alto, and cytosine is the soprano. As we listen
closely to the harmony, we hear the bass and the alto sing
in a specially close relation to each other (the guanine and
cytosine), while the tenor and the soprano (adenine and
thymine) are similarly linked.

While we have been watching, these slender, threadlike forms have been pulling closer together so that the
cords are beginning to swell, and now the whole altar, the
whole nucleus, begins to glide toward the center of the
nave preceded by the centriole "priests." The tempo of the
symphony accelerates and there are trumpet calls from behind the veil of the altar. The second movement, the pro-

phase, has begun. The priests move one to each side and suddenly the veil is torn asunder and dissolves in the sea of cytoplasm. We see the chromosome threads also parting, one part moving toward the left, the other to the right. The whole structure of the altar is quivering in a new rhythm. The two groups of chromosomes move to the exact center of the nave, while one priest glides toward the end of the nave where the altar originally stood, and the other priest is opposite, toward the other end of the nave, which is now to receive its own altar.

At this point the third movement begins, itself consisting of two parts, the metaphase and the anaphase. There are crashing chords that resound from the walls. The chromosomes fall apart, half of them moving back toward the original location of the altar and half moving toward the new location at the far end. Meanwhile, each centriole "priest" has wrapped his robe around him and, at the climax of division, suddenly unfolds the robe—and two priests, two centrioles, are revealed where one stood before. Each pair moves slowly toward an end of the nave—one pair returning to the original site of the altar with one of the newly formed altars gliding in their wake. The other pair moves toward the far end of the cathedral, followed by the other new altar. And now, at the spot in the middle of the nave where this strange fission took place, we see the cytoplasm congealing and a twin wall forming.

We are in the final movement, the telophase of the symphony. As the wall in the center extends and joins the original walls of the cells, we see a new veil forming over each altar with its attendant centriole priests and as the harmony moves through a final climactic fugue, the chromosomes uncoil and return to their tenuous, almost invisible structure that we first observed when we entered the cathedral. There is a final chromatic transposition in the harmony and once again we recognize the chords of the inter-

phase coming softly from the new altar, while the continuing antiphonal music of the flow of energy from the
mitochondria again fills the nave.

Silently, you and I float back to the passage where we
entered. As the echoes of melody and harmony still are
wafted to us, we recognize that in this language of music
we are hearing the assertion: "I am a rose. I am that special
essence of beauty that unfolds its petals and gives forth its
fragrance, the realization of the invisible form of that unheard melody which gave me birth. It is the melody whis-
pered *pianissimo* by my roots. It is the melody of stock and
branch. It is the melody of leaf and bud, the same melody
in each part, a theme with a thousand variations bursting
into its climactic, triumphant *fortissimo* when my flower
unfolds."

Perhaps this is the song that Gertrude Stein subconsciously heard when she wrote, "A rose is a rose is a rose."

You and I stand in the moonlight, returned to our normal stature. Actually, this symphony which we have just
heard has taken just about the same time in its performance
as would be taken by a real symphony in a concert hall. But
remember that this is a *real* symphony, too. Our ears are not
tuned to perceive it. Our eyes cannot discern the infinitesimal detail of movement that accompanies it. But all the
observations of science provide evidence that in the rose
garden, night and day, this symphony is being played over
and over again in the dynamism of life.

The Need for the New Perspective

The terms in which I have told the story of this imaginary journey into the heart of the rose are, of course, highly
imaginative. As I cautioned you in the first chapter, this
music of life is played on waves that cannot be perceived
by the human ear. These waves constitute a fabric so intangible that many scientists still refuse to admit its reality. But

I believe with Whitehead in the doctrine of the reality of things in terms of the modes of their functioning. I believe that all scientists will agree that electrons, atoms, and groups of atoms do function according to these dynamic wave patterns, that they have a character that is essentially *harmonic* in the broadest meaning of the term. In this brief chapter, I have been able to portray only the most minute part of the total dynamism of life as we observe it over the entire spectrum from the humblest, unicellular organism to man himself. But I hope that this brief glimpse will convince you that we must keep this harmonic aspect of the life process in mind when we try to understand life's meaning.

Today, with the help of the electron microscope, the new analytical methods of chromatography, the new evidence from investigations with the help of X-ray diffraction, we can draw the blueprints of the parts of the life process with an almost unbelievable fineness of detail. Our present portraits of life look like magnificent Rembrandts compared with the crude pictures of a decade ago which appear to be no more than drawings made by a child with a stick in the sand.

At first glance, it appears that this new and highly intimate knowledge of the parts of life reinforces the mechanistic and analytic perspective. Many scientists are even more firmly convinced today that life has been reduced to mere physics and chemistry. They cannot help but ask whether, after all, a human being is more than a highly complicated robot. Can there possibly be any deeper meaning in life than just wheels spinning within wheels? But I am convinced that they fail to see the forest because of the trees. I believe that, viewed in a truly balanced perspective, the life process is seen to be clearly *more* than the physico-chemico-mechanical interaction of parts. For the truly balanced perspective takes into account the fundamental nature of the reality of which the life process is itself a part. If we constantly remind ourselves that the basis of life is not matter but music, then I think we can retain the vision of the immensity of life, its beauty, its miraculous complexity, and its meaning, that far transcends the boundaries of materialism. This is why I have taken the liberty of portraying the cell and its dynamism in these unusual symphonic terms.

I hope that by this imagery I have not offended the thousands of scientists who have devoted their lives with such infinite patience and efforts to the hard task of deciphering bit by bit the secrets of this life process. In the heroic struggle to uncover just a little more truth, it is necessary to be starkly objective in criticizing one's own methods, in searching for possible sources of error, and in interpreting one's findings in a way that is free of every taint of prejudice or overoptimism. But unfortunately, this commendable attitude frequently narrows the focus of vision. I am convinced that there is an equal need every now and then to look through a wide-angle lens. To achieve a balanced frame of reference, one must be synthetic as well as analytic. It is with this in mind that I have tried in these last few pages to add just a little touch of fresh color to our picture of the life process in the hope that this chromatography may throw into relief certain of the dynamic patterns that otherwise may be camouflaged amid the unparalleled riches of detail with which today's life sciences are providing us.

In the next chapter, I want to point out how so many facets of this detail, seen in the perspective of dynamic form, provide evidence for the unity of life.

11

The Unity of Life

A FEW years ago when I was addressing a national symposium on science and medicine in Philadelphia, I stated in the introduction to my lecture that I was going to discuss the way in which atoms and molecules in the human body talked to one another. I could see the startled looks on the faces of a number of persons in the audience. One of the psychiatrists remarked later that the thought flashed through his mind that I had been put on the program not for the purpose of instruction but for observation. This is just another example of the danger of proposing an idea that is too far ahead of the times. You can imagine my satisfaction a couple of years later when I glanced at a copy of The American Scientist, one of the most authoritative and respected scientific periodicals, and found that in the first article the distinguished authors, one a Nobel laureate, announced that they were going to discuss "the way molecules interact with each other, i. e., *communicate* with each other."

The title of the article was "Atom to Adam." It is a fascinating discussion of our increasing knowledge of the pattern of evolution through which the interaction of inanimate atoms has grown in complexity to attain this incredibly intricate interplay that today we know as human life. There is little doubt that the coherence in this complexity has been attained by interatomic communication. Life is an interplay of dynamic forms. It is in this pattern of intercommunication that we find the essence of life's unity.

A number of the great scientists of the past have expressed a belief in this unity. Teilhard de Chardin writes: "By the force of orthogenesis the individual unit becomes part of a chain. From being a centre it is changed into being an intermediary, a link—no long *existing,* but *transmitting;* and, as it has been put, life is more real than lives." Later, in the same context he says: "I repeat this same thing like a refrain on every rung of the ladder that leads to man; for, if this thing is forgotten, nothing can be understood. To see life properly we must never lose sight of the unity of the biosphere that lies beyond the plurality and essential rivalry of individual beings. This unity was still diffuse in the early stages—a unity in origin, framework and dispersed impetus rather than in ordered grouping; yet a unity which, together with life's ascent, was to grow ever sharper in outline, to fold in upon itself, and, finally, to centre itself under our eyes."

Whenever a scientist uses a phrase like "unity of life," he exposes himself to a special brand of criticism. He opens the door to the accusation that he is using a high-sounding combination of words as a smoke screen to conceal his ignorance. There are countless examples in the history of science where not only a single scientist but large groups of scientists have had a vague awareness of an aspect of nature that they thought pointed toward a deep, underlying reality, but which they were unable to describe logically and clearly or to connect in a meaningful way with other concepts of established validity. The idea of a mysterious essence of life has hovered like an *ignis fatuus* in the dark swamp-fog of our ignorance concerning the true nature of life. As the light shed by painstaking objective scientific experimentation has penetrated further and further into this fog, dispelling it bit by bit, many of the arguments for accepting a belief in an essence of life have been removed one by one.

More than a hundred and fifty years ago, chemists

thought that there were certain organic chemical compounds produced by vital processes that never could be reproduced in the laboratory. With the synthesis of urea from ordinary inanimate carbon, hydrogen, and nitrogen, Wohler punctured the balloon of this myth.

Many of the vitalists argued that the fantastic process of heredity, the transmission of the million or more characteristics that give a complex organism like a mammal its unique individuality, could never be transmitted from one generation to the next by an ordinary physicochemical mechanism. The discovery of the structure of the genetic macromolecule DNA (deoxyribose nucleic acid) has destroyed the potency of this argument.

These are just two examples that can be cited from a host of similar discoveries that have forced scientists to abandon vague concepts clothed in high-sounding phrases and to accept physicochemical mechanism as the explanation for phenomena which were at first believed to be too complex to be explained in such materialistic terms. But in spite of the persuasive force exerted by these incidents of scientific discovery, many of the most eminent scientists and philosophers of science feel that there are aspects of vital essence that must not be ignored. They call our attention to the danger that the pendulum of scientific thought may swing from one bias to an opposite and equally threatening bias. Although many mysteries in the past have been explained finally in terms of familiar mechanism, we should not deny the possibility of discovering in the future some new, overarching realities that transcend familiar mechanism. We cannot ignore the voices that argue the possibility of someday uncovering evidence of all-pervasive phenomena whose reality can only be expressed in radically new integrative terms. We must set the lessons learned from Wohler and Watson and Crick side by side with the lessons learned from Planck and de Broglie. It is in this spirit that I want to explore with you the problem of the unity of life in the perspective provided by some of the latest evidence bearing upon the nature of interatomic communication.

Whitehead points out that life is the unity of all forces. Life is adventure. The unity of adventure includes among its components all individual realities. Weyl goes on to say that in exploring the nature of the life process we are dealing with combinatorial structures for the description of which our ordinary language is woefully inadequate.

Language itself is a striking example of such a combinatorial structure. One does not have to search very far to find examples of the difficulties inherent in recognizing some of the most significant integrative aspects of structure in language.

The Recognition of Communication Patterns

A few years ago one of my old college friends tried an experiment that provides a striking example of the difficulty of recognizing communication patterns. So that you can appreciate more fully the impact of this incident, I want to fill you in with respect to my friend's background. He holds the degree of Doctor of Philosophy in Physics from the University of Leiden, in the Netherlands, one of the most prominent centers of research both in experimental and theoretical physics anywhere in the world. He and I were roommates during the year that I held a post-doctoral fellowship at this same university. After a number of years of service on the faculty at several institutions including the University of California at Berkeley and The Johns Hopkins University in Baltimore, he accepted a commission in the Ordnance Corps of the United States Army. He served as Chief of Army Research and concluded his career as Commanding Officer of the United States Armies in Japan, holding the rank of Major General. His name is Chester W. Clark.

On one occasion, as a memento of his participation in a distinguished-service award, General Clark was presented with a recording of the address he made as part of the ceremony. A week or two later, he took the record home to play to his family. It happened that the family record player was not operating properly, and it played this record in reverse. If you have ever heard familiar speech played backward you are aware of the strange gibberish that comes out of the loudspeaker as a result of such an inversion. Inverted speech is common enough today but when General Clark's record player acquired the ability to go into reverse, our modern techniques of speech recording were still in the embryonic stage.

While the Clark family were enjoying the novelty of playing records backward, they had as their guest at dinner a language expert from the Department of State in Washington. Partly in response to the requirements of his position and partly as a hobby he had developed familiarity with languages both written and spoken that included both the highly developed patterns of communication used in the more civilized nations as well as countless aboriginal tongues. After dinner the conversation turned to the structure of language and General Clark remarked that they had a record with a rather unusual dialect which he wanted his friend to try to identify. So he put the record player into reverse and played his speech. The government official was stunned. He listened attentively to the end of the recording and with a look of complete frustration remarked that this was a language he had never heard before. He said that he was sure that he recognized all the earmarks of a very sophisticated vehicle of communication. There were patterns of complex repetition and syllabic variation that were sure signs of a highly developed structure. He concluded that it sounded like a language from some other planet, used by beings that had at least reached if not surpassed our own stage of sophistication in communication. Of course, General Clark then put the player into normal forward speed and the secret was revealed: it was just plain, ordinary English turned around.

I think there is a profound moral to this tale. Today, as Dr. Calvin so aptly puts it in his thought-provoking article "Atom to Adam," we are trying to learn the language by which atoms communicate with each other in the life process. We must expect to encounter many difficulties in this effort, difficulties that we may not even recognize as present. Merely quadrupling the speed at which a record is played can turn intelligible English into something that sounds like the chatter of excited monkeys. Slowing the record down below the normal speed by an equivalent amount results in an unintelligible series of groans like the moaning of the damned in the lowest circle of Dante's Hell. Merely playing the record backward but at normal speed makes the message indecipherable even to a language expert.

The language of life is uttered in part at a velocity of trillions of syllables per second. It certainly is possible that other parts of this message are spoken so deliberately that hours or days may be required for a single "sentence." We cannot assert that no message is there just because we are unable to perceive any signs of its presence in the myriad of "sounds" that make up this babble that is inaudible to the human ear and indecipherable by the centers of sound analysis in the human brain. This is the lesson we must keep in mind in our exploration of the aspect of *wholeness* in the phenomena of life.

The Miracle of Growth

In their classic work on plant physiology, Bernard S. Meyer and Donald B. Anderson remarked that the coordination and control of the physiological processes occurring in a plant is clear evidence that such an organism is more than a mere aggregation of genetically equivalent cells, and that control of cellular processes resides in the organism as a whole rather than within the individual cells. Obviously, if this conclusion is valid in the study of the growth of plants, it is even more germane in the study of the pre- and postnatal growth of a human body. Let us explore in a little more detail a few of the phases of this miraculous process.

In all except an extremely small number of instances, the process of the growth of living organisms takes place by the replication of cells. The new cells that constitute the expanding structure of the organism are derived from the fission and adaptation of a smaller number of "parent" cells. This process extends back to the original single cell that, in respect to the example of the organism we are considering, stands as the *Eve* from which the dozens of generations of cells are derived by reproduction to make up the totality of the organism. The original *Eve* cell itself was produced through the process of replication from a cell in the parent organism by the reproductive process characteristic of the species. Thus, there is an endless chain, cell to cell to cell to cell, *ad infinitum.* This is frequently summed up in the phrase *omnis cellula e cellula:* all cells come from cells.

In the preceding chapter we indulged in an imaginary visit to one of the cells of a rosebush as it replicated in preparation for the production of a rose. We focused our observation on the principal stages of this process of replication in the perspective of the transposition and variation of the harmonic dynamic forms that are the essence of the myriad of atoms participating in this replication. I now want to shift the focus and help you to visualize the variations that must accompany this replication as it provides through successive repetitions the hundreds of varieties of cells that are required for the total functioning organism. In order to make this pattern more meaningful, let us move from the domain of *flora* to the domain of *fauna.* Let us consider the

pattern of prenatal and postnatal growth of a member of
that species which, to many of us at least, stands at the
pinnacle of evolutionary growth. In the cynical words of
the poet e. e. cummings:

> "one stands supreme i mean the an
> imal without a heart."

So let us survey the growth of a human being from the
single initial cell, the *ovum,* to mature total body; this is the
problem of replicating from one cell almost a quadrillion
cells. Remember that if each cell were on the average about
the size of a dried pea, a quadrillion of them would be
enough to fill all the buildings from cellar to rooftop in
a city about the size of Philadelphia or Chicago.

In the period of gestation not only must the process of
growth produce by replication almost a quadrillion cells; it
must also produce variations in a systematic and coherent
way to provide hundreds of different types of cells all derived from the original prime egg; and these hundreds of
varieties found among the quadrillion cells must be located
in the proper geometric positions, and must be dynamically
coupled together so that after the proper intervals each
phase of the dynamics of the total life process is initiated and
linked dynamically with the total structure of dynamism.
The cells must cooperate so that breathing may begin at the
moment of birth, metabolism can be maintained, and the
subtle aspects of intellectual growth and emergence of personality may be fulfilled.

Instead of standing, as we did, in the cathedral-like cell
of the rose to watch its replication, let us imagine that we
are standing in the temple of human origin, the *ovum,* just
before the moment of conception.

I shall not try to describe in too great detail what one
might see if one could have such an experience. No doubt
the ovum if viewed from within would not be as suggestive
of the appearance of a cathedral as was the cell of the rose

that we selected as the seat of our last submicroscopic journey. The inside of the ovum might give the impression of a vast subterranean flooded cavern with a hemispherical domed ceiling a hundred or so feet high at the center (measured on the scale that we employed in our description of the cell of the rose). But we would see, as we did before, forms of incredible intricacy suspended in the cytoplasmic fluid that fills all the interior, that itself possesses intricate structure.

Standing thus, in the interior of the ovum, we would see the strange radiance of dozens of rainbow colors in the ternary, quaternary, quinary, and other successive octaves of the subvisible spectrum of radiation. We would hear the fundamental triad chord of water played with many variations as this basic dynamism of the cell surged endlessly back and forth. And in the cavern of the ovum, floating in the cytoplasm, we would recognize many of the forms that we saw before in the rose-cathedral cell. There are the mitochondria with their involuted surfaces, turning the energy brought in through the pores of this cell into molecular dynamic forms which carry it to the various parts of the cell where it is needed to activate the different cell functions. There are the ribosomes that are the weavers of the macromolecules, fabrics stitched together from the twenty-odd basic dynamic forms of the amino acids. And most prominent of all, there is the great veiled labyrinthine complex of thousands of interwoven spiral threads, the nucleus that we called the altar in the rose-cathedral. Here, in the ovum also the nucleus is the heart of the cell; this is the master dynamism that directs and activates the thousands upon thousands of wave patterns that in their total harmony constitute the life of the cell.

If we could listen to the symphonic prelude to a new life about to be born, I am sure that we would be overwhelmed with feelings of awe and of reverence as we stand

in the presence of and hear resounding about us these polydimensional chords of harmony that are the apex of significant meaning achieved through ten billion years of evolution. And now we are about to hear the music of conception,
a burst of unique harmony never before sounded throughout the history of the universe, the first notes in the unique
symphony of a unique new human being.

As we stand and watch and listen, there are dissonant
tones like trumpet calls without the walls of this temple-
cell. The walls quiver and slowly begin to part as wave upon
wave of thunderous chords shake the whole structure. We
see approaching through the fissure at the end of the temple
another great complex dynamic form, the millions of shining, intertwined, macromolecular threads that form the
antiphonal symphony which is about to merge with the nuclear symphony of the cell in which we have been standing.
Now the veil surrounding the maternal nucleus parts, the
paternal nucleus approaches, and the intricate contrapuntal
pavane is begun, the climax of the conceptual act.

We can conceive only faintly the unimaginable fugal
complexity of the symphony of the cell as the prime phase
of a life unfolds in this fundamental fusion. Think of the
most intricate polyphony of Palestrina. Think of the intertwining voices of the greatest fugues of Bach. Think of the
cosmic climaxes of the Ninth Symphony of Beethoven.
Think of the chromatic sforzandos of Brahms. Think of the
dissonances of ecstasy of Scriabin. Then think of a kaleidoscope of music poured out by a symphonic galaxy of a quadrillion instruments, and you begin to get a faint idea of the
dynamic reality in the creation of a new human life. And
all this is only the prelude to the vast symphony of a million
movements that ensues as this mother cell becomes two, two
become four, four become eight, until this concerto of replication has produced the quadrillion cells of the mature
human being.

Think how these twenty basic chromatic chords, the amino acids, are to be played in a series of symphonic variations to produce the tissues of the skin, the arteries, the veins, the heart, the nerves, the ears, the eyes, and the brain, together with those cells that must retain the primary genetic harmony to be passed on in turn to a new generation. Think of the nine prenatal months of darkness, but darkness luminous with the rainbow colors of the cluster of octaves of harmony produced by the genetic weaving of the embryonic tissues. Think of the new melody of life to whose notes the newborn infant responds with a cry as the first breath of oxygen and nitrogen floods the lungs.

Think of the infinite complexity of control of variations in cell structure, of finesse in cell location, that must have been exercised to produce the tiny bundle of fibers that will serve as the optic nerve, fibers that must have just the right size, just the right structure of extreme complexity to conduct the pulses produced by the millions of impacts per second of photons on the retina and to transmit these undistorted to the brain where their fusion yields vision. Think of the control needed so that the left arm is of comparable length with the right arm, both of the proper length to serve the many arm functions required for protection, for sustenance, for productivity.

I hope you will agree after meditating on all this that there must be a network of communication embracing the dynamism of the whole body, not only during the period of growth but throughout the entire period of life. Now take just a brief look at some of the possibilities by which this communication network may be maintained.

Intrabody Communication

Especially from studies in anatomy and physiology during the last hundred years we know something about a few of the channels by which the body does maintain a communication network. The most prominent and obvious channels of communication are the nerve fibers that connect a large portion of the body's components and carry messages both ways. The transmission of these neural messages is largely through pulses that involve both electrical and chemical changes. The speed of travel of such a pulse is very much slower than the speed by which an electrical pulse travels along a conducting wire of a metal like copper. Nevertheless, these pulses can be transmitted so that the interval between command and obedience can be a hundredth of a second or less. There are certainly networks of communication within the brain itself where the action of pulses may be even faster. We still do not have a sufficiently detailed knowledge of the neurophysiology of the brain to be sure of the extent to which brain intracommunication resembles the exterior nerve pattern; or whether there may be other mechanisms in the brain, chemical or electrical or electrochemical, that play a prominent part in transmitting, receiving, storing, and synthesizing these dynamic forms that comprise the body's interior language.

One of my former students, the choreographer of the chemical ballet that we produced in Baltimore in 1939, is now a professor at the Massachusetts Institute of Technology. He told me of an interesting conversation that he had with the great cybernetician Norbert Wiener, of the mathematics department at the Institute, concerning the mode of functioning of the brain. My friend had taken the local bus to go from Cambridge over to Boston to see his dentist and had just settled comfortably in a seat when the bus stopped again and Professor Wiener entered.

Wiener walked down the aisle, sat next to my friend, and immediately asked him, "Aren't you on the staff at the Institute?" My friend replied that he was indeed.

Wiener then inquired what his field of interest was and my young friend answered: "Infra-red spectroscopy." Quick as a flash, Wiener asked him, "Do you think that the brain functions by means of electron degeneracy?" My friend answered, "No, I think that it is by hydrogen bonding."

They rode over the bridge across the Charles River in silence and a few blocks farther on my friend rose, smiled at Professor Wiener, and walked to the door. Just as he was about to descend from the vehicle, Wiener shouted down the whole length of the bus, "Ah, it is proton degeneracy, then!" (I will not ask you to try to imagine what the thoughts of the other passengers on the bus may have been after such an exchange.)

Personally, I feel sure that there was a some truth in the conclusion of this dialogue. I believe that the peculiar nature of water with its hydrogen bonding and exchange of protons between molecules is a possibility for communication that should be considered seriously, at least under certain special conditions in the cell. Even today, we know so little about the nature of the liquid state of matter that we cannot say decisively the extent to which there might be directed communication of energy through exchange of protons or orientation of water molecules. A great many cytologists believe that there is a great deal of structure in the cytoplasm. It is certainly a possibility that alterations of this structure might provide a channel of communication. Whether such a channel should be called chemical or electrical or electrochemical, it is still premature to say. In a most interesting article on "Exploring the Brain with Chemicals" in the May, 1966 issue of the magazine called Discovery, Professor Sebastian P. Grossman of the Department of Psychology at the University of Chicago, remarks: "A cell's activity, however, and, just as important, its influence on neighboring cells, depends on *chemical* processes; the recorded electrical events only reflect these processes in a very gross and nonspecific way."

We must also keep in mind that there is constant interchange of energy in the form of radiation both through the cytoplasm within the cell and externally from cell to cell. This radiation is largely in the group of octaves lying between the ternary and the nonary subvisible octaves of the spectrum. I have wanted for many years to build an instrument to measure this intracellular radiation, both its color and the intensity in the different bands of frequency. I have a plan for the construction of such an instrument using an improved version of the superconducting bolometer that I built for the Navy and that measured the emission of this radiation from the surface of the body.

When I have discussed this project with representatives of some of the foundations which support this kind of work, they have expressed the belief that this radiation is so quickly absorbed by the molecules of the cytoplasm that I will get nothing but the well-known spectrum of the water molecule as the result of the painful and expensive labor of constructing such an instrument. I believe that they are wrong. I am sure that with present-day techniques this radiation can be observed and the changes in its spectrum can be followed as the cell goes through the different phases of metabolism and replication. I think that differences will be found between the intracellular radiation in normal cells and in malignant cells. I think that there may be most important clues to a better understanding of the functioning of the cell which can be uncovered through a study of this radiation. At any rate, the possibility of communication (both intracellular and intercellular) by means of radiation also must be kept as an item on the list of media that may play a part in the total communication network of the body. Radiative communication in all likelihood would be far more rapid than chemical or electro-chemical communication.

While we are considering all possible channels by which different parts of a cell or even different parts of the body may be sending messages back and forth, we should not fail to mention the possibility of gravity waves. We know that the changing patterns of vibration of different atoms in all probability set up changing patterns of gravity waves. We know almost nothing about how these gravity waves might be propagated or how they might be received. It may be "far out" to suggest that gravity waves may play a part in body communication, but while we are making this survey we ought to list all the possibilities we can think of. Of course, interaction with gravity waves would require such finely spaced energy levels that I believe thermal noise would prevent significant communication.

Finally, I want to point out that the de Broglie waves themselves certainly play a part in what might be called interatomic communication. There is ample evidence from many branches of chemistry that under certain conditions, which have been called somewhat ineptly *resonance* conditions, the de Broglie waves from neighboring atoms mingle and in their mingled chime produce very special conditions of energy resulting in characteristic modes of behavior found only when such resonance exists. In a sense, this resonance is an example of the phenomenon of feedback that we discussed earlier. It is a condition in which the whole is definitely more than the sum of the parts, as Professor Weyl has put it. In the complex pattern of interactions that undoubtedly exists inside the biological cell, we do not know to what distances significant de Broglie interaction may extend. It is perhaps premature to speculate in any detail at the present time. On the other hand, I think we should keep in mind that in the metallic state this kind of de Broglie interaction almost certainly extends over distances comparable to millions or more of atomic diameters. One of the most distinguished scientists of our time, twice Nobel laureate (once for his contributions to chemistry, once for his contributions to the cause of peace), Linus Pauling, made crucial contributions to our understanding of the nature of the metallic state by pointing out the role of this de Broglie resonance.

You remember the well-known example of a resonance phenomenon when a column of soldiers marches in step across a bridge and their coordinated rhythmic footfalls set the bridge vibrating so violently that it is in danger of collapse. The analogy is crude; but it is the ordered arrangement of the atoms in a metal, like the ordered arrangement of the soldiers in the column and the ordered pattern of footfall, that produces the strange pattern of energy in metals, completely different from any that we would have predicted on the basis of mechanistic behavior of the electron as contrasted with musical behavior. The Pauli exclusion principle operates in such a way that each electron in the block of metal is, so to speak, *aware* of the behavior of all the other electrons that are present. Thinking in terms of comparable size, the awareness of one electron of the behavior of another electron an inch or more away is comparable to the awareness of a man in New York of the behavior of a man in San Francisco, by the interaction of their de Broglie waves. In the case of the electrons the reality of this awareness has been established beyond any question of doubt by a number of laboratory experiments.

There is also evidence that the molecules of a gas have an awareness of each other's behavior, although I do not feel that the experimental proof of this is quite as incontrovertible as the proof of the awareness in the block of metal. However, I believe that a great many physicists would be willing to state that the Pauli exclusion principle might govern the behavior of the molecules of a gas under certain circumstances.

So far, I am not aware of any extensive investigation of the operation of the Pauli exclusion principle either inside the biological cell or between biological cells throughout the interior of the human body. Dr. Albert Szent-Gyorgyi, who was awarded the Nobel prize for his work in bio-chemistry, has suggested that this principle may play an important role in connection with the bands of energy levels in aggregates of biomolecules where there may be inter-action similar to that found in semi-metallic material. I feel that the problem at the present time is not so much the need to try to analyze in detail the possibilities for such inter-action, but rather the need to weigh the arguments for and against a perspective of thinking which leaves the door open for a kind of intrabody communication that can serve as the unifying guidance factor in this miraculous process of growth which we see happening before our eyes during every instant of our life.

The Perspective of Togetherness

You may recall that in reviewing our conclusions about the nature of music, I pointed out that the choice of a co-ordinate framework was quite arbitrary when we undertake to analyze the behavior of dynamic forms. In music, we are aware that there is far more significance in the relations of wholes, in the progression line of harmony, in the unity, than there is in trying to express music in terms of fre-quencies per second for individual notes. The significance lies in the wholes rather than in the parts; and we adapt our procedures of recognition, of appreciation, and of cre-ativity in the domain of music to this fact.

In analyzing the vibration of complex molecules, we are faced with an analogous problem. In a complex com-pound like an amino acid, we can try to think in terms of the vibration of each of the atoms present. As a rule, this leaves us with a mathematical problem that is beyond the possibility of solution even with the most advanced com-puters. On the other hand, we frequently find it more help-ful to abandon the effort to locate each atom at a particular coordinate of length, breadth, and height in space and, instead, shift our basis of analysis to *form coordinates.* This is very much like saying that we find it more useful to locate the position of a ship, not in terms of length, breadth, and height in a coordinate system with the center of coordinates at the center of the earth, but in angular coordinates that we express as latitude and longitude. Over the years latitude and longitude have provided the only functional way of expressing location in this type of problem.

I am proposing that we should adopt form coordinates in order to analyze and draw conclusions about the functioning of the cell and the functioning of the great clusters of cells that make up total organisms all the way up to the human body. I am not prepared at the present time to lay down the rules for the construction of these dynamic form coordinates. I can only go this far. I can only ask that you contrast the perspective of unity that may be achieved by thinking in terms of form coordinates with the fragmented perspective into which one is forced when one thinks of the phenomenon of life as taking place by the movement of particles and the shifting of potential fields in Newtonian space expressed in terms of Cartesian coordinates. I want you to contrast the "rules of the game" which are appropriate when we recognize that the essential basis of life is the interplay of dynamic forms with the "rules of the game" that are necessary if we are thinking in terms of Newtonian mechanism.

These two contrasting perspectives will be set forth in the concluding chapter of this division of the book that deals with the nature of life. I close with a final quotation from Whitehead: "Discussion of fundamental notions is merely for the purpose of disclosing their coherence . . . . the specializations that can be derived from their conjunction. . . . Life is adventure. The unity of adventure includes among its components all individual realities."

12

The Meaning of Life

A S WE conclude in this chapter our survey of the nature
of life from bacteria to mammals, this is a good
time to repeat the question, "What is life?" What
is the animate as distinct from the inanimate? When is something truly living? Let us try to define what it means to be
alive.

In his book on "Biological Order," Professor A. Lwoff,
of the Massachusetts Institute of Technology, comments on
the possibilities of discovery through definition. When in-
vading ignorance, let the definitions be distinct, let the symbols be sharp, as Cusanus reminded us centuries ago. Endeavor to make the definitions clear; and that effort in itself
may open doors to new knowledge. So let us first define
wholeness and *holism,* before we try to define life.

I have spoken many times in the preceding chapters of
what Weyl calls "wholeness" and what Whitehead calls
"togetherness." When one emphasizes "wholeness" or "togetherness" in a search for aspects of reality, it is frequently
said that one is employing the perspective of holism. This
philosophical term, *holism,* may be defined as the theory
that "wholes" (which are more than the mere sums of their
parts) are fundamental aspects of the real. A theory which
emphasizes this point of view is called holistic.

This term, *holistic,* is the first member of a trilogy of
definitions which open a most provocative article entitled
"A Thermodynamic Characterization of Self-Reproduc-
tion," published recently in Reviews of Modern Physics, by
Professor Philip Morrison of the Department of Physics

at the Newman Laboratory of Nuclear Studies at Cornell University, who starts by surveying the problem of casting a definition of life. He first quotes a quatrain from the Panchatra as translated from the Sanskrit by Arthur W. Ryder:

> "Horses, elephants, and iron,
> Water, woman, man,
> Sticks and stones and clothes are built
> On a different plan."

Morrison goes on to point out that in trying to cast a definition of life, three sorts of approaches are current: one which fixes its attention on holistic aspects; a second purely chemical one, which seems less than successful; and a third, that of the microbial geneticists, who describe life as an independent, specific, self-replicating system, possessing some sort of continuity with the general organic cycle. He goes on to say that "the acid, but perhaps not captious, critics who have observed that mules and prime ministers would then generally fail to be classed as alive, will not be fully content with the present approach either."

As you are surely aware by this time, I am urging the acceptance of a holistic definition of life, one that emphasizes its wholeness, its togetherness, its unity.

The Characteristics of Life

Although there are certain divergent, or we may even say aberrant, branches from the main channel of the stream of life which, though admittedly alive, are not self-replicating (such as mules and prime ministers), it is fair to claim that self-replication is the characteristic that distinguishes this dynamic pattern which we call life most sharply from the host of other dynamic patterns in the inanimate world.

A less emphasized but equally necessary characteristic of the pattern of life is the achievement of self-replication in

branching rather than *linear* chains. This multifoliate structure of the chain of life is necessitated by the fact of death.
As T. S. Eliot puts it:

> "Words move, music moves
> Only in time; but that which is only living
> Can only die."

If life were linear, there could be no life resembling the
pattern that we know. Down through the ages that vast
tapestry which we call evolution never could have been
woven from linear threads. The eminent biologist Lecomte
du Noüy, in his treatise on "Human Destiny," suggests that
the greatest invention of life is death; and part of the problem of defining life is the problem of defining death.

Viewed in the mechanistic perspective, death is not too
hard to define. It is the degradation of the pattern of dynamism, a loss of the holistic potential that makes self-replication possible. With life flowing in channels that continually split from *one* into *two* or more in a pattern of
branching chains, certain chains now and then terminate
in death; but there are always parallel chains that continue
life; and there simply would not be enough atoms to go
around to provide bodies for all the lives produced by replication if there were no death.

I think these ideas can be made clearer if we examine
a specific example. Let us consider the life cycle of a butterfly. The life cycle consists of three stages: egg, caterpillar,
butterfly. If we use the initial letter of each stage of development as a symbol to designate it, then a series of generations in the life cycle can be written thus: E-C-B-E-C-
B-E-C-B . . .

As in the conundrum, "Which came first, the chicken or
the egg?" it is completely arbitrary whether we start our
butterfly series with the egg, with the caterpillar, or with the
butterfly itself. However, we cannot help but feel that either

the caterpillar or the butterfly is a more functional expression of the life of the species than is the egg. It is an ascent in complexity to go from egg to caterpillar to butterfly; so let us start with the egg.

As we discussed in the previous chapters, the heart of the egg is the nucleus, and the heart of the nucleus is the macro-molecule formed of twin strands of sugar and phosphate which are joined by nucleic acid cross-rungs, the genetic *pilot* called DNA (deoxyribosenucleic acid). There are thousands of rungs on this tall DNA ladder, but essentially only four *kinds* of rungs. If we focus on the molecule that joins the left-hand side of the rung to the left upright "slab" of the ladder, we find only four kinds of molecules in this position: guanine (G), adenine (A), cytosine (C), and thymine (T); and we can characterize each rung by the molecule which it has in this left-hand position. As we go up the DNA ladder, we thus find the genetic message spelled out in a four-letter language, the GACT language.

Every kind of organism has its genetic name spelled out on the DNA ladder by a difference sequence of these four letters: G, A, C, and T. Thus in the DNA in the nucleus of the cell of a mouse we *might* find CATCATGAAA; in the DNA in the nucleus of the cell of a man we *might* find ACTACTACTGAT; in the DNA in the nucleus of the cell of a butterfly we *might* find the message TAGTAGATCG. We are just beginning to read these genetic code messages; my illustrations above are purely fanciful, but we are sure that every kind of living being from bacteria to man stems from the key code-word of thousands of letters, spelled out in terms of Guanine, Adenine, Cytosine, and Thymine on the rungs of the genetic ladder of DNA.

G, A, C, and T are the four chords of the genetic sonata rung on the carillon of the bells of hydrogen, oxygen, car-bon, nitrogen, and phosphorus that mingle together to form these four molecules. Somehow the blending of these chords into the tune TAGTAGATCG, like the tune of the Pied Piper of Hamelin, compels the neighboring bells of the notes of life (the hydrogen, oxygen, carbon, and nitrogen atoms in the immediate environment) to regroup, to play a new song, the song first of the caterpillar, and then the song of the creature of prismatic rainbow wings soaring in graceful flight over the meadow, the butterfly.

In all this we must not lose sight of the factor of *togetherness.* It is because the sonata of the DNA has the harmony that blends with the notes of hydrogen, oxygen, carbon, and nitrogen that we get the compulsion which brings these latter notes grouped into the chords and harmony through the miracle of replication and growth to compose the ultimate symphony that is the living creature. And then, of course, after a short span measured only by a handful of hours, the butterfly lays its eggs and the cycle starts again.

Thus we have this symphony of the life of the butterfly made up of movements sometimes concealing, sometimes revealing the sequential genetic melody in its full dynamic realization. In the egg, the melody is being played in the single, solitary sequence of the lone molecule of DNA. Through embryonic growth, this is multiplied into the quadrillion or so sequences in the cells that we find in the caterpillar. Through the metamorphosis, these are rearranged into the quadrillion or so sequences in all the cells of the full dynamic realization of the butterfly itself, winging its way through the air with incomparable beauty and grace of form. Finally, we have the act of replication, the laying of the eggs, with the potential for dozens of butterflies if each of the eggs hatches and develops into a full and mature life.

In trying to view this life cycle in the perspective of the whole, in trying to grasp the holistic significance, we should keep in mind not only the harmonic significance, the sequence of these unimaginably complex dynamic forms, but also the fact that these forms represent energy, that they participate in the *flow* of energy. As du Noüy pointed out over and over again, life is not equilibrium. It is constantly flowing forward. Professor Dewey, the great philosopher of Columbia University, put it in a different way: that habit is energy organized in certain channels. Thinking of life as the transmission of patterns of energy, I believe that it is instructive to consider the many points of analogy between the flow of energy in a life cycle like that of the butterfly and the flow of energy in what we may call the "life cycle" of a concert symphony.

The Life of a Symphony

Particularly in our modern methods of broadcasting, recording, and rebroadcasting music, we see a pattern that is suggestive of a life cycle. For example, take the "life" of a modern symphony. We can say that the symphony is born in the brain of the composer. In that unfathonable dynamic cerebral complex of de Broglie waves we must believe that from the pattern of notes, the patterns of chords, the patterns of melody, the patterns of harmony which the composer has heard during his previous lifetime, he selects, combines, and interweaves; and by the magic act of creation there is achieved the birth of the new symphony. Then the brain sends signals to the muscles of the composer's hand, the fingers guide the pen, and black marks appear on the blank score paper, the first written notes of the symphony.

But remember that as the symphony metamorphoses into marks of ink, it has not lost its dynamism. The de Broglie pattern of those ink marks merge with the de Broglie patterns of the carbon, hydrogen, and oxygen of the paper and we find, superimposed again on this immeasurable complexity of dynamic form, the pattern that will be transmitted as sequential waves of light to the eyes of the musicians of the orchestra, through the impulses of the optic nerve to the brain waves of these hundred men; and fused with the signals from the director of the orchestra, these will set up impulses to arm and finger and lip muscles so that all the vibrating strings, reeds, and drumheads will synchronize ... and the symphony metamorphoses again into the dynamic form of vibration of the oxygen and nitrogen molecules of the air in its first audible music.

Suppose now that we think of the first broadcasting of this symphony. The vibration, the dynamic energy pattern in the air, goes to the microphone, is transformed into electrical impulses, goes to the broadcasting station, is transformed into the energy of radio waves, darts with the speed of light across hundreds of miles and is picked up by the antenna of a receiving station, is transformed back to electrical impulses which are fed to a tape recorder, where the atoms of iron in the swiftly moving tape are magnetized into still another metamorophosis of the dynamic form of the symphony.

A year passes; the taped recording of the symphony is stored on the shelf, apparently lifeless and inert like a seed lying in the ground during the winter. Then on the composer's birthday the tape recording is brought out, placed in the tape player, and the symphony once more is broadcast. It becomes a throbbing complex of electrical waves; again at the antenna it goes out as radio waves; again it is picked up at hundreds of receiving stations, and perhaps is tape-recorded at a dozen other locations; and in a dozen different cities the symphony now exists again in the form of the vibrating atoms of iron in the tape.

It is easy to see the common pattern in the propagation of a life form and the propagation of the symphony. The butterfly through its genetic process distills the essence of its existence into the unheard symphony vibrating in the nucleus of its eggs. These eggs remain apparently dormant for a year with the butterfly-symphony vibrating only at the

atomic level. Then warmed by the spring sun, the metamorphosis begins, the atomic symphony in the egg replicates
itself with all the variations of cell structure that produce
the caterpillar. The caterpillar feeds and grows, wraps itself
in its cocoon, and again there is a metamorphosis from which
there emerges the full dynamic realization of the butterfly-
symphony in all its glowing radiance of color, symmetry
of wing, poetry of flight. Then comes the time for reproduction and the eggs are laid and the symphony, now replicated
into hundreds of new vibrant nuclei, is once more dormant.

How much this resembles the symphony of music! The
tape-egg lies dormant on a shelf at the broadcasting station
until the climate of awareness in human minds stimulates
the emergence into the first metamorphosis of radio waves.
Then at hundreds of locations, through the loudspeakers
the symphony bursts into the air, a hundred fully realized
dynamic forms winging through the atmosphere, some finding their way through human ears and human auditory
nerves to human brains, some finding their way through
microphones or other electronic channels back to the production of new tape-eggs.

Thus, we see the common pattern in the symphony of life
and the symphony of sound. Is it not reasonable to search
with an open mind in order to see whether there is not a
significant deep reality shared by life and music?

The Symphony Around Us

While we are meditating on this question, let us take a
little walk from my house on the Spanish River across the
bridge and over to the beach where the waves from the blue
Atlantic are breaking on the sand. We step from the patio
into our palm garden along the lagoon where the tide has
just risen from the estuary of the river. We listen with our
minds tuned to catch the music of the symphony of life that
is all around us.

As we step through the gate, we hear the rustle of the fronds of the Manila palm brushing against the house. Then we listen to a single frond and hear the music of its hundred billion cells singing in chorus. In each of the thousand fronds on this beautiful tree, arching gracefully in the tropical June sunshine, there is resounding a similar chorus of one hundred billion cells. In each of these living cells the symphony of replication and growth is ringing from the atomic carillon of its hundred trillion atoms. And this unheard symphony of *Adonidia merrillii* is radiating through the garden air all around us.

As we walk out on the lawn, a beautiful little Sago palm with its symmetric crown of arching branches sounds the song of *Cycas revoluta*. Directly before us the Latania palm with its stiff yard-wide gray-green leaves calls to us. Just beyond the little pygmy date palm is playing its melody of *Phoenix loueiri*. In between, on the ground, a hundred blossoms of multicolored African daisies are singing their gerberine polyphony, each voice with a different variation expressing in music the pink, red, crimson, orange, cerise, mauve, and purple shades of rainbow radiance. High above our heads the lordly coconut palms are chiming their own carillon of *Cocos nucifera* accompanied by the tympani of their great green nuts.

Even under our feet as we step across the soft turf, we hear each tiny blade of grass trilling its own sweet melody, each of the millions of individual blades singing its own unique song. We walk down the street listening to the myriad voices all around us, across the bridge over the river where the cacophony of the steel and concrete mirrors in music the stress and tension of the nonillion atoms linked together to arch the almost imperceptible flow of the estuary. We move slowly under the shade of the Australian pines on the dune listening to the thin fluting of their tiny gray-green needles and finally cross to the sand where the surf from the broad Atlantic is breaking at our feet. We hear the song of silica, each infinitesimal grain of sand singing its own little melody, a unique song coming from every one of the trillions of tiny specks on the beach stretching to the horizon.

We turn to listen to the music coming to us from the deep blue water. Now we perceive the dominant chords of the triad of H_2O intermingled with the chime of the sodium, the potassium, the magnesium, the chlorine, the bromine, the iodine, even the gold, the silver, and the copper. And entwined through these myriad tones we hear the echoes of the songs of the countless thousands of sea creatures moving silently in the blue-green depths, the tenor of the ragged claws scuttling on the sea floor, the reincarnation of Alfred Prufrock, the bass of the barracuda, shark, and dolphin, the contrabass of the whale. If we could only read the meaning in the symphony of the sea, perhaps we would understand the meaning of the symphony of life, for the sea is the mother of life.

The Core of Life's Meaning

As in imagination we face the mystery of the great deep, this is perhaps the time to focus our thoughts on the mystery of life.

First of all, we must admit and define clearly our areas of ignorance. We do not know the pattern of the bridge that links the dynamism of the atom to the dynamism of life; but we do know where the bridge begins and where it ends. We do know that atoms are far more music than matter. And we see about us with our own eyes all the visible forms of life in the grass, the flowers, the trees, the insects, the fish, the animals, and our fellow human beings which instinctively we know are far more than mechanical robots. We have proved that there is harmonic dynamism at the atomic level and we have seen that life flowers into dynamic forms, the breathing, moving, eating, sleeping, replicating creatures that are its macroscopic embodiment. But what is essential morphology of this bridge of dynamism from the atom to Adam? I want to discuss three of the attitudes that we can adopt as we face our ignorance of the nature of the bridge of life.

First, we can simply say: *"Ignoramus,* we do not know." We can agree that life might be mechanism, that life might be novel dynamism with significance that transcends mechanism, that life may be something so different from anything previously envisioned that it makes no sense either to talk about it or to think about it. In other words, we can say that we do not know and that we will keep our mind a *tabula rasa,* a slate remaining blank until something new is discovered that is worth writing on it.

Second, we can assert that life is mechanism. The tenets of this belief may be phrased in a variety of ways. I shall try to state them briefly, a summary of the views expressed by the mechanists with whom I have talked and whose books I have read. Reduced to the most primitive terms, the mechanist believes in a billiard-ball universe. A hundred years ago almost all scientists thought that atoms closely resembled elastic, spherical particles that obeyed the laws of billiard-ball mechanics. Every cause produced a unique effect. If you knew the velocity of motion of two particles and their momenta, you could predict with absolute accuracy the pattern of velocity and momentum resulting when they collided. Of course, they were many aspects of the universe that could not be described in such stark terms—for example, electrodynamics, molecular attraction, and chemical energy; but the mechanists were completely convinced that the same basic rules of the game applied in these other areas as were found to be obeyed in the realm of billiard-ball mechanics.

The first revolutionary challenge to this way of thinking

came from the ideas of de Broglie, reinforced by the experiments of Davisson and Germer, Bragg, and many of their contemporaries, and especially through the enlightened interpretations of Schrödinger, Heisenberg, von Neumann, Born, Dirac, and the other brilliant theoretical physicists who brought into being the new quantum mechanics. The pattern of behavior of wave particles led to the formulation of the principle of indeterminacy, which states that at the fundamental wave-particle level it is impossible to predict with complete accuracy the resultant pattern of energy with its components of velocity and momentum.

Did this really shatter the links in the chains of determinism? Many of those best qualified to judge thought it did. Von Neumann asserted that the morphology of the relationships, the structure of the mathematics, was such that there could never be any new discoveries to dethrone this acausal pattern of logic and reenthrone determinism. He asserted that indeterminacy was as much a built-in part of the universe as the relationship that two plus two equals four. He said that it was inconceivable that at any future time discoveries would be made to show conclusively that two plus two does not equal four, that it equals five or three, instead. Von Neumann believed that it was just as inconceivable that any future discovery would invalidate indeterminism.

Contrasted with this attitude, many physicists claimed that not only was it possible, but that it was highly probable that future discoveries would reenthrone determinism. They argued (and still argue) that when we know more about the factors that influence the behavior of wave particles, we will find that behind the "iron curtain" of indeterminacy, there are at work chains of action that keep the law of cause and effect in operation. They believe that the only reason we cannot predict with complete accuracy the results of fundamental particle interactions is that we simply do not know enough. They believe that some day we will have the facts to prove beyond any shadow of doubt that we live in a deterministic universe. As I have remarked before, this strikes me as just a longing to return to the "good old days." Even where facts are not available, one can sometimes observe certain symptoms that disclose habits of mind of the kind that are apt to lead one astray from the path of truth. And I suggest that the mechanistic attitude in confronting the mystery of life is an example of the same pattern of thinking that refuses to accept the validity of the principle of indeterminacy.

The biomechanists argue that the development of modern biology exhibits a whole series of examples where experimental fact removes the need for a postulating of any bio-function that is not consistent with physicochemical deterministic mechanism. This series of discoveries ranges all the way from Wohler's synthesis of urea (showing that chemical compounds previously believed to be made only by a *vital* process could be produced *in vitro* in the laboratory) to the work of Watson and Crick (showing that hereditary characteristics previously believed reproducible only by some mysterious vital mechanism were transmitted by relatively simple physicochemical means). By means of such arguments, the mechanists extrapolate to the conclusion that the now-mysterious bridge that links atom to Adam is sure to be revealed as physicochemical deterministic mechanism.

Contrasted with the "ignoramus" attitude, and with the attitude of the biomechanist, there is the third possibility expressed in the attitude of the *holist,* who admits that we do not know the nature of the bridge from the atom to Adam but who believes that the totality of evidence points to a bridge pattern with significance far beyond the mere functioning of mechanistic deterministic parts. The holist asserts that there are realities in the life process that are more than the sum of the parts.

As the foundation of the argument, the holist adopts the attitude of von Neumann that future discoveries at the fundamental wave-particle level will not lead to a retrogression restoring classical determinism, but rather will lead to a new understanding of the links between freedom at the atomic level and freedom at the human level. In other words, the holist starts from the premise that atoms are not imprisoned behind walls of causality.

The holist then surveys the nature of *inter*action at the fundamental wave-particle level and concludes along with Hermann Weyl that even here the whole is more than the sum of the parts. The holist examines the problem of identity at this level and concludes that even here the framework of classical Cartesian coordinates and classical mechanistic concepts does not provide the appropriate vocabulary, grammar, and syntax for the translation of the meaning contained in interatomic communication so that it can be understood by human minds. The holist believes that reality is revealed only in the totality and that this revelation can be apprehended only in holistic coordinates.

Of course, in adopting the holistic approach, one recognizes the necessity for analysis in order to grasp effectively the significance of the wholeness, the togetherness, that one observes. But when the wholeness is broken down into parts for analysis, the significance of the whole is not to be construed merely in terms of the significance of the parts. Analysis has a usefulness; but it is constructive usefulness only if its limits are given due recognition. Analysis destroys simultaneously as it reveals. We slay the virus in order to observe its structure under the electron microscope. Analysis can be prevented from injecting a destructive component into our thinking only if we recognize that it provides only a partial view of reality. (In writing that last sentence we really should write *partial* as *part*-ial.)

As we have constructed the new vocabulary, grammar,

and syntax of forms appropriate for dealing with the behavior of fundamental wave particles, the whole trend has been away from the interpretation in terms of parts and toward the interpretation in terms of wholes. If the trend at the fundamental wave-particle level points toward the pattern of holism, is it not logical to argue that this is the proper pattern for our thinking when we try to build the bridge from the wave-particle atom level up to the culmination of the life process in man? Whitehead says that life is a unity of all forms.

Life and Attitudes

If we decide to adopt the holistic attitude in trying to delve more deeply into the mysteries of the life process, what are some of the problems that we will have to face in continuing the journey along this road? At the present time, we do not have experimental facts to prove that life is *more* than mechanism. On the other hand, we do not have experimental facts to prove that life is *only* mechanism. If we adopt holistic thinking in our attempt to get new experimental facts and to interpret them, will this be an advantage or a handicap as contrasted with mechanistic thinking?

First of all, I believe that we must recognize the human weakness expressed in the saying that "we see what we look for." Or putting it another way, "we don't see what we don't want to see." In other words our attitude will, to a considerable extent, determine where we look, how we look, and what we think is worth looking for; and, of course, all this determines, finally, what we actually do see when we do look.

I believe that this all adds up to the overwhelming necessity of keeping an open mind as we pursue this investigation of the life process. Lecomte du Noüy comments that there are almost certain to be special laws for special molecules. In other words, we must keep our mind open for the appearance of phenomena so unusual, so different from what we are used to seeing, that it will be easy to overlook or dismiss these phenomena unless we are prepared in advance to keep an eye out for unfamiliar overtones.

There is a story about a famous chemist who, a little over fifty years ago, was trying to prepare the purest possible water for use in some physicochemical experiments. He checked the purity of the water by measuring its density, the weight per unit volume of water, the number of grams per cubic centimeter. The more he purified the water by distillation, the heavier it appeared to get. He said to himself that this is impossible. He finally concluded that he should be satisfied with the purity of the water already prepared; and he did not attempt to purify it further or to account for the increase in density. Looking back on these experiments in the light of our present knowledge of the isotopes of hydrogen, we can be reasonably sure that this chemist had "discovered" heavy water; but he failed to realize that he held in his hands the evidence for the existence of heavy hydrogen, the discovery that brought the Nobel prize to Harold Urey twenty years later.

I believe that one of the essential necessities for the recognition of the significance of unusual phenomena is an appropriate frame of reference for one's observation and thinking. I believe that we should give serious thought at the present time to an effort to construct a mathematics of form that will enable us to think in terms of form-space. Instinctively, we think of space as the space in which we breathe, move, and live, the space of length, breadth, and height. This is the three-dimensional Cartesian space that has been the framework of our thinking in the area of classical mechanics, and which has been so overwhelmingly successful in the domain of the macroscopic. I believe that with sufficient effort we can learn to think in terms of form-space, a pattern of thinking far more appropriate to the holistic aspects of the life process.

In some ways this may be urging a return to Plato, the father of so much of our present philosophy and of so many of our present thought patterns, who suggested forms as the ultimate reality. At this time, I can only indicate paths along which we might travel to make form-space a truly potent means for thinking about and solving some of the problems in the complex domain of life; but I hope that these indications will bear fruit. First of all, I suggest that we should see whether in a domain of forms, there might not be certain interactions of forms which under sufficiently *uniform* conditions result in an algebraic connection between form-space and Cartesian space. In other words, the interaction of the uniform aspects of forms might produce the kind of phenomena that, on the macroscopic level, are significantly interpreted in terms of familiar dynamics in length, breadth, and height. But as Ortega y Gasset rather acidly put it, conventional time and space are the stupid aspects of the universe; the truly significant aspects of the universe can never be cast, can never be expressed in the vocabulary, grammar, and syntax of ordinary time and space; the only proper language in which to express basic observations and deduce fundamental significance is the language of the domain of forms.

I suggest that we examine the kind of conclusion we may reach, the kind of new attitude we can assume if we are willing to say that the basic realities of life, the basic realities of the universe, are not the realities of matter and energy in time and space but are the realities of form, form both visible and invisible, form both audible and inaudible, form both tangible and intangible. I suggest that we postulate that the intangibles of truth and beauty, human freedom, courage, honor, and honesty are the core of the truly basic realities; and that the supposed realities which we see and touch and feel are really only shadows cast by these truly basic dynamic forms in their many embodiments.

Hocking, in his great book on "Science and the Idea of God," remarks that there must be an arena for life. It is the exploration of this arena that I am urging, the effort to construct a working vocabulary, grammar, and syntax not only of the forms appropriate for the understanding of the mystery of life in the bacteria, in the flower, and in man, but even the mystery of man's nature and destiny.

In the next division of this book devoted to a study of the nature of man, I want to explore with you some of the new insights which I believe we can acquire through this holistic point of view, through this perspective of unity, based on our new understanding of the music of the atom, and of the symphony of life.

Part IV

The Nature of Man

13

The Structure of Man

D ID YOU ever stop to think that you probably have in your body at least a million atoms which were once in the body of Julius Caesar? For after two thousand years Caesar's atoms are widely scattered.

"Imperious Caesar, dead and turn'd to clay,
Might stop a hole to keep the wind away:
O, that that earth, which kept the world in awe,
Should patch a wall to expel the winter's flaw!"

Without even the benefit of a course in freshman chemistry, Shakespeare had a sense of the diffusivity of atoms. With the facts of science at his disposal, he might have extrapolated Caesar's diffusion far beyond the hole in the wall. For example, it is quite easy to calculate the size of your own personal portion of Caesar.

As a rough guess, Caesar's body occupied a volume of a quarter of a cubic meter. Packed in that relatively small amount of space there were five octillion atoms—the hydrogen, the carbon, the oxygen, the nitrogen, and all the rest which vibrating toegther made Imperious Caesar. During the two thousand years since Caesar's death, Caesar's atoms have been scattered widely, carried by the waters of the Tiber, borne on the winds of the Apennines, floating through the Mediterranean, drifting beyond the pillars of Hercules, and ultimately diffused to the farthest reaches of the entire earth.

While some of Caesar undoubtedly is journeying up beyond the stratosphere into outer space and heading for a different star, it is a fair guess that most of his atoms are still contained in a spherical shell a few kilometers in thickness which embraces the surface of our own planet. Many of Caesar's hydrogen atoms are surely in the ocean and will remain there for a long time. Many of his carbon atoms are in the air as carbon dioxide; but even more are in the myriad plants and animals on the surface of the earth (including you). As a crude approximation let us estimate that your own body occupies one ten-quintillionth (10^{19}) of the total volume around the world into which Caesar's atoms have diffused. Since there are five octillion (5×10^{27}) of these atoms, it is easy to divide the latter figure by the former and get the result: you have in your body five hundred million of Caesar's atoms. Since this is a statistical calculation, let us be conservative and just say that you have probably at least a million of these atoms.

You can see how saturated with imperial Rome you are. Caesar is in your brain, Caesar is in your heart, Caesar is in your fingertips, Caesar is in your toes. Everytime you breathe out, you are expelling Caesar, and everytime you breathe in, the chances are you are inhaling more Caesar.

Of course, I just happened to pick Caesar as an example because of the quotation from Hamlet. Undoubtedly you have just as much of Cicero as you have of Caesar; you have some of Caesar's wife; and maybe some of Caesar's dog flows in your veins. As far as that goes, some of Caesar's atoms may be playing tag with some of Hamlet's atoms in your blood right now, with some of Shakespeare's atoms joining in the game; but of course there hasn't been quite as much time for Shakespeare to get around. Still, when you stop and think that all during his life, Shakespeare was breathing in oxygen and breathing out carbon dioxide, there is a good chance that even before his death a lot of the atoms that were once in Shakespeare drifted west to America and east to the Orient. So you have a little Shakespeare in you, too.

Man in Particle Perspective

This fanciful picture which I have just drawn is based on the concept of man in a particle perspective. It assumes that the human body is an assembly of about five octillion atoms. It also assumes that each of these atoms retains its identity as it drifts around here and there through the untold millions of years of its existence.

I can already hear some of my physicist friends shouting, "Stop, stop!" as they read these lines. For today it is generally agreed that atoms do not have individual identities. It does not make sense to say that a particular atom of carbon was in the body of Julius Caesar, happened to be breathed out in the form of carbon dioxide as Caesar was walking to his fatal rendezvous in the Roman Senate on the Ides of March, and drifted for centuries in the air until it was absorbed by a leaf of wheat in Kansas a year ago, then turned into flour, then into bread, then popped into your mouth and lodged in your brain as a link in the chain of one of your amino acids.

The proof that such logic is false rests on somewhat complex relationships which have been deduced from many kinds of observations of the behavior of matter; and this is not the place to try to unravel their intricacies. We must accept the lack of this kind of atomic identity as one of the certain aspects of the structure of our universe. But if we cannot think of the structure of the world around us, the structure of ourself in terms of assemblies of identifiable atoms, what is the proper vocabulary of thought in which to do our reasoning about such kinds of structure? Today the answer from science appears to be that we have to go back to Plato and think of the world around us, think of ourself, not as an assembly of particles but as an assembly of forms.

Man in Form Perspective

What is the structure of man? This is the question we are

trying to answer. What concept can we construct and say that here we truly have man?

Let me take Beethoven as an example. If I cannot say that Beethoven was a collection of a certain octillion of atoms, what *was* Beethoven? Would it be closer to the truth to say that Beethoven was a certain collection of quanta of energy? But energy quanta are even more slippery than atoms. They cannot be identified either. One cannot follow the course of a single quantum of energy down through the centuries. These "particles" of energy combine with each other and split up in an even more distracting way than do atoms.

Let me approach the problem another way. Suppose that in one of his tragically frustrating affairs of the heart, Beethoven gave a lock of his hair to one of the aristocratic young ladies of old Vienna. Suppose that this had been preserved during the last century and a half; and by a devious chain of circumstances it is now in your possession. One evening you open the vault in the wall of your library where you keep your most precious treasures; you bring out the little ivory box containing this relic of Beethoven and place it on your desk; and you open the lid so that you can gaze at this remnant of keratin from the head of the world's most titanic composer.

Now you go to your collection of phonograph records and take out the disk which has imprinted on it the first part of Beethoven's Ninth Symphony. You put this on your record player, settle yourself and lean back in your reclining chair as the initial thunder of this symphonic drama reverberates through the room.

What is really Beethoven? The atoms of hydrogen, carbon, oxygen, and nitrogen of the keratin filaments lying in the little ivory box, or the soul-shaking grandeur of the Ninth Symphony that is engulfing the room and surging in your brain?

Isn't it clear when we try to describe what Beethoven really was, the structure of this unique human being, that it is absurd to say that Beethoven was nothing but a collection of hydrogen, oxygen, carbon, nitrogen, and a few other kinds of atoms moving in a complex pattern of energy? The atoms were not Beethoven; the energy was not Beethoven; Beethoven was the total dynamic form, the essence of which is incandescent in his last monumental symphony.

Consider the ascending ladder of relationships starting from the simplest parts, Beethoven's protons, neutrons, and electrons, and rising through the complex relations that make atoms, molecules, amino acids, macromolecules, biological cells, anatomical organs, and finally the totality of Beethoven's body. If we assert that reality is associated only with the fundamental particles at the bottom of the ladder and possibly with the quanta of energy making these particles dynamic, is it not clear that we are looking through the wrong end of our observing instrument? As Goethe put it, by analyzing Beethoven into his fundamental parts as we search for his reality, we are discarding and destroying the essence of his reality. We are throwing out the spiritual links, the togetherness, that is the true vibrant reality. We have left only the fundamental parts, which are no more than distorted shadows of the reality of the whole that is the true Beethoven.

Beethoven's living spirit leapt into the air when the sounds of this great symphony first reverberated in the concert hall in Vienna a century and a half ago. Beethoven is literally alive in your room when this symphony again resounds around you. Beethoven is alive in your brain, once that total dynamic form has penetrated your being; and from now on Beethoven will be alive within you forever.

To me the overwhelming proof is in the uniqueness in what Beethoven created. Why is it that among all the thousands of composers of music since Beethoven's time, not one could write a *tenth* Beethoven symphony? Any such attempt would be detected immediately as a patent and crude forgery. To find the real Beethoven, to perceive the structure of reality that contained this unique creative dynamism, we must focus our gaze not in the perspective of particles but in the perspective of forms. We must try to envision the tapestry of dynamic interplay in that pinnacle symphony of life which was this supreme creative genius. Even in this perspective we can only hope for remote intimations of what that dynamic reality truly is. But as Professor Stace puts it so perceptively in his book "Time and Eternity," music almost breaks the walls of existence.

Form from Forms

The idea that forms are the ultimate basis of reality goes back many centuries and has appeared in human thought expressed in many ways. Plato is credited with one of the most original and refined statements of this doctrine. Today we are in the position where we can begin to clothe his skeletal ideas of form with flesh. From modern mathematics and its morphological relation to the data from atomic and molecular spectra, we begin to see the intimate details of these basic forms emerge, the forms that we call the atoms and molecules and their more complex combinations.

In trying to think of a human being as a synthesis of these forms, we are, of course, in danger of committing the same errors as those who think of a human being merely in terms of a synthesis of particles. However, I hope that in the preceding chapters of this book you have acquired a sense of "what it feels like to be an atom," in Whitehead's phrase, so that you can fuse the analytic and synthetic aspects of the picture into one integrated whole. So let us go back and try to think of the totality of dynamic forms that composed our composer, Beethoven.

At the bottom fundamental level there are primarily the electrons, the protons, and the neutrons we would find if we shattered Beethoven to the greatest possible degree of fineness. These are expressions of the basic mathematical character of the universe. Today there is a growing conviction among theoretical physicists that these and their somewhat more complex cousins like pions and muons are the embodiment of some of those subtle and elusive mathematical realities that we call algebraic *groups.*

At the next level of complexity above these fundamental entities, there are the atoms, the particles we would find if we "ground up" Beethoven a little less drastically. There are the hydrogen atoms making up about sixty-three per cent of his body, the oxygen atoms making up about twenty-six per cent, the carbon atoms making up about nine per cent, the nitrogen atoms about one per cent, plus the remaining one per cent of phosphorus, sodium, potassium, sulfur, iodine, and the rest. Remember that we thought of these vibrating aspects of the total form as the notes out of which the total symphony of life is composed.

At the next higher level of complexity, there are the molecules, the clusters of atoms formed by the fusion of the lesser patterns of vibration. Among these we see repeated over and over again the chords of harmony that the amino acids embody. At a still higher level of complexity, we have the woven fabric of the proteins of hundreds of different kinds, but distinguished to a high degree by the sequence as well as the choice of the twenty-odd amino acids that are their principal constituents.

Rising still higher in complexity, we find the biological cells, a hundred trillion in round numbers making up the total body. We find a remarkable similarity of form among all these hundred trillion cells, each in our somewhat fanciful language resembling a cathedral with nave and nuclear altar and a congregation of interior forms, ribosomes, centrioles, mitochondria, and all the rest. Then through the incredible miracle of differentiation these cells group together to form the different organs and the connecting links, the skin, the muscles, the bones, arteries, veins, the organs of metabolism, the organs of reproduction, the heart, the nerves and, crowning all, the brain. Keep clearly in mind that, although we speak of these as differentiated parts, life exists only because of the intimate dynamic linkages that fuse all these vibrant forms into the integrated vital whole.

Think also of the multiplicity of the dynamism. There is the visible dynamism of pulsating muscles, beating heart, flowing blood. There is the less visible dynamism of the complex circulation of energy that is the essence of the whole life process. There is the invisible incandescence of radiation glowing throughout the whole anatomical structure in the rainbows of the quaternary and quinary octaves of the subvisible. There is the music of the octillion harmonies of thermal vibration. There is the chanting of the poetry of neural communication . . . and, at the deepest dynamic level, the surging surf of the de Broglie waves.

Where in all this incredible complexity of the symphony of life do we find the deepest reality? I hope that you will agree that in this search we should focus on the part of life's music which we sum up broadly under the term *thought*.

The Cathedral of Thought

At this point the mechanist may claim a right to be heard. He may assert that all the recent experiments show that we find more and more evidence of physicochemical mechanism when we probe more and more deeply into the activities of the brain, using all the new techniques for measuring the dynamic nature of brain potentials together with the harmonic analysis of brain waves. We must remind ourself, however, that both the mechanists and the holists—both those who believe the ultimate explanation to be physicochemical mechanism and those who believe the ultimate explanation to be holistic dynamic forms—must admit ignorance, the inability to draw at the present time any detailed dynamic picture that links the little we know about action in nerve cells with the holistic pattern of human thought and human behavior.

Of course, there have been many attempts to suggest mechanisms of thought. Take the phenomenon of memory, for example. One can imagine that an act of memory is a process in which a chemical imprint is made at some particular point in the structure of the brain. In terms of this theory the brain may be regarded as a chemical filing system. If you want to remember that you met a man named John Mac-Pherson in Edinburgh on August 1, 1963, you shift the hydrogen atoms on the active ends of certain amino acids in your brain and set up a few new hydrogen bonds at appropriate locations. Later when the brain wave (which is the dynamic component of your search for the name of the man whom you met in Scotland) encounters the hydrogen bonds coding his name, the search wave is altered so that when it comes round to the nerve cells which give you the sensation of conscious thought, it sounds the name *John MacPherson.*

I cannot speak with any authority with regard to the most recent trends in our thinking about neurocerebral processes, but I gather that there is considerable doubt in the minds of many of the specialists in this field with regard to the validity of the chemical-filing-cabinet analogy. I believe that there is more and more recognition of the importance of the dynamic components of thought and less emphasis on more static changes of form.

Another contributing influence in our search for a better understanding of the nature of thought has been our experience in constructing computers. Both in the research aimed at improving the design of computers and in deepening our understanding of the essential nature of the computer problem, we are coming more and more to appreciate the true nature of information and the pattern of dynamism involved in the retrieval of that information. In a computer we have to store facts and we have to have a way of scanning the storage domain in order to get the fact back when we want it. A large part of the service that computers render consists of storing facts, retrieving them, and then recombining them under the influence of other facts into new dynamic patterns. In all of this we are appreciating more and more the importance of the cybernetic or feedback aspect of this dynamism.

You recall that we discussed an almost trivially simple example of feedback earlier in this book, the relation between the house furnace and the thermostat located in the area to be heated. The thermostat sends energy in the form of a signal to the furnace and the furnace responds by sending energy in the form of heat back up to the room and, of course, also to the thermostat. Thus, energy goes round and round and the pattern of this circulation determines the ultimate desired result, which is the maintenance of relatively constant temperature in the area to be heated.

Another pertinent example of a cybernetic mechanism is the automatic pilot of a ship. The compass mechanism on the captain's bridge is set with the "needle" pointing toward a selected direction, say northwest. If wind or wave turns the ship toward northwest-by-north, the compass signals the steering engine which at once turns the rudder slightly to bring the ship back on a true northwest course. As the ship responds and turns, the compass needle is slowly restored to the correct position of northwest, and terminates the signal to the steering engine. Thus a signal is fed from compass to rudder, and the action of the rudder *feeds back* a signal to the compass. It is in the *togetherness* of the relationship that the power of the process resides. If *being* is *power,* then here in the dynamic form of togetherness we find reality.

There is general agreement that this cybernetic or feedback process plays an important role in the dynamism of the brain. So keep this in mind as we try to see in more detail the interplay of these dynamic forms that constitute thought. Somehow in the brain there is achieved an interweaving of the de Broglie waves in the trillions of brain cells, so that they surge back and forth, converting information to action in a pattern governed by other information, creating still further information, ultimately resulting in the dynamic process that we call thought and finally producing signals that result in bodily action.

At this point I want to pose this crucial question: Can we ascribe reality to the *total* forms that constitute this thought? Of course, the mechanist is probably willing to say that thought is energy in some form or another and that energy is just as real as the mass which in the past he has regarded as the most fundamental aspect of reality. However, I am not arguing for a kind of undifferentiated reality of thought. Rather, I am arguing that, as the music of thought is transmitted back and forth resounding in the brain, there is a fundamental enduring reality that can be ascribed to *each* of the forms that constitute the components of this thought.

You remember, I hope, that I pointed out the pattern of invariance under transformation in the broadcasting of a symphony. You remember how the dynamic pattern that constitutes the symphony is woven together from the musical thoughts in the brain of the composer; fused in the dynamism of sound, transformed into electrical waves at the microphone, into radio waves at the broadcasting station, back into electrical waves at the receiving station, into sound waves at the loudspeaker, into neural waves in the ear and, finally, back into the brain waves that constitute the final perception of the music. You recall that I argued that this aspect of invariance under transformation should, at least, make us ask the question whether there is not a true reality of the symphony which transcends its individual manifestation as sound waves or electrical waves or even brain waves, a reality which has a far more fundamental claim to recognition than the temporary and evanescent reality of vibrating sound or vibrating electricity. In the same way, I suggest that we should at least ask the question whether we may not have an example of the most fundamental reality in these waves which through their resonance constitute the miracle of thought.

This suggestion is implicit in the writings of a number of scientists and philosophers who have considered this problem in the past. Whitehead goes on record as saying that man is thinking substance. He puts it in somewhat more detail by saying that the human body is indubitably a complex of occasions which are part of a special nature. It is a set of occasions miraculously coordinated so as to pour its inheritance into various regions within the brain.

You recall that I suggested that we could recognize these deeper realities of the intangible if we were willing to say that we exist not just in the three dimensions of length, breadth, and height (plus time), but that our reality is grounded in other dimensions that I have suggested might be called *form-space.* Teilhard de Chardin states that science . . . neglects . . . an entire dimension of the universe in its attitude toward thought. He speaks of the incandescence of thought beyond measure. He points out the role both of channeling or exclusion on the one hand and of interaction or cybernetics on the other in establishing the domain for thought.

In order to pursue these ideas a little further, let us

consider the nature of the stimuli under which our thinking substance evolves.

The Structure of Perception

I do not know whether psychologists believe that an infant child becomes aware of the world first through the sensation of touch, through the sensation of hearing, or through the sensation of vision. Perhaps it is a potpourri of all three. However, it may be logical to consider perception through hearing as involving the simplest sort of stimuli which can be coordinated to form the basis of thought structure. While sensations resulting from touch may be more basic and may occur at an earlier stage in the development (either prenatal or postnatal) of the infant, these do not offer the possibility of analysis into a simple mathematical pattern comparable with the sensation of hearing. This is because hearing partakes much more of the nature of a time sequence made up of components related to each other through the rather simple mathematical concept of frequency. Vision, on the other hand, has less the nature of a time sequence and more the nature of a total confrontation.

Of course, to a degree we have a total confrontation when we perceive sound. The ear acts as a harmonic analyzer and measures the intensity of the different tones that strike it simultaneously. To use a simple example, if you hear a major triad chord represented by *do-mi-sol,* the ear sends a succession of nerve pulses along the nerve fiber that comes from the generating mechanism in tune with *do;* simultaneously, a series of pulses are sent to indicate the intensity of the note *mi;* and lastly, a third series of nerve pulses are sent to indicate the intensity of the tone that corresponds to the note *sol.* So when you hear this major triad being played on the piano or on the pipe organ, you are confronted with three simultaneous sets of signals. The evidence is that these come to your brain as a series of electrochemical impulses, in which the rapidity of the pulse in each fiber indicates the intensity of the particular note stimulating that fiber.

Of course, when you hear this major triad played, the *total* process of perception is probably far more complicated than that which I have just described. Still, it is amazing that this series of "taps" from three nerve fibers can produce an interplay of brain waves to create this overwhelmingly beautiful sensation associated with this basic chord, the major triad. It seems reasonably clear that somehow in the mind there is present the recollection of this chord, possibly the recollection in context with the millions of times you have heard it played in church, in the concert hall, or even at football rallies and political conventions. How much the wave in your brain resounds back and forth between all these different memories, I do not know. I do think that part of the pleasure you derive in hearing this chord comes from its association with memories of the past. At any rate, I am sure that you recognize the chord in one instant act of perception and not as a conscious comparison of the frequencies of its three notes. It is a *gestalt* phenomenon, an instant perception of total form.

One could go on from this simple example to the perception of far more subtle harmony, the perception of shifting patterns of harmony, the perception of melodic line, the perception of polyphony. I believe that in all of this there is the element of *gestalt,* which may resemble the kind of process that we think of in radio transmission as *tuning.* We know that our radio set has to be *tuned in* to the frequency of the broadcasting station in order to have that energy brought in, amplified, and conveyed to us through the vibrations of the loudspeaker. We may have to be *tuned in* to recognize the elements of musical perception.

There is another simple experiment with tuning that you

can do with a piano. Depress the right hand pedal, removing the dampers from the strings. Then sing, as loudly as you can, the note of middle C. If you place your fingertips lightly on the piano string that corresponds to middle C, you will feel it vibrating. Because it is tuned to the frequency of the note you sing, it has absorbed some of your voice energy and has begun to vibrate in response to it. If you touch the neighboring strings you will not feel any similar degree of response. Of course, you may get some response from the closely related strings, such as those for the note *sol* in this key, and particularly for the notes an octave above or an octave below the note that you have sung.

If we think of memory as the presence in the mind of certain latent frequencies in this total complex of de Broglie waves, then it is understandable that when these frequencies are sounded through the act of perception, there is a feedback that stimulates overtones which increase the amplitude of certain wave forms and result in the sensation of recognition.

I am sure that the same concepts must apply to the perception of visual form. Just look up from this book for a moment; look out into the room around you. Stop for an instant and become aware of the fantastic complexity of the image with which you are totally confronted. I do not know just how many nerve fibers go from the retina of your eye to the visual center in your brain, but my guess is that it is at least one hundred thousand. In this single act of vision untold millions of these vibratory waves of visible light, these bundles of vibrant energy which we call *photons,* have entered your eye, have been absorbed in this miraculous complex of de Broglie waves called the retina, and have set up again this series of popping pulses that go to the brain. There these untold millions of pulses are somehow synchronized, fused in an instant to give you this fabulously complex awareness of the image of the room around you containing literally millions of components of color and form.

We should be aware of the countless miracles taking place at every moment of our life. Think how every act of sight involves the fusion of millions of waves in the incredible functioning of the eye and the brain to produce from this apparently chaotic bombardment of impulses the coordinated sensation of sight. One can multiply examples of the miracle of perception almost endlessly. But rather than explore this fascinating field further, I want to push on to reflect briefly on the greatest cerebral miracle of all, the miracle of creative imagination.

The Miracle of Imagination

In analyzing the functions of the brain, one of the more difficult problems is the definition of the difference between perception and thought. One way of illustrating this difficulty is to consider the problems faced by electrical engineers when they try to make an analogue of the brain employing computer techniques. There is a serious need today for "thinking" machines that will replace human beings in tasks that require a survey of mountainous information and the identification and comparison of certain items of this information, a process which might be characterized as *search and seizure.*

For example, in the United States Government Patent Office, the files of previously issued patents contain literally billions of words. When an inventor files an application for a new patent, it is necessary to search through all the files of previously issued patents to make sure that the invention has not been anticipated. And, of course, anticipation might be found not only in the patent file but in the previously published scientific and engineering literature. As we are all aware, in the last decade or two the rate of expansion of scientific and technical endeavor has accelerated markedly each year in a kind of astronomical mushroom growth (if I may be permitted to use a mixed metaphor that suggests the present muddled state of affairs).

It is obvious that one step to help solve this rapidly growing problem would be the development of a machine capable of reading previously issued patents and checking them against a new patent application. Unfortunately, the essence of many patents is expressed as much in drawings as in words. It is almost essential that such a machine should be able both to "listen" to English and to look at drawings intelligently. In effect, it must have both ears and eyes.

In many ways the modern television camera is the equivalent of an eye. Of course, the eye receives stimulation from a pattern of light and relays the result through a cable of communication to the brain, the optic nerve, which has many thousands of circuits; on the other hand, the television camera receives the same pattern but transforms it into a single-circuit channel where the pulses of information travel much faster. Thus, the large number of rather slow pulses in the many channels of the optic nerve are matched by the many rapid pulses in the single channel from the camera.

The single rapid sequence of pulses coming from the television camera can be recorded on electronic tape, making it possible for us to store the information received by the camera and reproduce it again in the form of a picture anytime that we wish. This process has revolutionized the whole pattern of television communication, making it possible to tape a live program and reproduce it with as much clarity as the original at a later time (which can be varied from a matter of seconds to a matter of years).

Whether we think of the recording of a scene from a drama or the recording of a drawing from a patent file, the act of "vision" by the television camera and the subsequent recording on television tape appears to be a close analogue of the act of perception. In the patent-office problem, for this perception to be meaningful, there must be some way of scanning a drawing and comparing the essential relationships expressed in it with another drawing which may be on a different scale, or which may employ different symbolism. There must be a similar scanning step in the mental process of vision in order that the series of signals transmitted to the brain by the optic nerve may be compared with previously stored information. It is this comparison, the checking of similarities and differences and the evaluation of the results of the checking, that properly may be called *thought*.

Now it is only a short step from the mental checking and identification of a new set of visual impressions coming directly from the eye to the brain, to the process of reflection or imagination in which a group of impressions perceived days, weeks, or months ago are compared with each other and synthesized into a new concept. Although it is difficult to define precisely in words, there is general agreement that here we are dealing with a very special kind of mental process. However, there is a disagreement between the mechanists and the vitalists on one essential part of this process. Is the act of imagination merely a continuing series of causes and effects? The photons of light stimulate the optic nerve and the nerve pulses travel to the brain by a physicochemical mechanism which appears to be clearly a chain of events—A causing event B causing event C causing event D, and so on. Is the subsequent mental process of comparing one previously received impression with another and from these synthesizing a new and original third—is this process merely event K causing event L causing event M causing event N and so on, until the chain is broken by boredom or sleep? The mechanist claims that all these cerebral processes are merely chains of cause and effect. The vitalist claims that in the act of creative imagination, the human psyche seizes the helm and the outcome is determined by the free will of the human being.

Here we reach a crucial nexus in the pattern of logic derived from the holistic perspective. Let me see if I can put this clearly and briefly, straight to the point.

The mechanist argues that the brain is merely an assembly of fundamental particles—that at the subatomic level, the atomic level, the molecular level, the macromolecular level, at all these levels, the law of cause and effect is obeyed. The brain is no more than the sum of its parts, therefore the mental processes are no more than chains of cause and effect. There is no psyche, no soul.

As opposed to this logic, I suggest that at the subatomic level, at the atomic level, at the molecular level, at the macromolecular level and so on right up to the brain itself, reality consists of wave patterns. At the atomic level, as Heisenberg first pointed out, the law of cause and effect no longer holds; there is indeterminacy. This indeterminacy is not just lack of knowledge about the outcome; the outcome in the complete sense of the word is not bound by the law of cause and effect. Consider that there are many reasons for believing that key steps in mental processes involve the action of such a small number of atoms that the outcome is also not bound by the law of cause and effect. Since at every stage of increasing complexity the assembly of the whole wave pattern is richer in its potentialities than the mere sum of its parts, since the nature of the combination to form the whole involves an intimacy, a togetherness that is far beyond mere summation, I assert that there is a *reality of the whole* above and beyond the reality of the parts, that this *reality* is not bound by the law of cause and effect, and that in this *reality of the whole* we find the guiding factor which governs the outcome of the mental process. This reality of the whole is a freedom that lifts its functioning out of the prison walls of *cause-and-effect* determinacy. This freedom is the human soul.

Along with Kierkegaard, I maintain that this freedom

of the spirit is not only a reality, infinitely more substantial, infinitely more potent than the illusory reality associated in primitive thinking with sticks and stones. I maintain with Plato that its supreme claim to reality is its potency. I believe with Plato that being is power.

Thus, the harmonic perspective of physics is not new in testifying to the reality of the human spirit. But it is adding new potency to the argument for this reality when it demonstrates through laboratory experimentation the wave character of fundamental particles and their combinations, the appropriateness of thinking about the universe as music rather than matter, and the necessity for applying the concept of determinacy only as a statistical law, binding on machines but not binding on men. In this way the new perspective of the universe as music opens the door to a new way of thinking about the dynamism of life and of the universe. It shows that the language for describing the behavior of assemblies of fundamental particles is the language of multidimensional space. This language has the power to coordinate old knowledge, to suggest new paths for the acquisition of new knowledge, and to make new predictions that are experimentally verified. The old language of three-dimensional space and one-dimensional time, the old language of Newtonian mechanics and determinacy lacks this power. If we believe that being is power, then we must direct our thinking to the exploration of the significance of life and of the universe conceived in terms of multidimensional existence where total forms are the realities.

We cannot *prove* the existence of the human soul, we cannot *prove* the existence of God. But we should place side by side the picture of man and the universe as matter, and the picture of man and the universe as music, and decide which has the most persuasive claim to our faith. To this end, the remaining chapters of this book are dedicated.

14

The Dynamism of Man

THIS MORNING as I write these lines I am seated at my desk in the library of our home on the bank of the Spanish River in southern Florida. I stop for a moment and look around me. Against three of the walls there are bookshelves from floor to ceiling filled with books, the varied hues of their bindings making a fascinating patchwork pattern of color. I see my desk cluttered with pencils and pens, notebooks, photographs, paper weights, a few odd seashells, a few pine cones, a Venetian glass ashtray, an agate mortar and pestle inherited from my grandfather, and a porcelain faun from New Hampshire. There is a maple armchair which my wife has been urging me to give to the Salvation Army every year for the last fifteen years. But it is an old friend acquired many years ago in my bachelor days and is still comfortable to sit in. There is another straight-backed chair with turned arms and legs, a convertible sofa, four filing cabinets, and a Persian rug on the floor. It is a collection of the useful and the useless, of the beautiful and the battered; and I somehow feel that all these things are part of me.

How do I see these things? Light waves, originating in the gigantic incandescent nuclear cauldron of our sun a few minutes ago, sped on their way through the hundred-million-odd miles of space, headed for southern Florida, zoomed down on our house, in through the window, bounced off the surfaces of all these objects, leaving energy behind and acquiring specific color, and then headed into the tiny opening in the iris of my eye and were captured and imprisoned in the nerve endings of the retina. What an anticlimax for a photon after this remarkable journey! Birth, perhaps, in the million-degree incandescence of the sun's hydrogen fusion, a maiden flight at hundreds of thousands of miles per second through space toward our relatively tiny planet, then a dash down through the atmosphere dodging capture by some atmospheric molecule, the final plunge through the glass of the library window, the bounce off the back of a book, a zip into my eye, and the exciting flight is terminated.

As I look at the many books directly in front of me and see all the details of the different bindings, even the titles on many, I think of the millions of these tiny light waves each second that have made this trip from the sun, that are pouring into my retina; and I meditate on the millions of neural impulses per second that are traveling along the thousands of nerve fibers to my brain and the inconceivably complex quivering of the de Broglie waves of my brain cells, all to give me this single sensation of an instant's vision of my wall of books.

This is the dynamism of one small portion of my conscious life. Why do I have this moment of consciousness? It is first because of the flow of energy, the energy coming from the sun in the form of light, a flow altered in its pattern by the reflection from the bindings of the books, then entering my eye and changed into energy in the nerve fibers, finally entering my brain and transformed into the energy of brain waves. But the moment of consciousness is more than just flow of energy, it is the flow of dynamic *form*. The relatively formless energy coming in from the sun had the form of the binding of my books stamped upon it in the act of selective reflection; and this new message, carried by the photons of light, was transformed in my eye; but it was transformed with the kind of invariance that brings the image of the bindings of the books to my brain where I am conscious of its form in a way that tells me the color and the shape of the bindings and the pattern of the letters stamped on their backs. Thus, a single act of vision may be characterized as a flow of dynamic form, the word *dynamic* emphasizing the energy aspect, and the word *form* emphasizing that it is energy in a specific kind of form.

Man as Action

The dynamism of man essentially is constructed from these two kinds of components: *energy* and *form*. Consider first the life of a human being as the flow of energy. This aspect is evident in metabolism at every turn. The advertising pages of our newspapers and magazines are shot through with pleas for us to live on low-calorie diets. A calorie, of course, is one of the most common scientific units in which to measure energy. Its abbreviation *cal* is worked into the trade names of patent foods whenever possible.

It is even fair to say that when you eat, you are really consuming not matter at all, but energy. First of all, you eat just to get energy in bulk. You need energy to keep you going, just in the way that a factory needs energy to keep its machines going. For the factory the energy arrives in the form of lumps of coal or gallons of fuel oil or pulses of electrons in copper wires or even in the push of H_2O molecules against the paddles of a millwheel. For the body the energy arrives in the "packaged" form of sugar, starch, and fat molecules, since we have not discovered how to put a socket on the abdomen and plug ourself into the house electrical circuit for a recharging, in the way we recharge a portable electric shaver. Through the almost miraculous process of digestion and the subsequent stages of metabolism, the energy of the sugar, starch, and fat molecules is distributed around the body, stored at strategic points and then used to activate the muscles of the heart and other internal organs as well as arms, legs, fingers, and eyes. It is also used to make possible the transmission of the many signals along the nerve fibers that control the feeding of energy to the muscles. It is used to energize the billions of brain cells that send out these control messages along the nerves and it is used to convey the information received by the organs of sensing along the nerve channels that lead from them up to the brain.

Of course, there are many other complex and subtle aspects of the dynamism of the body. We not only require gross calories; we also must have energy that is especially packaged in the tiny bundles which are the molecules of vitamins and hormones. These molecules also serve as special controlling factors along with the nerve impulses to keep the unbelievably intricate dynamism of the body playing the symphony of life in tune.

Of course, we also must have the right channels established for these streams of energy to flow in; the growth energy must be delivered to the right places in the right amounts; and the electrical, physicochemical, or chemical pulses of control must be conveyed to the right places at the right time. So it can be said that this requires a certain energy structure for the body. There must be arteries and veins; there must be contractile muscle tissue as well as tendons and bones to enable this energy to flow out of the body again as useful work. But remember that the walls of the veins and arteries, the contractile muscle tissue, the tendons and bones are themselves assemblies of de Broglie waves; thus even the most structural aspect of the body is still in essence dynamism. Most significantly of all, it is controlled dynamism.

Man as Communication Pattern

The control of the flowing energy that makes up the day-to-day pattern of human living may be divided into two principal kinds. There is the subconscious control, the pulses that keep the heart beating, the pulses that make the stomach and other digestive organs operate at the appropriate moment, the pulses that keep the body temperature relatively constant and control the chemical composition of the blood. But the network of control that makes you not only a being, but a *human* being, is the nexus of dynamic form that not only reflects your past experience, education, training in various kinds of skills but also embraces the mysterious operation of the *ego,* the arena of dynamism where you yourself live, the arena of the spirit of which Professor Hocking has written so persuasively.

The mechanist thinks of this pattern of control as just an unbelievably complicated network of physicochemical mechanism. The mechanist claims that all past experience, education, and training are merely a complex of physical and chemical causes, producing their imprint of structure on the physicochemical composition of the brain, thereby establishing a pattern which determines the effects that inexorably will be produced when future causes activate certain parts of the cerebral mechanism. But in assessing the validity of this mechanistic picture, it is well to recall that the deterministic law of cause and effect is based on observations of the behavior of *macroscopic* bodies. In fact, the most precise expression of cause and effect is to be found in Newton's laws of mechanics; and Newton was led to the enunciation of these laws both by the observation of the motion of the planets, bodies to which the application of the adjective *large* is somewhat of an understatement, and by observations of other bodies comparable in size to billiard balls. The mechanist asserts that the law of cause and effect can be extended from the very large (the planets) and the relatively large (the billiard balls) down to the domain of the atom where action takes place on a scale one hundred million times smaller. Now, we do not know exactly how many atoms are involved in the act of "storing" an item of information in the brain or in the act of fusing that information with other information to create a new impulse either of thought or of stimulus to action; but it is doubtful whether such an action is macroscopic in scope. It could involve less than one hundred atoms. We will consider this problem in more detail in just a moment.

In contrast with the above mechanistic hypotheses, the holist asserts that life is more than a concillium of tiny billiard balls. The holist points out that at the atomic level all the experimental evidence indicates that the law of cause and effect does not function in a deterministic way. He also points out that many like von Neumann are convinced that determinism cannot operate there. They also feel that the discovery of new evidence to reestablish determinism at the atomic level is about as unlikely as the discovery of evidence to show that two plus two equals five. In the light of this, the holist believes that the functioning of the brain is much more likely to have the character of atom dynamism than of billiard-ball dynamism. The holist concludes that in the complex dynamism of the human mind is a domain beyond determinism, an arena for the spirit.

In order to compare these two lines of argument in perspective, I think it is worthwhile to take a quick glance at the comparative size of a memory center, a brain cell, and a billiard ball. A billiard ball contains, roughly speaking, about septillion atoms. Expressed in the usual scientific manner, this is 10^{24}. Recall that a septillion peas would provide a four-foot layer covering the entire surface of about two hundred and fifty planets, each the size of our Earth.

Again, as a rough figure, the brain is made up of something close to a trillion biological cells (10^{12}) and as a rough figure each of these brain cells contains about one hundred trillion atoms (10^{14}). You remember that 10^{14} is equal to one followed by fourteen zeros.

We can summarize the relative numbers of atoms in a memory center, in the cell and in the billiard ball in the following way:

memory center --100 atoms
cell --------------------------------------100,000,000,000,000 atoms
billiard ball ....10,000,000,000,000,000,000,000,000 atoms

When an act of thought takes place it is reasonable to assume that the brain cell is not in any sense destroyed. How many of its one hundred trillion atoms are involved in the act of thought is difficult to say. We also do not know with any certainty how much energy is involved. In fact, it is extremely difficult to define precisely what we mean by one "act of thought." However, let us reflect on the idea expressed by Professor Norbert Wiener in his conversation on the bus with my friend, the young spectroscopist. Wiener suggested that thought might be the alteration in the hydrogen bonding connecting the different cells. If a single unit in the thought process is merely the shifting of a single hydrogen bond, then it puts the act of thought much closer to the single atom than it does to the billiard ball, and if it is even a hundred atoms, then its dynamics can certainly involve indeterminacy in a significant way.

This raises the interesting question of the differentiation within a single cell which might be involved in thought. Can a single cell with its 100,000,000,000,000 atoms participate in perhaps 100 thoughts, or in 1,000,000 thoughts, or even in 1,000,000,000 thoughts simultaneously?

The point which I am trying to make is this: There is good reason for believing that the fineness of action involved in the thinking process represents such a smallness of scale that it is far more logical to ascribe to the thought process atom dynamism rather than billiard ball dynamism. And if we accept atom dynamism as the most probable dynamism of thought, then it is logical to extend this perspective and try to envision not only the intracommunication in the mind but the intercommunication between minds in the dynamic pattern of society in terms of the interplay of dynamic forms which are not imprisoned behind the bars of determinacy.

Communication in Form Perspective

One of the great steps along the path toward an algebra of form was taken by the great French scientist, Jean-Baptiste-Joseph Fourier, a little more than one hundred and fifty years ago. Fourier had been trying to develop mathematical ways for explaining the way in which heat flows in varying patterns. For example, during the summer when the sun is high, heat flows deeper and deeper into the ground. In winter when the sun is lower on the horizon, heat flows back out of the ground. How, then, can one predict the average temperature of the ground at ten feet below the surface on the first of January? In one of the most brilliant and original intellectual feats of all time, Fourier showed that it was possible to approach the problem in terms of mathematical expressions which represent a series of waves beating at different frequencies. Having solved in this way a number of the major problems in heat flow, he went on to show that practically all mathematical functions (relationships between quantities) could be expressed in terms of this series, which has come to be known as the Fourier Series; there are only a few exceptional classes that are not amenable to such a treatment.

Today the generalized concept of Fourier's Series is the cornerstone of our modern theory of communication. Speaking broadly, the numbers that one inserts as the coefficients of terms in the Fourier Series characterize a dynamic form. If you will recall especially our discussion of the patterns of vibration of the square drum, you may remember that the drumhead may be made to vibrate in a number of different dynamic forms. We can make this membrane vibrate in a pattern like the flag of France, or a pattern like the flag of Japan with a circle in the center; or we can make it vibrate like the checkerboard design used on the flag waved by the starters on an auto race course. We characterized the flag of France as having a 1, 3 pattern, and the checkerboard flag as having a 5, 5 pattern. The numbers placed at the front of each of the terms in the Fourier Series also characterize the form which is represented mathematically by this series. In the development of the analytical theory of communication, this kind of approach has proved to be the only useful and significant way in which to solve problems and design new media of communication.

I do not know whether the engineers prefer to think that in the act of communication they are *really* transmitting forms, or whether they verbalize more in terms of billiard-ball mechanics and the transmission of discrete pulses. It depends somewhat on the nature of the problem. There are forms of communication, like the signaling of telephone numbers, where discrete pulses do play an important role. But it is fair to say that the majority of the patterns of communication can be thought of far more usefully in terms of the transmission of waves than of pulses. Actually we have the complementarity of wave and particle appearing just as we did in the behavior of the atom. In the case of the atom we found that most of the aspects of chemical behavior could be readily explained if we thought of de Broglie waves associated with the atom; these same phenomena were completely inexplicable in terms of circulating particles. This was a strong support for the point of view that de Broglie waves are real. In the same way it is logical to assert that the wave forms that make up a large part of our communication network are real.

Society as Action

In our analysis of the dynamism of the human body, we

recognized the importance of both the gross energy flow and the communication network that controlled this flow. We concluded that the character of the dynamism of the body was largely determined by the character of the dynamism of communication. When we turn to examine the dynamism of society, the collection of many individual human beings, the same idea emerges. In our typical twentieth-century society, there is a flow of energy and there is a communication dynamism that controls the flow of energy. As in the case of the individual human being, it is largely the dynamism of communication that determines the total dynamic character of the society as a whole.

Of course, the flow of gross energy is obvious. Once more, let me give a few brief examples. Let us consider the process that results in the manufacture of a lawnmower. As the first step, iron ore is removed from the ground, obviously a process requiring energy. As a second step, the ore is transported by train and by ship to the steel mill. Transportation again is a process that requires energy. At the steel mill the iron ore is heated (the introduction of thermal energy); it is chemically treated to remove the impurities and combine the iron with small amounts of carbon and other materials to produce steel (a pattern of changing chemical energy). The steel is forged under a hammer into the form of a blade; the forging hammer applies kinetic energy at the proper place on the steel to bend the pattern of iron atoms into the proper shape. Then the edge of the blade is ground to a sharp line by the application of energy from the motion of a grinding wheel. Finally, the parts of the lawnmower are assembled, probably by energy from human muscles, and the lawnmower is packed and transported to the store and eventually to the ultimate buyer and user. This is just one small example of a manufacturing process which is essentially a flow of energy from beginning to end.

There are, of course, thousands of other examples of the flow of energy in our modern social order. Consider the production and distribution of electrical energy. The sun's energy raises water from the ocean to clouds, the water is precipitated and comes down on mountains, it flows down rivers under the influence of gravity from a higher to a lower level, and is diverted into a hydroelectric generator. There this energy is turned into electrical energy, stepped up in voltage, sent out over a transmission line hundreds of miles long, and goes into the heart of a large city. There it is distributed and used to turn motors in factories, to light lights and to heat homes. The distribution of gasoline is another example of energy in chemical packages which "flows" around our nation and ultimately is used to produce energy of motion in vehicles. Actually, we live in houses because the walls of the houses provide protection against too much dissipation of energy from our bodies. We wear clothes as an energy barrier to conserve our bodily energy. The whole distribution and consumption of food is essentially a pattern of energy distribution and consumption.

In each of these instances the pattern of the flow of energy has to be planned to make it effective and useful. The flow of energy is controlled by a communication network. Sometimes this network is a direct and obvious one. In the great power networks through which energy in the form of electrical power flows from production plants to our cities, an intricate communications network is maintained by which this flow of energy is directed. In manufacturing, the communication network may not be quite so obvious, but frequently one finds steel mills, automobile assembly lines, and sales distribution points all linked by a communication network to make the manufacture and distribution of automobiles more efficient. These networks are usually in the form of telephone or radio communication channels.

We must not forget the communication networks of magazines and newspapers and even the postal system. You may object and say that this is not an energy communication network, but remember that every piece of paper with printed marks on it actually is just a collection of de Broglie waves vibrating in a dynamic pattern. Measured in gross amounts of energy there is a negligible transmission. But the real measure of the power of this energy to direct the flow of other energy lies in the potency of the forms. We all recognize the "power" of the press. If you could listen to a newspaper with your magic ears, you would hear the patterns of the de Broglie waves in the ink and the paper singing a symphony; and it is the pattern of harmony, melody, and counterpoint of this symphony that the energy is contained which exercises the controlling effect on human action. When light reflected from the surface of the newspaper conveys this pattern through the complex melody of vibration of light waves to the human eye, when the eye in turn transforms but keeps the essential pattern of information invariant and relays it via the optic nerve fibers to the brain, when this transposed symphony resounds in the brain and through tuning with the recognition centers conveys the *ideas* set forth in the newspaper to the brain centers, then we see the whole chain of the dynamism of communication in action.

This is obviously a long chain of different transformations; but I hope you will agree that there is a highly significant component of invariance running through all these transformations. This is the invariance that retains the meaning of the idea all the way from the mind of the person who wrote the newspaper dispatch through the transformation to the manuscript that went to the printer, through the printer's actions on the linotype, through the black marks that appear on the newspaper, through the light beam that carries the information to your eye, through the optic nerve, and finally through the distribution of this information to your own perception centers.

Anyone who would try to express such a process in terms of billiard-ball mechanics and old-fashioned height, length, and breadth coordinates would be regarded as stupid or crazy. We follow this transmission of information largely by following the pattern of the letters and the grouping of the letters under the laws of spelling, vocabulary, grammar, and syntax. Thus, when we express ideas in words which consist of letters, we are employing form coordinates. An alphabet is an example of form coordinates.

A number of these aspects of society as a flow of energy and as a communication network have been recognized and discussed in the past. The new point of view, which I wish to emphasize, is the assignment of reality to the forms, even to the ideas distributed in communication, a reality which I claim is even deeper than the reality that we have ascribed in the past to tangible, weighable matter. I am saying that matter is illusion, that form is reality. I am saying that if a bullet from an enemy soldier shatters the bone in your arm, it is not a piece of matter breaking another piece of matter; it is the kinetic energy conveyed by the bullet disturbing the chemical energy of the calcium, oxygen, and phosphorus atoms of your bone; and I am saying that this energy is a carrier of the aggressive idea that made the soldier your enemy. Because the energy that disrupted the energy of your arm bone was generated and directed by a pattern of aggression, it is the aggression that has shattered your arm. Again, if we believe with Plato that reality is power, we have to ascribe far more reality to the essence of aggression than we do to the rather illusory shadow that accompanied it, the so-called matter of the steel of the bullet that penetrated your arm.

The Social Community as a Dynamic Network

There are many reasons for believing that it is important

today to analyze our social dynamism in terms of the flow of energy and the control of energy by dynamic forms. As Whitehead points out in his book on the "Adventures of Ideas," we are now in the midst of a crisis of civilization which can be best understood in terms of these aspects of the dynamism of our society. As Norbert Wiener puts it, there has been a revolution in power and in control of power.

Look back over the last two thousand five hundred years and you see that, over a large part of this time, civilization coasted along on a rather flat level of power in the world. Society depended largely on energy derived from human muscles to do the work of the world, energy supplemented only to a small degree by a few windmills and waterwheels. From the time of Alexander the Great to the time of Napoleon, ships were borne across the sea largely by the power of the wind; and over this period of more than two thousand years there was no significant increase in the speed of marine travel. And Caesar's chariots may have traveled more rapidly over the Appian Way than did the carriages of George III in the ruts of the muddy roads of eighteenth-century England.

It is estimated that before the year 1800 the total flow of energy for doing the work of the world was less than a million horsepower. Then at about the beginning of the nineteenth century came the start of the power revolution. Our understanding of the conversion of heat into power deepened with the discovery of the laws of thermodynamics. Our better knowledge of the nature of electricity and magnetism developed into the production of electrical generators and motors. Our improved chemical technology led to the invention of the internal-combustion engine. With the development of machines for making machines and devices for controlling power, the flow of energy increased like a raging flood until in the year 1950 human muscle was supplemented by well over a billion horsepower. If the length of the average working day had shortened in proportion to the increase in power, it is fair to say that each of us would be working less than one minute per day.

There is every reason to believe that by the end of this present century this flow of energy may be amplified another ten to a hundredfold, *if* peace can be maintained in the world and *if* a large portion of our energy is not diverted into unproductive military activities.

Seen in the term of our perspective of dynamism, it is clear that we hold this enormous reservoir of energy in our hands today because of the development of the dynamism of the ideas of science and technology. Whitehead remarks: "Our period of history is the first break with routine in the last ten thousand years. Our age is characterized by the emergence of idea into power." A few pages later, he comments, "Mankind is now in one of its rare moods of shifting its outlook."

It needs no persuasive argument today to convince us of the ominous overtones hovering above this increase of energy in the world. Today mankind holds in its hands sufficient energy to encompass its own destruction. Some years ago Albert Schweitzer in a pessimistic mood wrote that the suicide of civilization was clearly in progress.

I think that it is good to meditate on two other remarks by Whitehead at this point. He wrote: "Catastrophes are disastrous to civilization. They are a plunge into the unknown; and civilization is not the average result of raw nature. It depends upon the long-term operation of selective agencies." He went on to say: "Nature is plastic. Modern history begins with new European selective agencies. Man is the supreme factor in nature. Plasticity is the introduction of novel law."

With all these aspects of today's civilization as a background, I urge that it is important to try to understand more deeply this dynamism of forms which is the agency that is controlling the vast power for good or for ill that we hold in our hands today. So I want to push the inquiry which we have been making just a little further. In addition to recognizing the reality in specific ideas that may be circulating in the dynamism of our social communication, I want to argue for the even deeper realities of the more generalized dynamism of beauty, truth, justice, loyalty, and freedom. In the acceptance of the reality of these holistic intangibles, in the understanding of the dynamic structure of their potency, and in the effective application of their power, we have the one and only pattern of hope for our future.

The Reality of Beauty and Truth

On the wall of my study there is hanging before me a beautiful etching by D. Y. Cameron of a mountain in Wales that is called "Ben Ledi." The Gaelic name *Ben Ledi*— "Hill of God"—is said to have originated in the Beltane mysteries celebrated on its summit. The foreground of this picture is dark; it is etched by many closely grouped strokes of the artist's stylus, suggesting a long vista of marsh and meadow stretching to the foot of the mountain; the shadows are broken only by the reflection of the sky on a small pond almost concealed in the reeds. In the center of the picture, the mountain rises abruptly. Above the marshes there is a narrow band of forest and then bare rock thrusting up in a pyramidal peak to the pointed summit. Above the peak there is clear sky with just a suggestion of high cirrus clouds at the upper left.

As I gaze at this picture I cannot help but feel that here before my eyes there is far more than just a pattern of ink on paper. Here is the harmony, melody, and counterpoint of these quintillion atoms of the carillon of hydrogen, carbon, oxygen, and nitrogen in the ink and the paper, there is singing the song that I would hear if I were standing on the bank of this marsh in Wales and by some magic could listen to the melody of the mountain. For those countless millions of tons of rock are not inert matter; they are really the song of silicon, of calcium and of oxygen mingled with the trillions of overtones that express not only the cosmic melodies of these elemental atom-bells but the history of the incandescent flowing rock, the matrix molded by preCambrian fluid force, chiseled and eroded by rain and frost to produce at last this majestic pinnacle. In the deep and mysterious contrabass overtones of the vibration of the rock which reflect in the domain of unheard music the noble profile of this "Hill of God," there is floating the intangible but super-actual reality of beauty.

And this dynamism of beauty is not only the impersonal beauty of this glorious portion of nature, it is the beauty stamped with the vision of the artist. No one but Cameron could have portrayed in this precise way both the mystery and the beauty of this vista. In the trillion overtones of the dynamism of this picture there is also present the melody that *is* Cameron.

You recall that I suggested that the reality in the melody, harmony, and counterpoint of the Ninth Symphony *is* Beethoven far more than any portion of Beethoven's body. I maintain that I have here in my study something of the living, dynamic soul of Cameron.

I maintain that in every object around me there is not only the vibrant reality of the elemental tones of the universe, the ninety-two chemical elements; there is also the vibrant reality of the souls of the thousands or even millions of human beings who somehow contributed to the composition of the total music that is embodied in these forms.

In the Persian rug on my floor, there is something of the soul of the designer (thousands of miles away and centuries ago) who envisioned that pattern of muted red, green, and blue. There is something of the souls of the artists who preceded him in the long evolution of Iranic art that provided the vocabulary, grammar, and syntax of form that flowers in this beautiful rug. There is something of the souls of the more humble artists who prepared the dyes, who twined the fibers into thread, and who contributed to all the other processes that resulted in this symphony of color and design.

Everywhere I go in our home, I feel the real presence of the thousands and millions who have contributed to make it what it is. Even in such humble objects as the lamps, the end tables, the ash trays, the water pitcher and the glasses, there are present the dynamic forms that contain the overtones of beauty, of honesty, of effort, of devoted skill. And these realities have survived the transformation from the minds and the muscles of the initial artists and artisans, have come to me with invariant reality, just as the reality of a symphony pursues the path from the brain of the composer through the musicians, through the embodiment as sound, to the form in which it is perceived as brain waves. These realities of the spirit about me have come to me invariant and real in the same way that my own spirit moves forward from day to day invariant, dynamic, real through the sextillions of metabolic and genetic transformations which are taking place constantly in my body during every hour of my life.

The walls of my house are standing because of the honesty of those who quarried the stone, who calcined the lime, who mixed the cement, who cut and aged the beams, and who assembled the total structure. In the frozen music of the architecture of our house, there is the dynamism of form, the dynamism of beauty but also the dynamism of honesty and truth.

The privilege that I have of living in this beautiful home, secure from the forces of aggression and evil, stems from the dynamism of law, the dynamism of justice, the dynamism of the loyalty of those who guard my rights at home and of those who fight on foreign fronts to protect our collective right to life, liberty, and the pursuit of happiness. Today we need more than ever a deepened awareness of the dynamic reality of these holistic intangibles—beauty, truth, justice, loyalty, and freedom.

The Reality of Freedom

Over a century ago the great Danish theologian Kierkegaard asked and answered the supreme question: "What is this myself? . . . It is the most abstract and yet at the same time the most concrete of all realities. It is freedom."

Today deep down at the level of the atom we have found that reality is harmony. We have seen how these harmonies are merged to give the reality of the symphony of life. We have seen how this symphony of life is realized in the dynamism of the human being. We have just examined the manifestation of similar intangible realities in the collective dynamism of the social order. But what is it which, at the end of the road, gives all of these realities their supreme human significance? I assert that it is the reality of that ultimate component crowning the symphony of life in each of us, the climactic sforzando of the spirit. But what is the essence of this supreme reality? I want to quote two of the wisest men who have meditated on this question.

At the beginning of his monumental book on "The Nature and Destiny of Man," the eminent theologian Reinhold Niebuhr states: "Man's essence is free self-determination. His sin is the wrong use of this freedom."

In his book on "The Phenomenon of Man," Teilhard de Chardin says: "That what is 'free,' even in man, can be broken down into determinisms, is no proof that the world is not based on freedom—as indeed I maintain that it is."

Kierkegaard's stark statement that the soul *is* freedom can, in its dazzling brilliance, leave us blind and groping. What does it mean to say that the soul is made of freedom?

What does it mean to say that freedom is the kind of reality out of which something can be made?

I think our bewilderment when we face this perspective for the first time is akin to the perplexity of the nineteenth-century scientists when they realized that light waves were not waves *in* anything. When earlier experiments indicated beyond any shadow of doubt that light had a wave character, the general opinion was that light must be waves *in* something. Water waves were obviously waves *on* water. Sound waves were waves *in* air. So the concept of the luminiferous ether was invented to provide a medium that light could vibrate *in*. Nobody had ever seen ether or felt ether. No experiment had been carried out to demonstrate the existence of ether. But nearly all scientists felt that there had to be an ether to provide a medium for the light waves; otherwise light waves simply could not exist.

You can imagine the wrinkled brows and the head-shaking when the experiments of Michelson and Morley showed that the speed of light was completely independent of the path of the light and of the position of the earth in its orbit around the sun. This forced the abandonment of the concept of the imaginary ether and the acceptance of the fact that light existed *in its own right* without having to be a vibration *in* something. Thus, science was forced to recognize that light is one of the fundamental components out of which the universe is constructed. Although light has no material mass, it has reality.

Light is a form of energy. In a sense, it is pure energy. If energy in the form of light has reality, isn't it logical that energy in any form should have reality? Since the acceptance of the principles of the theory of relativity, this argument has even greater potency. Einstein's famous relation between energy and mass, $E = mc^2$, relates energy and mass. In this equation, E stands for energy, m stands for mass and c is the velocity of light in a vacuum.

One more step toward intangible reality carries us to the question of the reality of the de Broglie waves associated with fundamental particles. Take the proton which is the nucleus of the hydrogen atom as an example. The proton certainly has mass. It has a positive electrical charge. It also behaves in reflection experiments as if it were a bundle of de Broglie waves. Do these waves have reality?

As Hermann Weyl has pointed out so many times, the combination of waves possesses something more than its component parts. Does this "something more" have reality? As we pass step by step along this chain of logic, can we find any valid reason for saying that reality extends thus far and no futher? Right from the beginning of this chain, we associate reality with power, with a pattern of action; and we see each link in the chain possessing a valid claim to reality. So all consistency, all logic, point to the reality of the last link of the chain, the supreme all-pervading reality of the human being, the reality of the free will, the reality of the spirit.

In the next chapter, we turn to explore the nature of this supreme reality in terms of the perspective of the reality of forms, a reality that stakes its claim on such a wide variety of scientific experimentation.

15

The Unity of Man

D URING THE thirty-six years of my service on the faculty of The Johns Hopkins University in Baltimore, one of my closest friends was Arthur Oncken Lovejoy, Chairman of the Department of Philosophy. We spent many hours together discussing problems in the area between his field and mine; and shared other days and evenings in such nonphilosophical and nonchemical pursuits as the enjoyment of the operas of Richard Strauss. My wife and I had the privilege of his presence at our Thanksgiving dinner table on numerous occasions.

I know of no better way to begin the discussion of the subject of this chapter than by quoting several sentences from the introduction to his profound philosophical treatise "The Revolt Against Dualism."

Lovejoy begins the preface of his book with a statement that is an expression of his eagerness to share his thoughts and pleasures with others. He writes: "The practise of philosophizing *in vacuo* I have always regarded with distaste and suspicion. Philosophy seems to me essentially a collective and cooperative business. Effective cooperation among philosophers consists, it is true, primarily in disagreement. For, given a sufficiently well-defined problem, philosophy can really get forward with it only by bringing together in their logical interconnection all the considerations which have occurred, or are likely to occur, to acute and philosophically initiated minds as significantly pertinent to that problem."

My problem in this chapter is to present to you the evidence for the reality of the human spirit. The problem is so vast and so profoundly significant that it needs to be seen in a wide variety of perspectives, viewed through many philosophical eyes of divergent focus, in order to be understood with any degree of depth. I hope that in the fusion of these diverse views, you will see emerging the evidence that the human spirit is, in Whitehead's phrase an eternal verity transcending time and space, grounded on more than perishing occasions.

Whitehead summarizes this idea: "The unity of personality is an inescapable fact, a concilium of subtle atoms, the complex dimensionality of the body that is spirit." But as the wealth of experimental facts regarding the functioning of the human body and brain have accumulated, the belief in the reality of this unity appears to be on the wane. As Reinhold Niebuhr puts it, our greater understanding of nature has caused our greater confusion about human nature.

Is the human spirit real? Do both the animate spirit and inanimate matter partake of a common reality? Or is matter, exemplified by the solidity of stone, the only reality? Or is there a dualism in nature, a domain of the spirit and a domain of matter separated by an unbridgeable gulf, subject to sets of unrelated laws?

A large part of Professor Lovejoy's book is devoted to a discussion of these problems. In the first chapter he writes: "From those early days of the century to the present, the attack upon dualism has been carried on by two distinct philosophical groups, operating from different positions— one of these groups, the less radical one, being active chiefly though not exclusively in Great Britain, the other chiefly though not exclusively in the United States. The former, following the original doctrine of Mr. Moore, has continued to admit the reality of 'consciousness' or 'awareness' as a unique, non-physical type of phenomenon, and thus retains a residuam of psycho-physical dualism; while the other party, following James in rejecting 'consciousness' altogether, has, insofar as its program has become clear-cut and consistent (as it was not in the case of James, himself), tended toward behaviorism or materialism. (I disregard, for the present, the fact that both movements have been further divided through the growth of powerful heretical sects who would elevate the objects of sense perception itself

'In die schönen regionen
Wo die reinen formen wohnen,'

making of the patch of color I see at a definite place in my visual field, or the musical tone I fleetingly hear, eternal platonic essences.)"

As you do not need to be told at this point, I am a member of one of these heretical sects, but I am confident that I am in good company. Along with the other heretics referred to above, I believe that music is an eternal Platonic essence with its reality grounded in "the beautiful regions where the pure forms dwell." In order to show where our heretical holistic philosophy breaks away to new ground, I want to review once more from a slightly different point of view the materialist's concept of reality.

The Materialist's Concept of Reality

The typical materialist is convinced that he *knows* that sticks and stones are *real.* Lovejoy makes a penetrating evaluation of the validity of this knowing which I want to quote at length:

"In knowing, or attempting to know, Man makes certain claims or pretentions, the remarkable nature of which he usually fails to see, because he makes them so confidently and so habitually. He assumes that, insofar as he ever succeeds in one or another form of the cognitive enterprise, some very curious things must be true about the known fact's or object's relation to himself and his act of knowing. These assumptions are no far-fetched inventions of the philosopher; they are all manifestations of the primary and most universal faith of Man, his inexpugnable realism, his two-fold belief that he is on the one hand in the midst of realities which are not himself nor mere obsequious shadows of himself, a world which transcends the narrow confines of his own transient being; and, on the other hand, that he can himself somehow reach beyond those confines and bring these external existences within the compass of his own life, yet without annulment of their transcendence. It is precisely this achievement that men naturally mean by 'knowing'; I have but put in general and explicit terms what everyone (except, possibly, a few philosophers) supposes himself to be doing when he is engaged in true perception, retrospection, forecast, or social communication. In the persistent human demand that this singular achievement shall be possible, of describing precisely what happens when it is accomplished, lie the perennial sources of that most human of all activities of reflective thought which is called epistemology. Man, in short, is by nature an epistemological animal; for his irrepressible knowledge-claim is itself a thesis *about* knowledge, and therefore about himself and his relation to Nature and to the life of his self; and it is a thesis which cries out for clarification, and for correlation with the conclusions about other natural phenomena to which this natural phenomenon of knowing has brought him. So long as he continues to feel any normal curiosity about himself and his role amid the rest of things, he will necessarily wish to know himself *as* knower, and therefore to understand the seeming mystery and challenging paradox of knowledge—the possibility which it implies of going abroad while keeping at home, the knower's apparent transcendence of the existential limits within which he must yet, at every moment of his knowing, confess himself to be contained."

Within the perspective of these thoughts let us once
more reexamine the materialistic doctrine of the reality of
sticks and stones. Pick up a stone and hold it in your hand.
Squeeze it. It refuses to grow smaller under the pressure of
your fingers. In imagination (I hesitate to urge you to com-
mit the act), throw it at your window. The glass shatters.
The stone has done something. Go outside the window and
(hopefully without cutting your fingers on the imaginary
broken pieces of glass) pick up the stone and bring it back
inside the house. Throw it (again in imagination) through
another window. It exerts the same power as before, again
shattering the glass.

The conclusion from this somewhat destructive experiment is obvious. The stone has retained its identity, its essential characteristics, its *power* throughout the period of
time of the experiment, throughout its transition through
space from your hand out the window, back inside the
house, out the window again. The stone has remained invariant under transformation both in time and in space.
This invariance under time and space transformation is accepted by the materialists as the true proof of the stone's
reality.

Now let me quote Lovejoy's comments on invariance
as the test of reality:

"The only object of reference of which you can legiti-
mately claim, under the circumstances assumed, to know the
character (beyond that of being *something* belonging in that
casual series), is the ultimate effect, *i.e.,* the percept conceived as a strictly private possession of your own. And
even the abstract property of being a member of the causal
series, you can be said to *know* only if your judgment about
the existence of an original causal object and of other
members of that series is assumed to be not relative to your
standpoint, to be itself innocent of perspectivity.

"The (in this sense) non-relativistic implications of the

notion of the objective are, of course, copiously illustrated in the history of science, and nowhere better than in recent theoretical physics, despite the potent influence therein of some contrary tendencies. In the scientific investigation of Nature, men have been looking for views of things which have, at the minimum, *some* degree of generality, and are *not* relative to particular contexts or standpoints. You approach the truth about a thing, both commonsense and science have usually supposed, only when, after changing your standpoint, you find some of the characters of the thing remaining the same; the more changes of standpoint you make, the more justification you have for identifying the characters found to be common in all with the sort of object knowledge aims at."

In other words, by throwing the stone, you have changed your standpoint. When it travels through the air you are viewing it in a different perspective; when you pick it up outside the house, you are viewing it from still another standpoint. If it has remained invariant under these transformations, it has a claim to be real.

Lovejoy continues: "The constructive part of Einstein's reasoning, in short, has throughout been determined by the principle that 'the test of objectivity is invariance for all observers'; and it was through the application of this test that his reasoning led to the conclusion that, 'unless we wish to continue to talk about such shadows as space and time, it is in the space-time world and there alone that we shall obtain universal objectivity.' It is precisely in the degree in which he denied that 'what the world is perceived as from any or all' potentially differing 'points of view constitutes the essential part of its objective nature for physical science,' that Einstein really continued 'the high tradition of scientific objectivity.' Insofar as objective relativism in philosophy has been inspired by the theory of relativity in physics, it has been by the part of that theory which is regarded (though undeniably, with much wavering and equivocation) by its author and by most physicists as proving that the world of actual appearance, at least in those respects in which it varies with standpoints, is not 'objective.'

"The business of knowing, then—if by the word we mean anything more than bare sensation or pure reverie— is the business of transcending standpoints; it is the quest of content which can be believed to have some character identical in nature (if not in existence) with the character which belongs to (or is present in) the specified object or locus of reference independently of the knowing and within its own limits."

As through the eyes of science we take a look at the stone in its arc from your hand through the windowpane, we see that its valid reality shrinks and diffuses into something far less deserving of the word *tangible*. First let us regard this process of window-breaking in the perspective of energy flow. While you held the stone in your hands and your muscles contracted to initiate this act of violence, as your hand moved in a semicircle, energy was flowing from the chemical wells in your blood through the contracting ligaments and into the atoms of the stone. As your fingers released the stone and it began its flight of destruction, this energy was present as kinetic energy, the energy of motion. As the de Broglie waves of the stone first achieved intensive penetration of the de Broglie waves of the silicon, calcium, and oxygen of the glass, some of this energy of motion was transformed into chemical energy, disrupting the bonds between the atoms of the glass. If we interpret this action with the most precise scientific accuracy, the bulk of the matter of the stone never touched the matter of the glass. The matter or mass of the stone is essentially contained in the nuclei of the atoms, these very tiny points of concentration that in an atom, visualized as having the size of a football field, are only about the size of a pinhead.

Strictly, it was the penetration of the de Broglie waves of the stone with the de Broglie waves of the windowpane that permitted the transfer of energy which, in turn, disrupted a few of the de Broglie wave patterns between the atoms of the glass, the patterns which were binding them together, the patterns referred to by the chemist as *bonds.* With these bonds broken, another part of the energy of motion of the stone flowed into the shattered fragments of the glass, giving them also energy of motion which carried them beyond the window where they fell in chaotic array on the grass.

Insofar as this process of window-breaking indicates any reality according to Plato's doctrine that being is power, it is testifying not to the reality of the stone but to the reality of the energy that the stone carried. Perhaps you want to argue that the stone was able to carry the energy only because it had mass. The mass, *i. e.,* the matter, contained in these pinhead atomic nuclei remained essentially invariant throughout this transformation. But I counter by questioning whether this transformation of the atomic nuclei of the stone through time and space is the proper transformation to test invariance. If we want to find out whether the stone is really real because of its mass, we should subject this mass to a nuclear transformation, since mass is nuclear in character (as the experiments of Rutherford demonstrated so clearly).

Just as soon as we start talking about nuclear transformations, we have to place before us the all-pervasive equation of Einstein expressing the equivalence of mass and energy:

$$E = mc^2$$

It has been demonstrated (both in a number of laboratory experiments and in the rather persuasive detonations of atomic and thermonuclear weapons) that mass has an energy equivalent. We can no longer have the mental satisfaction of following, even in imagination, the infinitesimal bits of mass, the nuclei of atoms, and saying that they persist through transformations of time and space just like billiard balls rolling around and bouncing against each other on the billiard table. At least part of the billiard-ball nucleus of the uranium atom transforms into something of a quite different character when it is released in the process of fission and sets up a destructive shock wave like that which flattened Hiroshima.

During the last ten years the variety of transformations of energy and mass have multiplied more than a thousand-fold in the experiments of nuclear physics and especially high-energy physics, which have revealed all the strange kinds of matter-energy such as pions, muons, neutrinos, positrons, and their dozens of cousins.

We can no longer think of reality as identifiable with some *thing* existing at a particular place at a particular time, like a billiard ball or a sub-sub-miniature billiard ball such as a proton. Most striking of all, the character of these different, almost infinitesimal, fundamental aspects of matter-energy can best be understood in terms of mathematical *forms,* especially those mathematical forms called algebraic *groups.* There appears to be a common morphology between the fundamental particles of nature and the fundamental forms of mathematics. Again let us recall Sir James Jeans' famous remark that "God is a mathematician." So even if we try to follow the materialist's line of logic to its most fundamental origin, we end up with a discussion of reality in terms of forms.

Just as soon as we try to establish the network of relations between forms we are immediately aware that familiar Cartesian space with its three dimensions of length, breadth, and height is not the appropriate domain for our purpose. So let us turn now to examine again the nature of the proper domain in which to express the interrelationships of forms.

The Region of Forms

We will now explore *"die schönen regionen wo die reinen formen wohnen,"* the beautiful regions where the pure forms dwell. Before we start our journey we should receive some further instruction from Professor Lovejoy.

"We observed in the first lecture that the early modern dualists fell into an unhappy confusion of terminology, if not from ideas, when they defined 'mental' entities as unextended and non-spacial, and at the same time included 'sensations' (*i. e.,* sensa) among mental entities. That visual and tactual and perhaps auditory content is given as located and extended in *some* space or other we have accepted as a primary fact of experience. That in this general sense, space-occupancy is attributable to some sensa seems beyond reasonable dispute. But this alone does not go far toward vindicating their 'objectivity.' For there are recognized in recent philosophy and physics not merely many possible kinds of space, but many possible separate spaces of a single kind. It is not evident that your visual sensa are given in a space identical with that in which mine are given, or even that your own visual and tactual sensa are both given in a common space. It is furthermore not evident that any sensa exist in the space in which physical objects are commonly supposed to exist—or at all events, that if we say they exist there, we are using words of the same meaning as when we say that the physical objects exist there. Broad has lucidly set forth the considerations which make it seem 'clear that either (1) sensible determinates (such as some particular shade of red) do not inhere in regions of physical space-time, but in regions of some other space-time; or (2) that if they do inhere in regions of physical space-time, they must inhere in the latter in some different way from that in which physical determinates (like physical motion) do so.' We appear to be confronted with this dilemma: either there is one sense of inherence in many different space-times, or there is one space-time in many different senses of inherence. And aside from these difficulties about the localization of sensa in the same space with one another and with physical objects, there are the (logically prior) difficulties attaching to the supposition of a single absolute space in which to locate physical objects themselves. These difficulties have been notorious for more than two centuries; and the results of the Michelson-Morley and kindred experiments, with the reasonings of Einstein concerning them, have, it is now even more notorious, seemed to most mathematicians and physicists to give a notion of an absolute space its *coup de grace.* But if there is no absolute space even for physical objects, to *what* space are we to assign sensa in order to invest them with the desired objectivity? It will perhaps be answered that they may be assigned to the Minkowskian four-dimensional continuum of space-time which in relativity physics has taken the place of Newtonian absolute space. But visual sensa are *not* in this space-time. For, as Mr. Bertrand Russell has remarked, 'In the world of percepts the distinction between space and time does really exist, and space does really have certain properties which (Einsteinian) relativity denies to physical space,' that is to say, to space-time. The 'events' of relativity physics are thus not even in the same kind of space, or quasi-space, with our percepts.

"Before, then, we could assign any specific meaning to the objective relativist's general thesis—as we are now interpreting it—we should need to know what in that thesis is meant by space, or the space-time, in which (some) sensa are declared to be situated. Such information is not, so far as I can recall, usually afforded us by those who propound this philosophy. To deal fairly with it we should therefore be obliged to reconstruct for ourselves all the views which might conceivably be held about physical space or space-time and the relation to these of the space of perception, and examine into it the tenability of each of these views. This would demand an exceedingly long and complicated analysis."

While Professor Lovejoy's comments are directed more at the spaces associated with the human psyche in its acts of perception, I feel that the same questions arise as we face the broader problem of exploring the space in which to view the reality of the psyche in its more profound function of thought and moral decision. It seems clear from the conclusions of Lovejoy, Russell, and their associates that there *is* a problem to be solved. It is also clear, as Professor Lovejoy puts it in his last sentence quoted above, that this solution demands an exceedingly long and complicated analysis. In what follows I can only sketch certain of the more obvious features of the kind of space we need in which to view the human spirit in proper perspective.

In our ordinary Cartesian space of length, breadth, and height, we recognize the property of distance. I sit on one side of the room; you sit on the opposite side of the room; we are separated by a distance of ten feet. For the concept of distance to be significant in ordinary space, we must have a *measure* of distance. As I stated in the above example, we are separated by a distance of ten feet. The *foot* is here agreed on as the unit of our measure of distance. As Einstein and his associates in the development of the theory of relativity have pointed out, the concept of measure is an extremely subtle one. In domains of more complicated mathematical relationships this concept of measure has been a key that unlocks many secrets, as explained in the particularly original approach of the great French mathematician Lebesgue.

If there is no distance between you and me, then we are at the same place. Of course this concept of lack of separation is complicated by the principle that the same space cannot be occupied by two different bodies at the same time. If we are shaking hands, it is perhaps correct to say that there is no separation between the skin of your right hand and the skin of my right hand where they are in contact, but obviously we can never merge ourselves completely. If there were no distance separating any part of us, we would be the same person. On the other hand, we feel that when we are sitting on opposite sides of the room we are not as widely separated as if we were situated on opposite sides of the earth.

The same consideration holds for the dimension of time. We think of a *separation* in time; and to express this quantitatively and significantly we have to have a *measure* of time. We can talk of two events being separated in time by a matter of seconds, like the event of the stone leaving your hand and the event of the stone crashing through the windowpane. We can also think of events separated by minutes, hours, days, weeks, months, years, centuries, or millenia. In both space and time the concept of separation has an instinctive visualizable meaning.

Now what does *separation* mean in this strange domain of forms that we have talked about so much? Suppose that there is a piece of blank paper in front of you. You draw a triangle in the upper left-hand corner and another triangle in the lower right-hand corner of this sheet of paper. Obviously, the triangles are separated by a certain distance, say six inches. But this is not the kind of separation that we talk of in form-space. In form-space, because both of these forms are triangles, we regard them as very close. If they are identical in size, shape, and every other respect, we then say that we are dealing not with two triangles but with one triangle. If one is larger than the other then we say they are closely related but congruent, if each of the angles of one is equal to the corresponding angles of the other. If one of the figures you draw is a triangle and the other is a hexagon, then these are still fairly closely related but have greater difference of form. If you draw a line on the one hand and a triangle on the other, you have an open figure in the form of a line and a closed figure in the form of the triangle; and this difference is a separation in form-space. If you draw a triangle in the upper left corner and a circle in the lower right corner, these are both closed figures and therefore related but profoundly different in that one consists of straight lines joined together and the other is a single line in the form of a circle.

If we express such figures by means of mathematical algebraic symbolism, we can construct ways of representing forms by collections of symbols. One of the most fruitful kinds of mathematical symbolism is the matrix, which is a collection of a square array of symbols such as three horizontal rows of symbols with three symbols in each row. The matrix thus can be regarded as either three rows or three columns. In general, a matrix may be taken as the representation of a member of an even deeper mathematical entity called the algebraic *group*. A *group* is one of the most elusive and at the same time one of the most profound and significant concepts in the whole domain of mathematics. Suppose that I write the following symbols:

abc
acb
bac
bca
cab
cba

Here I have a representation of the permutation group on three elements. If I draw a triangle (Figure 1) and label the three vertices a, b, and c, respectively, and then proceed to interchange the letters on these vertices in every possible way, I also have a representation of this group. I also can represent it by writing six algebraic matrices (Figure 1). I

FIGURE I

REPRESENTATIONS of a GROUP

```
1  0  0        0  1  0        0  0  1
0  1  0        0  0  1        1  0  0
0  0  1        1  0  0        0  1  0


1  0  0        0  0  1        0  1  0
0  0  1        0  1  0        1  0  0
0  1  0        1  0  0        0  0  1
```

can represent it by twisting objects in space. But each of these is only a *representation* of the group, we cannot say that it is the group. A group is thus a pattern of relationships, an intangible that lies far deeper in reality than anything that can be put on paper with symbols or even imagined visually. Relations can be set up between these algebraic groups that provide a domain in which forms can be represented and logically connected.

I think that nearly every philosopher, scientist, or layman who has ever given serious thought to the problem will agree that there is a reality to the concept of numbers. The number *one* has meaning beyond any material embodiment as a single object; in a similar way the number *two* has a meaning. In this sense numbers are perhaps the simplest example of the eternal verities, the platonic forms, which have been believed by so many to represent ultimate reality. In the same way, *algebraic groups* have a claim to the title of eternal verities.

One of the most fascinating mathematical games is the transformation of the matrices that can be constructed to represent these groups. The particular representation depends upon the particular set of mathematical coordinates selected. As one shifts from one set of coordinates to another, the symbols of the matrix shift. Sometimes, if we are dealing with numbers, these numbers appear to have relations so chaotic that one cannot discern even with considerable study just what kind of group possesses this particular member. Then a transformation, particularly one that will put the matrix in so-called diagonal form, suddenly reveals the essence of the group. In the diagonal form all the terms in the matrix are zero except those lying on the diagonal starting at the upper left-hand corner and terminating in the lower right-hand corner. In this form the matrix can be represented directly as a sheaf of orthogonal vectors.

The concept of the vector is a kind of bridge between

the ordinary Cartesian space or extensions thereof in more than three dimensions, and the more subtle varieties of form-space. A vector is frequently defined as a quantity that has both length and direction. If you take a familiar lead pencil and place it so that the eraser is on the surface of your desk and the point is up in the air, then you have a representation of a vector. The pencil has length; the point is like an arrowhead. You can leave the eraser on the desk and by twisting the pencil make it point in any direction that you wish.

Whether we are dealing with form-space or group-space, it is similarities of form, similarities of symmetries that make it proper for us to say that two things are "close together." It is extreme dissimilarities in form, extreme dissimilarities in symmetry that make it proper for us to say that two entities are widely separated in form-space.

In the same way, with two vectors, it can be the direction in which they are pointing that determines their "separation". Put two pencils with the erasers side by side on the top of your desk and have both pencils pointing directly up. You would have no hesitancy in saying that they are close together as they are contiguous. Have both erasers at the same point but one pencil pointing straight up in the air and the other lying flat on the desk. In this situation, you might say they are still close together because their erasers are touching, but from the point of view of vector considerations, the point of view of the elements of groups that the pencils might represent, they are far apart. One lies in the plane of the desk, the other lies in a plane perpendicular to this—and that difference could be the equivalent of infinite separation.

I think you can see that the consideration of the distance of separation of waves also involves distinctions other than those of normal distance in familiar Cartesian space. The room in which you sit at this moment is filled with radio waves. These waves are overlapping, interpenetrating, forming one thick, three-dimensional tapestry of dynamic form. In this sense they are all close together. On the other hand consider what happens when you flip the switch on your radio to pick up a program. If the radio is properly constructed, you will not pick up the whole mass of programs; you will pick up only the program to which you are tuned. In the sense of form-space, the program coming from one station on a certain wavelength station (perhaps near you in the city) is widely separated from the program coming from another station in a neighboring city on a different wavelength. You may have to turn the dial on your tuner through a large angle to go from one to the other. It is the difference in wavelengths and not the difference in physical space location that determines the separation or the "distance" between the two programs.

I now want to examine the concept of the human psyche in some of these new concepts that have originated from our examination of form-space.

The Ego Vector

In our exploration of the relationships between the new wave (or musical) concepts in modern physics and the human psyche, we are searching for a portrayal of the essence of the human spirit that will combine both an expression of its unity and of its diversity; we are seeking a portrayal that will express its dynamism side by side with a delineation of its character as eternal verity.

I now want to consider with you the portrayal of the human ego as a vector in form-space. From the beginning we must be aware that any portrayal of this supreme essence of a human being is inadequate. No matter how carefully we select words, no matter how thoughtfully we construct images, no matter how astute we are in weaving together subtle concepts of form, our finite minds can never hope to

FIGURE 2

VECTORS

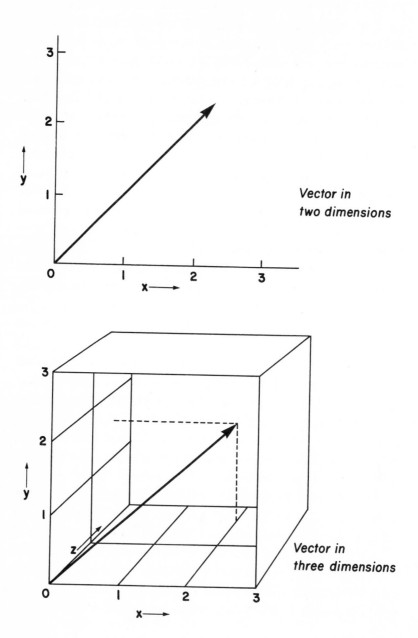

Vector in
two dimensions

Vector in
three dimensions

do more than sketch in the crudest lines this transfinite flame that burns in the core of each one of us. In full awareness of this, nevertheless, let us proceed.

In its simplest mathematical representation, a vector is usually shown as a line with an arrow on one end. This arrow can be called the head of the vector and the other end of the line the base of the vector. Again, for the simplest demonstration of vector properties, the base of a line is generally located at that point in the graph that denotes the zero of all the coordinates. A picture of this sort is most simply drawn on a piece of flat paper (Figure 2). The paper represents a two-dimensional space; it has the dimension of breadth to the right and to the left, and of height toward the top and toward the bottom of the paper. To establish a frame of reference, we can draw a horizontal line from the left edge to the right edge passing through a point in the exact center of the paper and call this the axis of the x coordinate. Similarly, we can draw a vertical line up and down through the center of the paper from the top edge to the bottom edge and call this the axis of the y coordinate. We refer to the intersection of these lines at the exact center of the paper as the origin of the coordinates. We say that at this point x has the value 0. We set up a scale arbitrarily and say, for example, that one inch to the right of this point, x has the value of 1; two inches to the right, x has the value of 2; three inches to the right x has the value of 3, and so on. In the same way, along the vertical line we say that at the exact center y has the value of 0; that one inch above the center on this line y has the value of 1; two inches above the center y has the value of 2, and so on. We have thus established the familiar Cartesian set of x, y coordinates.

Suppose that now we draw a line starting at the origin of the coordinates where our vertical and our horizontal coordinate-line axes intersect and extend this line up toward the upper right-hand corner of the paper drawing it so that it bisects the angle between the horizontal and the vertical. In other words, this line rises off to the right at an angle of forty-five degrees. We terminate the line where it is two inches to the right of the center of the paper and two inches above the center of the paper; in other words, where the line ends is exactly above the point corresponding to 2 on the *x* axis and exactly to the right of the point corresponding to 2 on the *y* axis. At this end of the line we draw an arrowhead. This line starting at the point representing zero and ending out in the plane is the representation of a vector. It has both length and direction.

You may argue that any straight line you draw on a piece of paper will have both length and direction necessarily. I grant that it will always have a defined length, if you make clear as you draw the line just where it starts and where it ends and do not let it taper off into such a fine streak of grayness that it is impossible to tell where the line ends and space resumes. But when you claim it has direction, you have to say that it has direction *with respect to something*. If you happen to have lined up the edge of the paper with the direction of true North at the point where you are sitting, then it is correct to say that it has a direction with respect to the North Pole. You can also claim that it has direction with respect to the edge of the paper but if you do this you are arbitrarily implying that the edge of the paper is your coordinate system. When you say that your line is a vector, then you are saying that it is a quantity which has a significant direction; and in the particular example which we are considering, it is the direction *with respect* to the coordinate axes.

In this illustration I have merely sharpened up a little the vaguer example which we were discussing in terms of the lead pencil sitting with the eraser on the surface of your desk and the point out at an angle somewhere in space. In this example of the vector drawn on the paper, the direction is determined by saying that the angle between the horizontal coordinate axis and the vector is forty-five degrees. The length of the vector is determined by the usual Pythagorean theorem which I hope you remember from your high school geometry. The vector is the hypotenuse of a right-angled triangle. Therefore, we can determine its length from the fact that the square of the length of the hypotenuse is equal to the sum of the squares of the lengths of the two sides of the triangle. Since each one of the two legs is two inches long and two squared is equal to four, the sum of the squares of the two legs is $4 + 4$ or 8; thus, the length of the vector is equal to the square root of 8 or 2.828 . . . inches. If you want to check me on this, lay a ruler on the diagram and see for yourself.

This line on the paper is an example of a vector in two-dimensional space, the plane of the paper. To specify where the head of the vector is, we need to tell the point on the x axis *above* which it lies and the point on the y axis *across* from which it lies. This is just another way of saying that the paper has length and breadth.

As contrasted with the two-dimensional vector on the paper, the lead pencil with its eraser or base resting on the surface of your desk and the point off at an angle somewhere represents a three-dimensional vector. To say precisely where the point of the vector pencil is, we need three coordinates (*x, y, z* coordinates) instead of just the two coordinates, the *x, y* coordinates which were required to specify where the head of the vector line on the paper lay. This is because the pencil is protruding out into space and the familiar space around us has the three coordinates of length, breadth, and height.

Now I want to ask you really to stretch your imagination. You will not be able to visualize this, but perhaps you can feel instinctively that there might exist somewhere a space of four dimensions. Imagine that the pencil is sticking out into a space of four dimensions, the dimensions of *length, breadth, height,* and *gropeth. Gropeth* is my own private way of designating this mysterious entity, the extra fourth dimension. I doubt whether you have ever heard it called by that name before. As you can easily guess, in order to designate just where the end of the pencil is in this four dimensional space, we need to specify four coordinates. If we use the letter w to specify the coordinate of gropeth, just as we used x for length, y for breadth and z for height, then, naturally, our four coordinates are $w, x, y,$ and z.

It is relatively easy to extend the principles of geometry into four-dimensional space. We can construct a four-dimensional algebra and write mathematical equations that are analogues of the familiar equations in two and three-dimensional space. As I mentioned once before, we can even define four-dimensional geometric figures that are the analogues of our familiar three-dimensional figures like the sphere and the cube. The analogue of the cube in four dimensions is called a *tesserac.* Just as a cube has two dimensional squares for its faces, the *tesserac* has cubes for its "faces." We can even calculate the imaginary musical chord which would be vibrating in the imaginary tesserac as it quivers with imaginary thermal energy in its imaginary four dimensions. And even though this may suggest harmony as imaginary as Sir Arthur Sullivan's famous "Lost Chord," the ratios of the tesserac's tones are easily computed; and when I am able to construct my polydimensional electronic organ, I will be able to play for you a tesserac sonata.

Although it is impossible to visualize a space of more than four dimensions, although such spaces are imaginary in the sense that they cannot be directly pictured, the relationships that exist in them are capable of rational analysis and even of tangible embodiment through such devices as the superposition of waves. In this sense, if I am able to construct a polydimensional electronic organ and play on it the chord of the tesserac for you, I will be making the fourth dimension directly tangible to you through your auditory channel of perception even though it is impossible for you ever to see four dimensions directly.

The point of all this long discussion is to convince you that I am not talking nonsense when I discuss form-space. And I hope that you feel that it makes sense to try to visualize a space of far more than four dimensions, a space of billions, trillions, quadrillions or more of dimensions in which your ego-vector is continually executing the dance of life.

To me the image of the ego as vector is appealing first because of its emphasis on unity. The vector is a single definite, unified, coherent concept. It is the embodiment of oneness. It is the unitary thrust into the unknown. Its arrow signifies dynamism. It is a bridge from the point of all zeros at its base, the origin where all is nothingness, a bridge out into the plenum of all forms.

Of course, this is still a most inadequate concept to suggest the fullness and richness and dynamism of the human spirit. We should add that because this vector is a vector in form-space, it is far more than a line with an arrow at one end; in its fullness it is more like the complex dynamic form of a symphony.

For a little over half a century, mathematicians have been employing most fruitfully the concept of a space of infinite dimensions. The real father of this space was the great German mathematician David Hilbert, who was Professor of Mathematics at the University of Göttingen in Germany for many years. When this space is used to represent mathematical functions by means of a vector, it is called *function*-space or more usually *Hilbert*-space in honor of its discoverer. A mathematical function can be represented as a vector in Hilbert-space.

In much the same way we can envision a space of infinite

dimensions which contains all possible musical forms. Every chord, every melody, every sonata, every fugue, every symphony ever written in the past or that can ever be written in the future, is representable as just a single vector in this music-space. Thus we can think of the total musical creativity of Beethoven as a vector in this space moving from dimension to dimension as his prodigious creations one by one took form.

You see that I am suggesting that the space of our spiritual existence and this space of all music, past and future, are really congruent, one and the same. I am suggesting that this vector that thrusts into this polydimensional infinite space of musical forms searching and embodying the quartets, the quintets, the sonatas and the symphonies, was really Beethoven himself. I am asking you to consider whether you yourself are not really a dynamic vector in this domain of infinity, the arena of the spirit of which Hocking wrote.

I grant that you have a tangible body, eyes that see, ears that hear, a torso, arms, hands, legs and feet. But even from the *particle* point of view, consider what these tangible parts are. In your electrons and your protons your totality partakes of the oneness of the universe. In your electrons with their positive and negative spin, their *yin* and their *yang,* you partake of the twoness of the universe. In your carbon and nitrogen, oxygen and phosphorus atoms you partake of the threeness of the universe. In the harmony of their s-orbitals you partake of the roundness of the universe. You are a fusion of these eternal verities. Is it not logical to think that as these verities intertwine to form the water of your blood, the amino acids of your protein, the mitochondria, the ribosomes, the centrioles, and the nuclei of your cells, that these concilia also are eternal verities like the electron, the proton, and the photon? And why should we stop there? In the heart of your cells, in the cell nucleus we have the assembly of all these verities in the melodic sequence of DNA which from the particle point of view comes closest to representing your essence. Why should we say that this is anything different? Is not the chain of logic overwhelmingly persuasive that *you yourself* are an eternal verity?

Think back briefly over the dynamism during the years since your birth which has made you what you are. From birth, during the sheltered years of infancy and youngest childhood, the dynamic forms through the media of your senses entered your brain and became part of your essential dynamism. You began to recognize the forms of objects around you, the possibilities of locomotion, the dynamic aspects of movements, and the rudiments of communication with other human beings. During your school years the more complex dynamic forms flowed into your brain through a refined vision that could perceive subtleties of form and in particular the letters of the alphabet, their combinations, words, sentences, paragraphs, and the ideas embodied in these dynamic forms. The dimensions in which your ego vector could move multiplied year by year. In the cybernetic process by which your mental capacity grew, the accumulation of recognition patterns in your total dynamism enlarged the dimensions of your intellectual and emotional world; and the deepest dimensions of all, the dimensions of the creative imagination and the creative spirit, unfolded.

Not only were larger, impersonal dimensions open to you through the addition to your dynamism of knowledge and skill. Gradually the dynamism of your human associates became part of your total dynamism. At the beginning this was the dynamism of parents, the dynamism of family, the dynamism of friends. But as the area of your perception enlarged, the dynamism of the great minds of the past flowed in and became part of you. As you listened to music, Bach, Beethoven, Brahms, Verdi, Wagner all began to live within you. As you saw paintings and sculpture, Pericles, Donatello,

Michelangelo, Rembrandt, El Greco, Monet, Manet, Picasso, van Gogh all began to live within you. In the incredible intricacy of your septillion cranial atoms all this dynamism of the inanimate world, all this dynamism of human beings past and present fused to make this total dynamism that you are today. And yet, like the dominant trumpeting thematic core of a symphony, your own ego vector plunges and thrusts, explores and creates and guides the forging of your own personal destiny.

Let me again quote just a few of the passages that have been such an inspiration to me in trying to express in this inadequate way the reality which, in the words of Teilhard de Chardin, is the immensity not only around, behind, and in front of us, but most significantly of all, within us. Reinhold Niebuhr, in the second part of his treatise on the "Nature and Destiny of Man," says that the alternatives are: to reduce life to meaninglessness of natural order, or to translate it into dimensions of pure reason, *i.e.,* pure eternity.

Whitehead in the "Adventures of Ideas" comments, "The human psyche activity thus contains the origins of precious harmonies within the transient world."

The Reality of the Spirit

To bring the thoughts of this chapter to a conclusion, let us explore the relationship in the dynamism of this ego vector with the overarching eternal verities such as beauty, truth, justice, love, and freedom. Let us try to see, if only dimly, the full dimensions of the human spirit.

I think that Niebuhr was hinting at this contrast between the particle and the form perspective when he commented that in the use of speculative reason Ulysses shared with foxes but Plato shared with God. He also stated that in idealistic rationalism (far beyond modern naturalism) we come closer to realizing the full dimensions of the human spirit. Teilhard de Chardin puts it a little differently:

"Stability is not at the bottom in the elementary sphere but at the top in the ultra-synthesis."

In the preceding chapter, I tried to give you an idea of the way in which the dynamic forms of objects around you not only thrust into your being the dynamisms of their shapes, their own particular melodies of form and color, the symphonies of their own particular beauty, but also that in this very thrust the living dynamism of beauty itself was becoming part of the *living you.* I tried to suggest that the reason that the walls of your house are standing, the reason that they can shelter you from the buffeting of wind and weather, is the living honesty of the architects and builders, of the artisans who made the materials, vibrating within the total structure.

In the same way, I believe that there is in the total dynamism of communal life a living, vibrant dynamism of justice, the force that protects us and enables us to live in civilization. Unfortunately, it is clear that the dynamism of the world contains not only these dynamisms of the good that I have enumerated but also the dynamisms of destruction. If we wish to expand the dimensions of the domain of the spirit to their supreme totality we must recognize that in addition to all the specific dynamisms of the inanimate, all the dynamisms of human beings past and present, all the dynamisms of the overarching verities of beauty, truth and justice, there is the final all-embracing dynamism of the supreme good, the dynamism of God, the dynamism of dynamisms, the harmony of harmonies within us.

I will wait until the final division of this book, "The Nature of the Universe," to explore the way in which the new perspective of the universe as music can help us to attain a clearer vision of the divine countenance. Here I want to focus our attention on this supreme component of our total dynamism, the portion of the creativity of the universe within us, this essence of ourself, *freedom.* Here is the nexus of the human spirit. As Niebuhr puts it: "Man is not measured in a dimension sufficiently high or deep to do full justice to either his stature or his capacity for both good or evil."

If you are more than a puppet dancing on the strings of fate, if you are more than a network of deterministic chains of cause and effect, then somewhere in the welter of this unimaginably complex dynamism that is the result of your physical growth and total life experience, you possess this ego vector whose direction you yourself control. While the dynamism of your natural structure and the dynamism of your total life experience influence profoundly the directions in which your ego vector points, you yourself can determine the course of its ultimate destiny. Like the ship moving across the surface of the ocean, twisted and turned by the force of waves and the blast of the wind, pushed now this way, now that way, you are moving through these infinite dimensions of the domain of the spirit. But although the currents of good and evil, although the waves toward the constructive or toward the destructive push you this way and that, although the winds of approbation or disapprobation of your fellow human beings divert the prow, your hand is on the helm; you can exert the final, telling twist of the wheel that day by day, month by month, year by year, holds your vector on the course of a high destiny.

Does it make sense to say that this ultimate *you* is freedom? How can there be a *reality* in this capacity to make decisive choice? But stop and think of the nature of those aspects of the universe to which we now ascribe ultimate reality. A hundred years ago, to many the arguments seemed almost overwhelmingly strong that reality was in the tangible, that which you could see and feel and wield, like a stone. When it was discovered that light was not just vibration in some tangible reality but was a reality in itself, the first great revolution in the scientific concept of reality was achieved. Light in and of and by itself is an eternal verity. Then we had the revolution which showed that energy and action are congruent with patterns of waves, the de Broglie waves. Like light, the de Broglie waves are not waves *in* anything. Today it is clear that these waves, like light, are among the eternal verities of the universe. But we find in these waves this strange component of freedom from the chains of cause and effect, this component of indeterminacy. Thus it appears that freedom, like light and like the de Broglie waves, is an essential component of the universe, a reality, an eternal verity. Is it any great leap of logic, then, to accept the essence of the human spirit as freedom, as a reality in its own right, the supreme reality?

In asserting this close relationship between the nature of light as a self-reality, an eternal verity, and the freedom of the spirit as a self-reality, an eternal verity, I am immediately aware of the image of the spirit as light which is found so frequently in the Christian Gospels. Is it not more than metaphor when we read "in him was life, and the life was the light of men. The light shines in the darkness, and the darkness has not overcome it"? Are we not asserting more than an image when we say, "God of God, light of light, very God of very God"?

It is also clear, I think, that in viewing the dynamism of the human spirit in this perspective we must consider not only the relation of the dynamism to the supreme dynamism of the supreme good, God, but also the relation of each personal dynamism to the dynamism of our fellow human beings.

For centuries it has been written that Jesus Christ is the light of the world. In our own time especially, Jesus Christ is referred to as the Man for others. It is in the pattern of togetherness that He exemplified that we find the evidence of the light of the world glowing most brightly.

The concept of the human spirit as an ego vector is in

no sense a static concept. As we keep stressing the dynamism of the concept, we should also stress that it is not what the physicists call a steady-state dynamism; rather, it is a dynamism of growth. Somehow in the near-infinite sequences of decisions that our spiritual freedom makes as we vibrate through each moment of living, there is a pattern of change. This can be a pattern of growth, the continual unfolding of larger and larger dimensions for the spirit; or tragically, it can be a pattern of decay, the widening of the gulfs of misunderstanding and selfishness that confine us on narrow islands of solitude and despair. It is in the "tuning in" to others, the sharing of dynamism, the abnegation of self in the fuller dimensions of service that we find our own freedom growing and expanding.

If we are willing to accept the domain of the spirit as resembling in its structure this form-space of which I have been speaking, if we are willing to think of juxtaposition and separation not in terms of *less* physical distance or *more* physical distance, but in terms of tuning in and tuning out, then perhaps we can make the reality of this spiritual domain part of the pattern of our thinking and our living, and achieve the wisdom and strength to go forward to attain the full stature that is our destiny; and we may also help others to do likewise.

But what is our destiny? If all these concepts that we have discussed at such length are in truth eternal verities, then it must also be true that the human spirit itself is more than mortal. It is to this consideration that I wish to turn in the next chapter. But before proceeding to this even more challenging domain where the finitude of our minds tries to understand something of the infinite, I want to put a few last touches to this portrait of the dynamism of the human spirit by quoting seven passages from those who have expressed these thoughts far more adequately than I am able to do.

Whitehead speaks of the complex dimensionality of the body that is spirit. Teilhard de Chardin writes of personality, the flame of the torch. Niebuhr writes of the integrity of the spirit that has validity in eternity. Henri Bergson says: "We shall see that individuality admits of any number of degrees, and that it is not fully realized anywhere, even in man. But that is no reason for thinking it is not a characteristic property of life."

A few pages later, Bergson writes: "In this sense it might be said of life, as of consciousness, that at every moment it is creating something. But against this idea of the absolute originality and unforeseeability of forms, our whole intellect rises in revolt. The essential function of our intellect, as evolution of life has fashioned it, is to be a light for our conduct, to make ready for our action on things, to foresee, for a given situation, the events, favorable or unfavorable, which may follow thereupon. Intellect, therefore, instinctively selects in a given situation whatever is like something already known; it seeks this out, in order that it may apply its principle that 'like produces like.' In just this does the prevision of the future by commonsense consist. Science carries this faculty to the highest possible degree of exactitude and precision, but does not alter its essential character. Like ordinary knowledge, in dealing with things science is concerned only with the aspect of *repetition.* Though the whole be original, science will always manage to analyze it into elements or aspects which are approximately a reproduction of the past. Science can work only on what is supposed to repeat itself—that is to say, on what is withdrawn, by hypothesis, from the action of real time. Anything that is irreducible and irreversible in the successive moments of a history eludes science. To get a notion of this irreducability and irreversibility, we must break with scientific habits which are adapted to the fundamental requirements of thought, we must do violence to the mind, go counter to the natural bent of the intellect. But that is just the function of philosophy."

Hermann Weyl, in exploring the relationship of the human spirit to the inanimate, writes: "Of myself, I know that I am open toward a purely spiritual world of images. Here lies the origin of my free insight and of my concern for truth as well as of my free action and my responsibility."

I want to close with a sentence from Whitehead, a thought that I have mentioned before and that I shall quote again: "There is a freedom lying beyond circumstance, derived from the direct intuition that life can be grounded upon its absorption in what is changeless amid change."

16

The Meaning of Man

D OES THE meaning of man transcend time and space? Does your own personal meaning reach beyond space into infinity, beyond time into eternity? At this moment you are alive, you are perceiving, you are conscious, you are thinking, you possess identity. In all of this do you also possess a timeless core that carries your personal identity—conscious, perceiving, thinking, acting—past the limitations of mortality into a domain beyond distance and beyond duration? Does this personal, identical *you* contain a reality that is invariant under the transformation that transports it into the mansions of eternity?

Since the beginning of humanity itself, men have been trying to answer these questions. And from a host of the most penetrating thinkers that have ever lived, there comes a series of affirmative answers. One of the greatest of these is Whitehead's affirmation: "There is a freedom lying beyond circumstance, derived from the direct intuition that life can be grounded upon its absorption in what is changeless amid change." This freedom, that which is the essence of you, is truly an eternal verity.

The Eternal Verity of Man

As we have observed man in the perspective of the new basic concepts of chemistry and physics today, we have found that the ground of man's reality is to be sought not in the parts, not in the particles of which he is composed, but in his whole, total being. For we have found that the fundamental particles of nature *as particles* are in essence

335

evanescent shadows. They transform back and forth from
one kind to another kind in an iridescent kaleidoscope of
form. It is a shifting pattern much like the transformation in
a radio broadcast of the form of the symphony from the
musician's brain waves to vibration in air, to electrical vibrations, to radio vibrations, to electrical vibrations, to air
vibrations and back into brain waves. We cannot say that
the symphony *is* the vibrations in air any more than it *is* the
electrical vibrations, the radio vibrations, or the brain vibrations. In the same way, we cannot say that the essential
reality of a particle *is* one form any more than it *is* any one
of a number of other forms into which the particle can be
transformed. So we concluded that the forms of the particles
are but shifting shadows of a deeper, underlying, invariant
verity. Thus the reality lies in the verity.

As we ascend the ladder of form from those eternal
verities of oneness, twoness, threeness, and their symmetries
associated with the fundamental particles, to the coalescence
of these particles into atoms, we deal with greater and
greater intricacy of form. We find complexities far beyond
our capacity to comprehend or express in any mathematical
or formal language today at our command. But there is still
every reason to believe that these atoms are again embodiments of forms that deserve the appellation of eternal
verities. Going up another rung on the ladder to those molecular forms that are the coalescence of atoms we again find
such clear and sharp identity of structure and function that
we feel once more that we hold in our hands the embodiment
of eternal verities.

Nowhere in this progression from the fundamental particles through the atoms up to the molecular level is there
any reason for saying that at any particular point we have
passed beyond the boundary of the eternal verities and are
no longer dealing with total eternal forms but merely groups
of parts. In the same way as we climb the ladder of com-

plexity still farther through the macromolecules, the proteins, right up to the biological cell, we pass no barrier suggesting that the reality of eternal verity no longer attaches. In fact, when we see the unity of life, when we realize that the cell is the unit of structure of all living matter, we have an overwhelming reason for accepting the eternal verity present in the essence of the cell. When we combine the dynamism of particles, the dynamism of atoms, the dynamism of molecules, the dynamism of macromolecules, the dynamism of cells all into the dynamism of total man, we again pass no border with a sign saying that "Here eternal verity stops." Again, the very nature of the dynamism of man is an argument that we have been rising on this ladder of complexity through a continuous ascending order of eternal verities to arrive finally at the supreme pinnacle of the eternal verity in man. So it is logical to ask whether in this portrayal of man as a dynamic form of eternal verity we can see evidence of the dynamism of man's participation in eternity. In this frame of mind let us try to find answers to the questions raised at the beginning of this chapter, the questions regarding man's immortality.

The Meaning of Immortality

In his provocative book on "The Human Use of Human Beings," Norbert Wiener remarks that to be less than a man is to be less than divine. What do we mean when we say that man's spirit partakes of the divine? What do we mean by asserting that man is immortal?

Clearly an answer to this question must be interpreted within the context of our concept of time. If we assert the opposite prosposition, that man is mortal, we are saying that man's existence is *limited* in time; we are equating the existence of a human being to that period in time from birth to death during which there is a dynamic concilium of atoms that fulfills the definition of what it means to be alive.

When we assert that a human being is immortal, we are saying that the existence of an individual human being is *not* confined within this limitation of time from birth to death, but that in some way the quality of aliveness extends throughout all time, and beyond time, beyond even the endless horizon of the infinity of time into the supra-domain of eternity.

To make this assertion meaningful, we must examine carefully once more our concept of what it means to be alive. We are now thinking not of the undifferentiated dynamism of life that consists of metabolism and a relatively simple level of intra- and intercellular communication. We are thinking of life in the *fullest* sense for a human being. To be fully alive, a human being must be conscious. Consciousness consists of perception, of reflection, of action, of imagination, and of the supreme dynamism of freedom, the action of free will. In each aspect of this dynamism there is the quality of the whole, the cybernetic interrelationship. More than that, since the essence of freedom is both the ability to choose and the act of choosing itself, there is the implication of the possibility of *growth* in this total dynamism, the growth and deepening of perception, the growth and deepening of reflection, the growth and deepening of imagination, the growth and deepening of freedom itself.

Does this new perspective of the universe as music enable us to see more clearly a structure of truly vital dynamism of growth that transcends time and space into eternity?

The Space Aspect of Immortality

In "The Adventures of Ideas," Whitehead asks the question, "How far does the soul extend beyond the body?" He goes on to say that to answer this question we must first determine on what scale in time and space we shall attempt to find coherence. What are the wavelengths and frequencies of the rhythms of the soul? Is life the gradual shifting of localized body wavelengths to wavelengths in the eternal? Is life a synthesizing of the soul? Niebuhr directs our attention to the thought of St. Augustine that the *mind* transcends its finiteness into the eternal. In order to see in the perspective of the universe as music the true dimensions of the extent of the spirit, let us first look within the familiar perspective of time and three-dimensional space to see where we really are. What does it mean in ordinary terms to say that *you* are *here?*

Presumably at this moment you are sitting in a room in a particular chair, reading this book. You can be located in terms of your nearness to certain objects in your environment and your distance from other objects. You are quite near to (in fact, you are undoubtedly *touching*) the chair in which you are sitting; but you are separated by some distance from the walls of your room. You are separated by an even greater distance from other buildings in the neighborhood, and so on and on.

Of course, even touching itself has varying degrees of proximity. Your clothes separate your skin from the actual substance of the chair. Even if you place your hand on the arm of the chair, the chances are that there is a very thin film of moisture on your hand and even some absorbed molecules of oxygen and nitrogen from the air that separate the actual hydrogen and carbon of your skin from the hydrogen and carbon of the material of the chair itself. However, as a working definition we think of your location in terms of nearness to some things and farness from other things; and this nearness and farness is measured in terms of units of distance which may be inches or fractions of an inch, or feet, or miles, or even light-years.

But are we to limit the definition of your proximity to the *material* atoms of your body? Do we have to say that your atoms are *in contact* with other atoms for you to be touching them? As we have seen, the definition of an atom making contact with another atom is extremely difficult to phrase in any precise and meaningful way. We have recognized that the energy within you is perhaps more significantly *you* even than are your atoms. If some of your vibrational energy is mingling with and affecting an object near you, is that not as meaningful an act of touching as the contact of atoms?

You may remember my story of the infrared television camera which I developed during World War II. With this camera I was able to project on a television screen the glowing image of the aura of the quinary rainbows of radiation that emanate from my body. At this moment your radiation is touching every object in the room around you. You may question the significance of this kind of radiative touching. I agree that the amount of energy involved here is very slight. But how should we evaluate the significance of slight amounts of energy? As the energy gets smaller and smaller, when do we reach the point of no significance? The energy involved in a single act of thought must be extremely small, yet we have to admit the high degree of significance in thought.

You are also emitting an aura of radio waves. These radio waves extend in theory out to infinity, although their intensity diminishes markedly as the distance from your body gets greater. But when does the significance of your radio presence cease, as distance gets greater? At a foot, at a mile, at a light-year?

Here, you see, we are forced to shift the perspective of our thinking about nearness and farness from distance measured in feet and miles to distance measured in tuning. In the domain of waves, nearness and farness are measured by being in tune and out of tune, rather than in distance.

You have another aura that extends without limit: your aura of gravity. Why are you sitting comfortably in your chair and not floating around up near the ceiling? Because every atom in your body is linked by a thread of gravity with every atom of the untold trillions of tons of matrix rock in the core of the earth. This aura of gravity from your body may be thought of as penetrating and mingling with the aura of gravity from the core of the earth, producing the force that holds you in your chair, enables you to walk along the floor, and gives you a most useful kind of stability in the actions of your daily life. But, of course, your field of gravity goes up as well as down, and extends out into the universe without limit as far as we know. Every time your heart beats, there is projected into the universe a pulse of gravity which within a few minutes will disturb the sun, within a few years will produce a push on a neighboring star, and which millions of years from now may be causing effects in a distant nebula. I believe it was Francis Thompson who said, "Thou canst not pluck a flower without troubling a star."

It is not unreasonable to conclude that every act of human thought projects some kind of gravity wave. This means that not only every action of your entire life but every thought that has ever crossed your mind has been projected and recorded on the pages of the universe. We can imagine that there is a dynamism expanding out into the universe that is a replication, in terms of form, of every act and every thought of your entire life up to this point. Perhaps the myth of St. Peter's ledger is not so fantastic after all!

If we accept the arguments for the reality of the de Broglie waves, we have evidence of still another aura emanating from your body. The structure of the mathematics that conforms to the observable patterns of electron behavior suggests that these de Broglie waves extend to infinity. It seems reasonable to believe that every action and every thought modifies your total de Broglie wave pattern; and this again enters a dynamic form on the ledger of the universe which wings its way on throughout all time. Thus in the perspective of form-space, where we forget about ordinary space and ordinary distances, we can see all these phenomena as aspects of the thrust of your ego vector in the domain of the spirit.

As we remarked in our survey of the *collective* dynamism of society, you stamp something of your personal dynamism in the mind of every person with whom you come in contact. After living a few decades some of your own dynamism is vibrating in the minds of millions of other human beings here on earth, present not only in the minds of those whom you have seen and touched but transmitted from them to others, and from them to still others in an endless chain. This is relatively obvious when we think of the great creative artists and thinkers of the past. If we are willing to accept the reality of dynamic forms, we must feel that we have within us, living and vibrant, the spirits of Socrates and Plato, of Caesar and Horace, of Shakespeare and Jonson, Bach and Beethoven, Goethe and Schiller and countless other great men. But in the billions of your brain cells, in the total dynamism of their septillion atoms, you also have something of the living dynamism of trillions of other, humbler human beings from out of the past. And by the same token, you are projecting your dynamism not only into those now living but into future generations extending to the very horizon of time.

Do you agree that man transcends space?

Man Transcends Time

From all of these considerations, it is also clear that man transcends not only space but time as well. In your dynamism rushing out into the universe as radiation, as radio waves, as gravity waves, as de Broglie waves, in your dynamism spreading through the minds of present and future generations of mankind, you are transcending both space and time. But just as we are compelled to examine man's transcendence of space, not only in terms of Cartesian space but in the deeper perspective of form-space, we must project man's transcendence of time against different perspectives of time in order to gain deeper insight into the nature of this transcendence.

In his book "The Revolt Against Dualism," Professor Lovejoy comments on the usefulness of viewing time in different perspectives. He begins with a discussion of a paper by Edwin A. Burtt in the Proceedings of the Sixth International Congress of Philosophy (in this discussion the italics are Professor Lovejoy's) :

"Another writer has had the acumen and the boldness in paradox to 'extend radically the doctrine of perspectives' so that it may apply—as it unquestionably should—to the concepts of time and evolution. The doctrine, in general terms, is thus formulated: whatever is found empirically to happen always involves the compresence of an intelligent organism, and (which is more important metaphysically) the way in which it happens is, in the last analysis, *the way in which it comes to play the part that it does play in the development of the perspectives or centers of experience through which it gains its place in the objective order that we will call the world.*

"Now the standpoint which determines any actually given perspective is always a present standpoint. What, then, is the past from the standpoint of the present? Are not its nature and the order of events composing it those which it empirically exhibits *within* the standpoint, *i.e.,* within the present from which it is viewed? If this question is answered, as the doctrine of perspectives seems to require, in the affirmative, it follows that the world always takes shape from the present outward. It expands into the past as knowledge of the past is needed to satisfy present desires . . . but it remains within the present all the while, in fact, it only generates a vastly larger present. Thus, real time begins only with organisms whose presence include temporal perspectives of the past; the 'time of science,' conceived of as something independent of such perspectives and prior to the existence of the intelligent organisms experiencing them, is a mere 'abstract time.' It 'does not characterize the world at the beginning, it only emerges when the expanding process of real time has gone far enough for the meaning of a successive continuity to be clearly seized and the habit acquired of fitting events into it. Real evolution is thus not a temporal process if we mean thereby the time of physics.' And this, generalized, means that the order of discovery is the order of reality."

It is clear to many of those who have made an effort to understand the nature of time that time is not just a simple linear flow. Time is a tapestry. For example, it may well be that to the dynamic form in the interior of an atom of radium, there is no passage of time until the critical moment comes when it expels an alpha-particle and is metamorphosed from the hard, bright, compact metal to a molecule of the tenuous and invisible gas *radon*. It may well be that time is a tapestry woven of the threads of the metamorphoses of dynamic forms.

What do we see when we look back toward the beginning of time? I want to discuss this at greater length in the chapter on "The Dynamism of the Universe" that follows in the next section. I merely remark here that the evidence is that ten billion years ago the state of the universe may have been very different from what it is now. It may have been a kind of primordial flux, a uniform sea of photons. There are those who say that the universe began with a big bang, an emergence from nothing into a ball of light which in its emergence, diffusion, and condensation created time, space, and matter. "In the beginning . . . God said, 'Let there be light'; and there was light."

(You may recall the remark of St. Augustine, who was

asked by someone what the Lord was doing before He created the universe. St. Augustine replied that He was making a special kind of hell for persons who asked such questions.)

It is clear that there is considerable evidence to make us conclude that in looking back toward the beginning of time we cannot make a *linear* extrapolation. We cannot assume that time goes back in a monotonous flow forever and ever. In fact, it is clear that such a concept of undifferentiated infinite past time is itself unimaginable. An infinite past cannot be grasped by finite minds.

To me, the most logical approach to this problem is the recognition that the beginning of time is a boundary; and that as we approach boundaries, we must expect the rules of the game to change. We must expect a different kind of structural relationship to appear, different laws to operate at the border.

Such boundary conditions are familiar in many areas of physics. As we go from objects of familiar size to smaller and smaller sizes, we find that at the boundary of the subatomic in the domain of fundamental particles there is exactly this kind of change in structural relationships, exactly this kind of shift in the laws that operate. We have to use *quantum* mechanics instead of *Newtonian* mechanics. Turning from the very small to the very large, the evidence is, as we go from distances of familiar size like feet or miles to the vast astronomical distances expressed in terms of light-years, that at the boundary of the very large there is also a change in structural relationships, a change in the nature of the laws that operate; here we find that space relations must be expressed not in familiar Cartesian coordinates but in Minkowskian curved coordinates envisioned in the framework of the principles of relativity. For reasons of this sort, I feel that the beginning of time must be viewed in a different perspective from familiar, everyday time.

There are dozens of articles in scientific and philosophical literature dealing with speculations about the origin of time, the origin of space, the origin of matter, the origin of the universe. But I have never run across any scientific articles discussing the complementary boundary which is the terminus of time, space, and the universe. Of course, religious literature is full of speculation about the end of things. My own feeling is that this terminus, this ultimate destiny must also be viewed in the same perspective as the origin. I believe that, as the universe approaches the fulfillment of its destiny, again the whole structure will change, there will be a change in the laws that operate. I want to go into this in considerably more detail in the final chapters of this book. But it is also in this perspective that we should now take a look at patterns of immortality consonant with our new concept of the universe as music.

Patterns of Immortality

Can we envision any kind of extrapolation of the existence of the human spirit into eternity? If we think of eternity as undifferentiated and timeless, we are confronted with a paradox in embedding dynamic aliveness into this kind of adynamism. Someone once remarked that it is impossible to think of a joyous eternal life in heaven, when the average human being can hardly survive the boredom of a long Sunday afternoon. Niebuhr continually emphasizes that eternity is more than undifferentiated infinity.

You may feel that it is not province of finite minds to speculate on the pattern of the infinite. You may claim that such an exploration is tasteless, impudent, and sacrilegious. If so, please skip the remaining pages of this chapter. For I can readily understand that my boldness in suggesting some of these thoughts may appear to you to violate the canons of good taste, propriety, and reverence. But if you can accept my speculation as just another humble effort to see a little more clearly some aspects of eternal Truth, then please bear with me.

First of all, if we grant that the eternal verities are ultimate reality, we may find it plausible to believe that they comprize not only the familiar universe which we perceive during our natural life, but that they also are the foundation of the universe of the dimensions of the eternal spirit. I believe that *two plus two equals four* here on earth and also in heaven. I also believe that in the domain of eternity we find a structure which embraces not only the simple but the complex verities, the verities of atoms, molecules, cells, and even human bodies. In the embodiment of these verities in the universe of our mortal life, there is always the component of imperfection which is perhaps associated with the dimension of time and change. We may speculate that, in the *transfinite* domain, this imperfection vanishes and we have the eternal verities from the simple to the complex embodied in scintillating perfection.

Reasoning along these lines we can think of a transfinite domain where the human spirit is made corporeal through the eternal verities moving *in* familiar recognizable form *among* familiar recognizable forms. In this trans-domain we may find the grass, the flowers, the plants, the trees, the forests around us in an eternal embodiment. There may be transfinite fauna as well as flora. I cannot think of anything more satisfying than to begin my transfinite life in a little house with a garden on the edge of a forest near the shore of a lake, with birds and animals for company.

But if my ego vector has somehow made this leap of penetration into this transfinite domain, if it has somehow achieved the tuning of immortality that carries me into this transfinite world of eternal dynamic forms, what will be the nature of my transfinite consciousness? First of all, as the *ground* of my consciousness, I suggest that I will have a concilium of forms of transfinite atoms grouped in trans-

finite cells which are assembled to provide me with a transfinite body and a transfinite brain. In the transfinite domain,
two plus two will still equal four; the slightly more complicated mathematical reality of the dynamism of the polydimensional chord of carbon still embodies the same harmony; I expect the melody of protein to remain invariant
in these new dimensions; I expect the dynamism of the life
cell to remain invariant; I expect the symphony of life to
play on. I believe that the transformation of my symphony of
life from the finite to the transfinite, from mortality to immortality, will be no more disrupting than the change found
in the transformation of Beethoven's Ninth Symphony from
vibration of sound to vibration of radio waves. His symphony is in essence not sound waves, nor radio waves, but
an eternal verity of which these sound and radio waves are
only evanescent embodiments. My own personal symphony
of life is not atom waves nor energy waves, but an eternal
verity of which my mortal atoms and photons are only an
evanescent embodiment. Just as the Beethoven symphony
passes invariant from embodiment to embodiment, my personal symphony will pass invariant from mortality into the
transfinite domain of eternity with its notes, chords, melody,
total structure resounding in the transfigured dynamism of
infinite perfection. And this transformation is not a leap
over light-years of distance to a heaven "up there" or "out
there." It is only a single step through the thin veil that
hangs between the familiar dimensions of the seen, the
heard, the tangible all around us—only a single step into
the dimensions of the unseen, the unheard, and the intangible which surrounds us during every moment of our living,
the domain of the eternal where our reality truly resides.
This transformation is no more than a small twist of the
dial that shifts the tuning of the soul from the mortal to
the immortal.

I am also sure that this transfinite dynamism of immortality is more than the dynamism of a sustained chord, a changeless harmony sounding without melody through eternity. I feel sure that the dynamism of the transfinite is truly a symphony, not only with harmony but with infinite melodic progression. Just as dynamic growth is the essence of life here on earth, I am convinced that dynamic growth is the essence of life in the hereafter.

Is it unreasonable to expect a continual deepening and expanding of the power of perception in the transfinite domain? During our mortal life we continue to perceive more and more deeply what we hear and what we see. I confidently look forward to a change from viewing *through the glass darkly* to a seeing *face to face.*

At the beginning of this book we talked about an experiment with a magic wand that endowed one with the perception of both the visible and invisible, both the audible and inaudible, the perception of all dynamic forms. We also commented on the fact that the sudden acquisition of infinite perception might be overwhelming to a finite mind. If immortality is dynamic existence it must have the component of growth. It must be that as we move down the vistas of eternity that we grow in perception and in understanding. I cannot think of any more exciting way to spend some aeons than in learning how to see into the heart of a rose and how to hear the symphony of its intricate and beautiful dynamic form. If my transfinite growth includes the deepening and enriching of communication, I can look forward to the possibility of at last achieving communication and understanding with the myriad other forms of life that I have viewed here in our familiar world. I shall learn to listen to the song of the violet, the lily, the chrysanthemum; I shall spend an aeon or two in the gardens of eternity hearing the symphonies of every living flower and tree, and mingling their beauty and harmony in my eternally deepening consciousness.

I shall spend a dozen or so more aeons conversing with and making part of me the symphonies of the insects and the animals. Someone once wrote that he did not want to go to heaven unless his dog would be there too. Perhaps, as in the fable, animals will speak and we will understand and our mutual love will be articulate. Albert Schweitzer in his doctrine of reverence for life implied the potential of this kind of community of understanding with all of animate existence.

Of course, a still greater significance of the growth of perception and understanding in a transfinite existence may be the enrichment of communication with those others who, like ourself, have entered the infinite domain of the spirit. Could there not be an enriched pattern of communication, an opportunity in the aeons of eternity to meet face to face not only with those we have loved but also with all mankind? In such communion one could enjoy infinities of time. Perhaps we can not only deepen our own perception and understanding and togetherness; but we can also give of ourself to others in a total process of enrichment of transfinite being. If the act of living as *someone-for-others* here on earth is the supreme channel for the growth and enrichment of the spirit, is it not logical to think that *giving* may be a continuing component in transfinite life? And at the summit of this growth of perception and understanding, and giving, we can finally envision the achievement of communion with the supreme total reality of the universe, a oneness with God, a fusion with the infinite Unity.

I close with a quotation from Hermann Weyl: "Thus the ultimate answer lies beyond all knowledge in God alone; emanating from him, the light of consciousness, its own origin hidden from it, grasps itself in self-penetration, divided and suspended between subject and object, between meaning and being."

Part V

The Nature of the Universe

"Talking with physicists, biologists, and other scientists who are unaware of a crisis in musical thought, one is always profoundly surprised to how great an extent they operate with concepts analogous to those in musical creation. We have already seen how time and space have their musical equivalents, and there apparently exist similar equivalents to basic laws in the physical sciences. This could lead us to the belief that there is some foundation in the ancient idea of a universe regulated by musical laws—or to be more modest, a universe whose laws of construction and operation are complemented by a spiritual reflection in musical organisms. The time may perhaps return when musical rules will be, as they were in olden times, an essential part of the code of the physical sciences."

—*Paul Hindemith*

17

The Structure of the Universe

FASTEN your seatbelt. We are starting on a trip to the end of the universe. For I want you to have a look at the very, very large in the same way that you viewed the very, very small with your magic eyesight on our trip inside the rose. I want you to hear the symphony of the stars as well as the symphony of the atoms.

We are going to travel in a twenty-first-century rocket ship propelled with nuclear fuel. You recall that a bathtub full of water has enough nuclear energy (if fully utilized) to light all the lights and run all the factories in the entire United States for several weeks. By taking along several thousand gallons of water for our fuel, we will have a supply sufficient for quite a long trip, even though we travel in a good-sized ship, maybe three hundred feet long and fifty feet across. We have staterooms with private baths, lounges, a movie projection room, a well-equipped library, dining facilities well-stocked with food, even a swimming pool for exercise. Most important of all we have some refrigerated beds equipped with special alarm clocks, because on our flight we shall be taking several extended naps of a million or even a billion years. When that time comes we simply crawl into bed, swallow a pill to prevent our blood from crystallizing, and then freeze ourself to a temperature of 250° below zero centigrade. When the alarm clock goes off, we warm up, wake up, and have a swim in the pool to be thoroughly alert for another long day of observation.

So if you are ready, let's go.

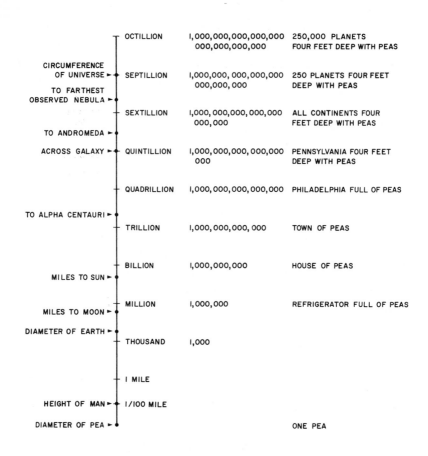

FIGURE I

GALACTIC DISTANCES

The Scale of Space

We have several objectives in making this trip. First of all, we want to get some feel for the magnitude of the distances that must be traversed in traveling from one part of the universe to another. In the second place, we want to take a look at the different kinds of stars and the way they are grouped together in galaxies and super-galaxies. In the third place, we want to make all these observations in a way that permits us to see the universe in the perspective of our new ideas about its structure as music.

As you can well imagine, the distances between different parts of the universe are enormous. In order to give you some *feel* for the relative magnitudes of these distances, I want to employ the same device that we used in getting the feel of the number of atoms in the body. We try to visualize the large numbers in terms of the areas covered by a four foot blanket of peas. In Figure 1 I have provided a scale to refresh your memory. On the right of the figure you see that a million peas are about enough to fill a household refrigerator. You see that a quintillion peas will cover the state of Pennsylvania four feet deep; the number of peas corresponding to the number of atoms in the human body, five octillion will cover one million, two hundred and fifty thousand planets, each four feet deep with peas. On the left of Figure 1, some of the more significant cosmic distances are given in miles.

Now that we are all set for our celestial navigation, let's blast off and head for the moon. We turn on just the right amount of nuclear power in the tail rockets so that the ship continues to move faster and faster at a rate corresponding to the acceleration of gravity. In this way we can walk around through the different rooms of the ship, eat our meals, and bathe in the swimming pool with just the same kind of comfort and security we have here on earth. Under this condition of acceleration, each of us will have his normal weight and all the objects around us will have their normal weight too, so that it will be a perfectly normal environment, except for the views out of the window. Whenever we want to get a more extended look at some celestial body, we can slow the ship down by turning off the rocket motors temporarily, maneuvering the ship through a complete reverse turn, and then using the rocket motors to decrease our speed with a deceleration also just sufficient to give us again our normal weight. Of course, during this maneuver there may have to be a few special precautions, such as a way of controlling the water in the swimming pool when we turn upside-down.

If we want to make our journey at this comfortable acceleration, with the ease of normal weight, it may take a few hours to get out to the moon. We can spend the time enjoying the remarkable views of our Earth as it recedes into the distance and the new views of the stars with their brilliance undimmed by the passage of their light through the Earth's atmosphere. We employ our magic eyesight to observe the beams of radio waves coming in toward us from various places in the universe, along with the cosmic waves from outer space.

We may even pass a meteor now and then. If you notice a slight jar once in a while, it just means that the electric eyes on the front of the ship have detected a meteor coming toward us on a collision course and have activated the disintegrator guns to blow it away as dust. Hitting a meteor at one hundred thousand miles an hour would be considerably worse than running into an iceberg on a transatlantic crossing.

As we approach the moon we slow down a little and glide in closer to the surface so that we can see some of the lunar observation stations placed there by the older, chemical-rocket techniques. We observe the mountains, valleys, and craters, but do not linger long as we have so far to go on the trip ahead of us.

We soon zoom off and take a quick flight by the planets Venus and Mercury, both of which are so obscured by clouds that there is not much to see. Then we head toward the sun, being careful to check the operation of our nuclear power so that there is no danger of being trapped in the gravitational field of the sun and pulled into its fiery surface. On our trip to the moon we covered a distance of approximately two hundred and forty thousand miles. The trip to the sun is considerably longer, about one hundred million miles. Adding a pea for each mile would give us about one hundred normal household refrigerators full of peas, which really isn't much compared with what we will soon have.

As we approach the sun, we realize that it is a heavenly body enormously larger than the Earth. It is just a little under a million miles in diameter contrasted with the Earth's diameter of only eight thousand miles. The surface of the sun has a temperature of about six thousand degrees centigrade; but that is almost freezing cold compared with the interior, where the temperature probably climbs to something like ten million degrees centigrade. We notice that the surface of the sun is literally a sea of gaseous flame, with waves thousands of miles high and spray flung off into the reaches of space. We could spend days observing this incandescent dynamism with its incredible beauty of color extending through the dozens of rainbow hues both above and below the range normally visible to our unaided eyes. We could spend weeks listening to the symphony of the sun, with its clusters of cosmic trumpet cadenzas. But we are going to see sextillions of suns on our trip, suns of enormous ranges in size, color, temperature and dynamic structure. We are going to hear sextillions of solar symphonies of every conceivable kind of melodic and harmonic structure and rhythm. So let us turn the ship out into space again and head for the nearest star, Proxima Centauri.

The journey from our own sun to its nearest neighbor will take almost five years, even though we push the speed of our own spaceship up almost to the maximum possible velocity with which anything can travel in our universe, the speed of light. This speed has the almost incredible value of seven hundred million miles per hour; but even with this fast flight, it will take us almost five years to get to our destination, the star Proxima Centauri. As we flash through the outer limits of our own planetary system, we cross the orbits of Mars, Saturn, Jupiter, Neptune, and Pluto during the first week of our journey. Pluto, on the average, is thirty-five billion miles away from the sun. But our journey has scarcely begun at this point.

From here on out, the view will be somewhat monotonous. Our own sun will gradually get dimmer and dimmer until it appears to be no more than an unusually bright star. With four years of nothing special to see, this is a good time to try out our refrigerated beds, so we each take a pill in preparation for the long sleep, set our alarm clock for about four and a half years, say "Good night" to each other, climb into our bunks, and start the refrigeration mechanism. Within a minute or two, we have fallen into a deep sleep and as we lose consciousness, our temperature drops fifty, a hundred, a hundred and fifty, two hundred degrees, until it levels off at about two hundred and fifty degrees below zero. During this long night, we do not have to worry about kicking off the blankets. We are completely in a state of suspended animation and I doubt if we are even troubled with dreams. So the weeks and months and years slip by while the automatic pilot guides the ship; and then the great day comes when the alarm clock begins to buzz and heat is sent back into our bodies. A few hours later, we open our eyes with the light of Alpha Centauri streaming brightly through the windows.

I will not speculate as to what we will find in this distant part of the universe. Astronomical evidence indicates that Proxima Centauri is one of a group of three stars known collectively as Alpha Centauri. So when we look out the window, we see three suns in the sky, instead of one as we see normally on Earth. There is no way of telling whether these triplet stars have a strange intertwining system of planets. If they do, it certainly would be tempting to stop and visit for a while. However, after we have had a brief look-around, we must be on our way, because we have far greater distances to explore.

Our next object is to complete the trip straight across the incredibly vast collection of stars that we see in the sky as the Milky Way. Our own sun is just one member of a group of about one hundred billion stars that lie in space forming an enormous saucer. This saucer, our own galaxy, is in motion. It is revolving and also moving through space at an enormous velocity. Thus, it is a kind of flying cosmic saucer. Our own sun lies near the outer edge of the saucer, so far from the center that it takes us over thirty thousand years traveling at the speed of light to go from Earth to the middle of the galaxy. The average distance between the stars as we travel through the galaxy is about ten trillion miles. (You recall that ten trillion peas is just about enough to fill all the buildings in a city with a population of one hundred thousand people.) This "flying saucer" galaxy thins out quite a bit at the edges so that it is difficult to define exactly the distance across it; but roughly speaking it is about a quintillion miles from one edge of the galaxy across to the other edge. (You recall that a quintillion peas is enough to cover the state of Pennsylvania with a layer of peas four feet deep. Matching a pea to a mile, this gives you some feeling for the vast distance across the galaxy.)

As we press on from the Alpha Centauri group toward the other edge of the galaxy we spend most of our time safely tucked away under the sheets of the cryogenic bed in a state of suspended animation. But in order not to miss some of the excitement of the trip, we wake up every thousand years or so and have a look around. We pass thousands of planetary systems as we speed across the galaxy. Some of these have only one star like our own, some have two stars at their center, some have three stars. Thus the solar systems are very much like the top-ranking men in uniform who wander around the Pentagon Building in Washington—the one-star, two-star, and three-star generals.

We shoot through great regions of stardust appearing like clouds of black fog on the horizon. If we sample the space through which we travel, we find that the most common chemical element is hydrogen. There is evidence that all space has some hydrogen atoms floating around in it. Thus listening to the music of the universe, we hear the overwhelming symphony coming from each star with the antiphonal music of its planets, with the monotone of hydrogen as a background, the embodiment of the oneness of the universe.

In the course of our observations of stars in crossing the galaxy, we may observe a number that are far smaller than our own sun. These are the dwarf stars. We also will pass stars like Sirius, twins with a size twenty-six times that of our own sun. The star Antares is believed to be about four hundred and fifty times the size of our sun. It is so vast that if the center of Antares were placed at the center of our sun, its incandescent cauldron of energy would extend even out beyond the orbit of Mars.

We also notice that some of the stars are not steady in their intensity like our sun. The star Betelgeuse oscillates, the strength of its radiation changing over a period of three years from an intensity of about two hundred times that of our sun to an intensity something like three hundred times our solar radiation. It then diminishes its light and at the end of another period is back at the lower level. We see some stars where the surface temperature is greater than fifty thousand degrees centigrade as compared with the mere six thousand degrees centigrade of our own sun. We pass very tiny stars about the size of planets, the white dwarfs which have a high temperature and a density in the interior one hundred thousand times that of water.

If we happen to be looking out the window at the right time, we may see a star suddenly increase its radiation, growing brighter and brighter and, in the course of two days, becoming a million times brighter than its original incandescence. The end of this process may be a stellar explosion. From back on Earth there is one such *nova* star observed about every month. And about once in every four hundred years a *supernova* star appears in the sky, with a radiation which can be one hundred million times brighter than that of our sun.

At last, after a period of waking and sleeping, waking and sleeping, we draw near to the farthest edge of our own galaxy and prepare for the plunge into the real vastness of the universe out beyond the Milky Way. We set the course of our ship now for the neighboring galaxy of Andromeda, about forty quintillion miles away. So the distance we have to cover corresponds, (matching miles to peas) to forty states each the size of Pennsylvania covered with peas four feet deep.

I will not continue to describe the details of the journey as we sleep away almost two million years getting to Andromeda. After a look there, we go on and on farther out into the universe, passing another galaxy or nebula about every two million years. After traveling a sextillion miles we are now out among the nebulae that are as far from Earth as it has been possible to observe with the help of our most powerful telescopes. It is estimated that there are at least one hundred billion of these nebulae and that each has something like a hundred billion stars in it. Just as a very rough figure, there are ten sextillion stars in the universe. Remember that one sextillion peas would cover all the continents of the entire globe with a layer of peas four feet deep; make this layer forty feet deep and you will have something like the number of peas corresponding to the number of stars.

But you may ask a question at this point: How is it possible to say how many stars there are in the universe? Does not the universe extend on and on to infinity?

Just let us keep our spaceship headed in a straight line and you will see the answer that many astronomers are giving to these questions. We let our spaceship coast along on what appears to be a straight-line course until we have covered about a septillion miles. (A septillion peas would cover two hundred and fifty planets each the size of our Earth with a blanket of peas four feet deep). Now, if we look out the window, we see a galaxy ahead; and on the edge of that galaxy we see a star with seven planets circling around it; and we look closely and recognize some familiar continents on the third planet and begin to tidy up our spaceship for the arrival back home. By moving in a straight line we have come back to the place from which we started. We have demonstrated that space is not the familiar Cartesian space of length, breadth, and height but that space is curved. We have proved the famous space-curvature conclusion from Einstein's theory of relativity.

But we may be in for some surprises in making our landing. The spaceport may have changed somewhat, for we have been away from home for thirty-five billion years. Will there be anyone there to welcome us? Will there be anyone with any interest in the results of our vast journey? Will there be anyone with whom we can converse, anyone that we will recognize as human?

I have sketched this trip around the universe with a

rather free hand; and I hope my astronomer friends will not be too critical of the places where I have painted with rather broad strokes. I have pictured the trip in this way primarily to give you an idea of the vastness of the universe. But it will become clear in the next chapter that there are several paradoxes involved in such a picture. We have evidence that the universe is not remaining constant in size as I implied in my description of our imaginary journey, but that it is expanding. Indeed it is expanding at such a rapid rate that we might find it impossible to come back to the origin of our trip. But before we get into that rather involved question, I want to tell briefly the story of the way in which the idea of curved space was born.

Curved Space

The concept of curved space originated a number of years ago in the minds of mathematicians who were speculating about various kinds of geometries. Minkowski is generally credited with laying the important foundations for these concepts. With the development of the theory of relativity by Albert Einstein, it became more and more evident that there was a possibility that we live in a kind of curved space. The theory of relativity made a number of predictions about the bending of light rays and other effects on light which could be verified with instruments like telescopes and spectroscopes. It took a while for the scientific community at large to accept the results, but today it is generally agreed that the broad conclusions of the theory of relativity are correct, although there is still some question about details. It is generally agreed that our space is curved, but there is some question about the exact nature of this curvature.

For our purposes, I want to consider the kind of curvature that makes our space into the kind of geometrical figure that can be called a hypersphere. While I am not enough of an expert to make a significant poll of the opinions of astronomers today, I believe that a substantial number of those best qualified to judge feel that the preponderance of the evidence favors this kind of space. Of those who have tried to express this concept in lay language, one of the most successful has been the famed British astronomer Sir Arthur Eddington. I will describe the analogy that he employs.

Imagine a rubber balloon about a yard in diameter, inflated and hanging in the air in front of you. The surface of the balloon is covered with polka dots, each dot being about a quarter of an inch across and the dots spaced about four inches apart more or less uniformly over the whole surface of the balloon. Now imagine an ant crawling on the surface of the balloon. The insect can move in any direction it wishes. It can crawl anywhere on the surface of the balloon. But if it moves in a "straight line" like an equator drawn around the middle of the balloon, then by following this "straight path" it eventually returns to the place where it started. The surface of the balloon is an example of a two-dimensional space. Like the surface of the Earth, one needs to specify latitude and longitude in order to denote a point on this surface. *Two* coordinates are necessary. But this is a two-dimensional space without any boundary. The ant can crawl as long and as far as it likes in any direction. There is nothing ever to stop the ant's crawling. Its space is unbounded, has no limits, and yet is not infinite. Because the space folds back upon itself; it is in the form of a sphere it contains a finite number of square inches. In this particular instance, the area of the surface of the balloon one yard in diameter is 3.1416 square yards. These digits are only the first five of the infinite number needed to express this number which is the quantity denoted by the Greek letter *pi,* the ratio of the circumference to the diameter of a circle. Thus the two-dimensional "space" of the surface of the balloon has just a little more than three square yards although it is unbounded; there is no limit anywhere to stop anything like an ant from moving anywhere at all on the surface.

The balloon is a two-dimensional analogy of the kind of hypersphere of space envisioned by the theory of relativity as our own dwelling place. To push the analogy a little further, the ant is our spaceship and the polka dots are the nebulae. If the ant continues crawling right around the equator of our balloon, it will end up where it started. This is like the imaginary trip which I described for our spaceship, where we moved in a straight line out through the nebulae and ended up where we started. Just as I calculated that the surface of the balloon had 3.1416 square yards, it is possible to calculate that the volume of space in our universe is 100,000,000,000,000,000,000,000,000,000,000,000,000, 000,000,000,000,000,000, 000,000,000,000,000 cubic miles. Of course we may be in error by quite a few zeros in writing this figure, but it gives us an idea of the size of space. It is a vast number, so vast that as far as I know, no one has given it a name. On the other hand, we have quite a different situation when space is limited to this size, as contrasted with the infinite space of the universe postulated by those who believe that space goes on and on forever without curvature.

You may recall that in the last chapter I pointed out the way in which the laws of nature are likely to change as we approach the boundaries either of the very small or of the very large. When we are dealing with such small amounts of space as those which contain atoms, we find that the concepts of classical Newtonian mechanics must be given up and replaced by the laws of quantum mechanics. I believe that it is another example of this boundary principle when we find that in moving out to distances of sextillion miles we must think of space as curved, and that we must replace classical Newtonian mechanics and Cartesian orthogonal coordinates with the new framework of the theory of relativity.

If space is finite though unbounded, then probably there

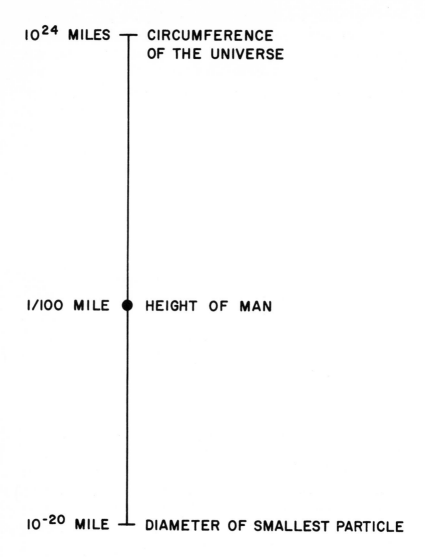

10^{24} MILES — CIRCUMFERENCE OF THE UNIVERSE

1/100 MILE ● HEIGHT OF MAN

10^{-20} MILE — DIAMETER OF SMALLEST PARTICLE

FIGURE 2

COMPARATIVE STATURE OF MAN

is only a finite amount of mass contained within this space. The figure for the mass of the universe as quoted by Hermann Weyl is 10,000,000,000,000,000,000,000,000,000,000, 000,000,000,000,000,000,000,000 grams. Thinking of this mass as made up of particles, Eddington has calculated that our universe may contain 1,000,000,000,000,000,000, 000,000,000,000,000,000,000,000,000,000,000,000,000, 000,000,000,000,000,000,000 *nucleons* (when this term is used to embrace the kinds of particles found in the nuclei of atoms).

Man in a Finite Universe

I have written these large figures derived from the theory of relativity as a string of zeros rather than in the usual mathematical form (the number ten with an exponent), because I am trying to give you some kind of instinctive grasp of these relative magnitudes. We were able to use the analogy of peas to gain an idea of the magnitude of numbers like five followed by twenty-seven zeros—five octillion, the number of atoms in the average human body. When we get up to a number like one followed by eighty-one zeros, then we are completely lost in our search for any analogy. But it is still important to remember that this number although large is still finite in size; and that makes it something very different from the kind of number we are suggesting when we talk of an infinite universe. In fact, by having a limit to the largeness of things from the theory of relativity and a limit to the smallness of things from the atomic theory, we can see where man stands in relation to the very large and to the very small.

In Figure 2 I have tried to convey some sense of this proportion. As in the drawing that showed us relative cosmic distances, we employ here not a linear scale but a ratio scale, a logarithmic scale. On this scale you see that man stands in ratio to the smallest size that we recognize as significant in the interior of the nucleus, as the size of the universe stands in ratio to man. It is a striking fact, pointed out by a number of cosmologists, that man in proportion is almost exactly midway between the very smallest and the very largest.

Let us think of this collection of five octillion atoms composing each one of us as a kind of private, interior universe. Here we have this miraculous coherence of dynamism that we call human life. The universe without us may seem inconceivably vast; yet its size in ratio to us is just about the same as our size in ratio to our particles. If within us, within our private, interior universe, there is this coherence, this dynamism of the human spirit which unifies our particles, is it any more miraculous to find in the universe a similar spiritual dynamism? This is a question I want to discuss in the chapter on "The Unity of the Universe."

There is another ratio involving man and the universe that is of equal significance. This is the span of man's normal lifetime in ratio on the one hand to the shortest interval of time that occurs significantly within us and in ratio on the other hand to the longest interval of time that we recognize in cosmology, the age of the universe. Here again we shall see that man stands just about midway between the very shortest and the very longest.

I want to close this chapter with a brief discussion of the structure of the universe as seen in the perspective of form.

The Universe in Form Perspective

Although the vistas we have just enjoyed give us a feeling of the immensity of the universe, we should set side by side with the vast picture the concept of the universe as music.

You remember that Whitehead raises the question of the relationship between the human soul and space. He writes:

"How far this soul finds a support for its existence beyond the body is another question. The everlasting nature of God, which in a sense is non-temporal and in another sense is temporal, may establish with the soul a peculiarly intense relationship of mutual immanence. Thus in some important sense the existence of the soul may be freed from its complete dependence upon the bodily organization."

You remember that we discussed the ways in which the dynamism of the human spirit extends beyond the space limitations of the body. First of all, there is the aura of ever-changing radiation that streams out from the body, reflecting in its shifting patterns the internal dynamism of the body and of the mind. There is the aura of radio waves which are sent out because of the chemical changes within the body that in turn are due partly to muscular action and metabolism and partly to thought itself. Again there is the aura of gravity waves, pulses originating from every thought and impulse that streams out into the universe. Finally, there is the pattern of de Broglie waves that extend out from the complex wave pattern of the body, a pattern that reflects not only the static structure but the dynamism of body and mind itself.

You recall that for the purposes of understanding this dynamism, form-space can be far more significant than the ordinary Cartesian or relativistic space. The fact is that the space of distance, even cosmic distance, is in many ways a construction of the mind. Hermann Weyl in his book entitled "Mind and Nature" remarks that space and time are intuitive forms, not realities. He also points out that Leibniz called our attention to the fact that space is really the order of all positions assumed to be possible.

Suppose that we accept the fact that the essential reality of everything in the universe is music rather than matter. We recognize that not only ourself, all the objects around us here on Earth, not only the Earth itself but the sun and all the other stars with their planets are essentially unimaginably vast complexes of harmony. We take into account that this harmony in the perspective of ordinary space interpenetrates the whole vast volume of the universe, more than vintillion cubic miles. (I am not sure of my Latin derivative for this figure but with your permission I will use this word to denote the number of cubic miles that we wrote out as one followed by sixty-three zeros.)

There is every reason to believe that every bit of matter (as matter) in this vast space is linked to every other bit of matter by gravity. There is every reason to believe that the de Broglie music of every portion of this space penetrates every other portion of it. So I ask you to consider the view of the universe in the perspective of a space of musical form with well over vintillion dimensions. Then nearness or farness is not a question of *space separation* but a question of *tuning.*

I am suggesting that in the perspective of this space of cosmic harmony where we see man's music mingled with the music of the entire universe, we can understand far more clearly the meaning of what Whitehead calls our mutual immanence with God. It is in this perspective that we get a clear vision of the unity of the universe. But in order to appreciate this incandescence of the universe in its full vitality we must now turn and reflect on its dynamism.

18

The Dynamism of the Universe

TODAY we are going to take a journey back into time. As you and I stand in the front hall of my home in Boca Raton, Florida, I explain the nature of this trip. You have asked me to take you back through time so that you can see with your own eyes the evolution of our Earth. So by means of magic, I have contrived a distortion of space and time so that for every foot that we move away from the door of my house, we move back in time through a hundred years. We will walk back through the first few centuries and then take my time-helicopter to speed up the passing of the years as we fly north, up the peninsula of Florida across the Carolinas and Virginia, over Washington, Philadelphia, and New York, continuing northward across Canada over the Pole and completing the circuit around our globe. On the scale of one hundred years to a foot, this is just about the distance that we must travel in order to see the story of our universe from the beginning of time.

A Journey to the Beginning of Time

I open the door and we step out on the front porch. George Washington is there waiting to greet us. Beyond him, just at the edge of the lawn, we see Christopher Columbus. We walk past with a smile and wave of the hand and meet Caesar and Alexander the Great out on the street. Moving swiftly on, it takes us only a short walk to catch up with our prehistoric ancestors, men and women clothed in animal pelts, short and stocky with apelike physiognomy. Just a hundred feet down the street we get into my time-helicopter and with whirling blades rise into the air, soar over the Spanish River, and commence our journey up the shore. In just a minute or two we are over Highland Beach, about two miles north of Boca Raton, and looking below we see that even the last cavemen have disappeared; in the open spaces between the palm trees there are only animals and birds. We fly swiftly northward, observing Palm Beach swarming with monkeys of many kinds. We quickly cover the two hundred miles to Daytona Beach, still seeing monkeys, gorillas, and chimpanzees; and then as we near Jacksonville, we notice the first huge prehistoric monsters, the dinosaurs browsing along the edges of the swamps of the St. John's River.

We fly over swamps for another two hundred miles and by the time we get to Savannah, the dinosaurs have disappeared and the banks of the river below us are crawling with snakes, small and large. As we keep on into South Carolina the reptile population increases. There are even some long wriggling serpents with wings that fly up around us to see the strange new monster with whirling blades which has invaded their private domain. Then as we leave South Carolina and cross the border to North Carolina we leave the land of snakes and enter the land of insects. The fields below us are crawling with giant cockroaches. Insects abound for another hundred miles or so, mingled here and there on the shore of the ocean with strange fish that come out with puffing bladders to rest on the sand. We swing the helicopter up the Potomac River and when we arrive over Washington, we find it crawling with snails. There are snails all across Maryland, across Pennsylvania, getting smaller and smaller until finally, when we reach the mouth of the Hudson River, we see that New York is nothing but green slime, mold and algae. We have traversed five hundred million years back in time.

We now set our course due north, and push the throttle

to full speed. As we cross into Canada, the land below is nothing but barren rock, not a sign of life anywhere. This is the bare magma that constituted our Earth a billion years ago. We move on back in time, two billion, three billion, four billion, five billion years and observe that the rock is beginning to glow with red heat. It is well that we have a magic helicopter because the atmosphere has taken on quite a different quality.

What will we see during the last stages of our journey corresponding to another five billion years back in time? In distance, this would just about take us around the Earth, over Asia and the Indian Ocean, over the South Pole, up across South America, and back to Florida once more. But it is certain that there would be no Florida there when we arrived. Would there even be any planet? Would we look out into the universe and see any stars at all? Would we find ourselves in an incandescent inferno of photons at a temperature of trillions of degrees? Would the whole universe be a single condensed ball of fire containing within itself the prismatic womb of time and space?

These are the questions so ardently explored by cosmologists today. Here is the crux of the dynamism of our universe.

Before we go on to survey some of the current thinking about these problems, I do want to apologize for a few of the liberties I took in conducting you along this magic journey into time. For instance, by the time we had reached the site of New York City, I doubt if there would have been any Hudson River there, because the geology of the Earth would certainly have changed very markedly over the period of five hundred million years. As I have remarked before, in these pictures that we draw in order to convey a more vivid image of aspects of the universe around us, it is always necessary to distort the perspective in order to emphasize the point. In telling the story of this journey, I wanted most to give you a little feel for the brief period of man's sojourn *as man* here on Earth, a million years out of the ten-billion-year existence of our universe, only a short distance of two miles along the twenty-thousand-mile path of cosmic history, only the two-mile stretch of shore between Boca Raton and Highland Beach as compared with the entire circumference of our Earth.

But what makes us think that the universe has a history of only ten billion years? Does not time go back forever and ever? Doesn't it *have* to? Isn't anything else unthinkable? In order to answer these questions let us look at the evidence.

Cosmological Theories

Scientists have been raising questions about the infinite nature of space and time during many past decades. It may seem unthinkable that time should have a beginning and that space should have an end; but the concepts of infinite time and infinite space also involve some paradoxes. Take the question of the dark background of the night sky, for example. If the universe were infinite, if it were uniformly populated with stars, then the *whole sky* should be blazing with the brightness of the sun both day and night. Wherever you looked overhead, you would see a star; and their images would be so close together so that the diminution of their light due to distance would be compensated by the infinitely dense nature of their images. Thus, we would have a solid bowl of "sun" overhead and everything on Earth would be instantly burned to a crisp (if not vaporized). Instead of this unhappy situation, actually we have the deep dark velvet of the night sky. The significance of this fact was first pointed out by the astronomer H. W. M. Olbers in 1826, and is frequently called "Olbers' Paradox." Olbers concluded that the universe was infinite but that there was dust between the stars to absorb the light. Of course, if this were the case, the dust would eventually become incandescent and give out as much light as it received; so, in the end, we would still have a blazing night sky if the universe were infinite.

The infinite nature of space was questioned again when cosmologists began to draw extended conclusions from Einstein's principles of relativity. Early in the development of this theory during the first two decades of our own century, it became clear that space might be curved; and that if it were curved, it might fold back upon itself and not have infinite volume. This was such a revolutionary idea that many scientists were skeptical. But they soon realized that there was a chance to test the new theory of relativity during an eclipse of the sun. If the light from a star passing near the sun was bent from its straight course according to the predictions of the theory, if this displacement of the image of the star could be observed, then there would be solid support for the new theory.

There was to be an eclipse of the sun in May, 1919, and to observe it, expeditions went both to Brazil and to North Africa. The observations completely validated the theory of relativity. Professor Whitehead was at the meeting of the Royal Society when the Astronomer Royal described the results and he tells the story of this dramatic incident: "The whole atmosphere of tense interest was exactly that of the Greek drama: we were the chorus commenting on the decree of Destiny as disclosed in the development of the supreme incident. There was the dramatic quality in the very staging—the traditional ceremonial, and in the background the picture of Newton to remind us that the greatest of scientific generalizations was now, after more than two centuries, to receive its first modification. Nor was the personal interest wanting; a great adventure in thought had at length come safe to shore."

Scientists had scarcely recovered from the shock of this "shaking of the foundations" when further astronomical observations brought forth another revolutionary suggestion. The great one-hundred-inch telescope at the Mount Wilson Observatory in California made it possible to see farther and farther out into the universe, and as a result more and more nebulae became visible. (You recall that we visited a number of these when we made our space trip in the last chapter.) Professor Hubbell of the Mount Wilson Observatory not only photographed these nebulae, but also measured the color of their light spectroscopically. He found that the farther away a galaxy was, the redder its light became. This is commonly referred to as the "red shift." The logical explanation was that the light of these distant nebulae changed because they were rushing away from us at incredibly fast speeds. The shift in color was due to the Doppler effect.

If you are not familiar with this phenomenon, it may help you to recall our magic piano with the keys glowing in rainbow colors. On this instrument, the note of *sol* glows a green color; the note of *do,* below it in pitch, glows with a red color. As pitch gets lower, color shifts from green to red. Color is a measure of the pitch or frequency of the light, and red has a lower pitch or frequency than green.

On some occasion you must have been waiting in your car at a railroad crossing while a train approached at high speed from the left and with its whistle shrieking a warning, zoomed by and went speeding off to the right. You must have observed the way in which the high-pitched whistle of the locomotive suddenly slid down the scale to a lower note as the motion of the train changed from approaching to receding. This is an example of the Doppler effect. The speed of the approaching train pushes the frequency higher; the speed of the receding train pulls it lower.

There is every reason to believe that the speed of stars approaching us or receding from us affects the frequency of their radiation in exactly the same way. So the speed of the motion of the nebulae can be calculated from the increasing redness of their light. It is also possible by independent means to get some measure of the distance of the different nebulae. Hubbell was thus able to deduce the law that the speed of recession of a nebula increases proportionately with its distance from us. Since we observe nebulae in every direction out in space and since the farther nebulae seem to be rushing away from us faster, the inevitable conclusion is that our universe is expanding. There are only a few scientists who deny the validity of this conclusion today.

It is also generally accepted that here on Earth, circling around our own sun, embedded in our own nebula, we do not occupy a position that is any different in character from that of any of the other nebulae. This is the cosmological principle which asserts the uniformity of the universe. It is thus clear that as time goes by, all the stars are getting farther apart. They appear to be rushing away from us; but if we were sitting on a planet on a distant nebula, according to the cosmological principle, they would still all appear to be rushing away from *that* nebula. How can this be?

Recall the analogy of the universe as an extended balloon, the cosmic model that we discussed in the last chapter. You remember that by thinking of a universe in two dimensions instead of three, we can say that the space of such a universe corresponds to the surface of the balloon. We think of the balloon as covered with polka dots, each polka dot representing a nebula. We are now saying that the balloon continues to expand, that it is blown up larger and larger as time goes by. Thus, with the rubber expanding, each polka dot is farther from every other polka dot.

Now if you are an ant sitting on a particular polka dot, you will see all the other polka dots in your neighborhood getting farther and farther away from you. It does not make any difference at all on which polka dot you happen to be sitting. It will always be true that all the other polka dots appear to be rushing away from you. This is the cosmological principle.

But now what happens if we turn the handle of our time machine backward; what happens if instead of going forward in time, we recede in time? It seems clear then that the balloon will deflate, the polka dots will all get closer together. This is what was happening when we took our trip in the magic helicopter back into time. Observing the sky, we would have seen the stars getting closer and closer to us, the nebulae rushing toward us.

Now you can think of an expansion as going on forever, if you have an infinite space into which you can expand; but you cannot think of a contraction as going on forever if the contraction continues at a uniform rate. Sooner or later, if the stars keep getting closer together, they are going to get so close that they will be touching each other. This is exactly the conclusion to which we have been led by the development of a number of the theories of our cosmos.

It is not a complicated calculation to compute the amount of time back from the present to the period in history when "all the stars were touching each other." Of course, it is necessary to assume that, from *that original point in time* to the present, the universe has been expanding at a constant rate; and this is an assumption which must be regarded with a critical eye. But it is interesting to make this assumption and to see how long ago the expansion started. The latest conclusion is that this expansion of the universe started about ten billion years ago. This is the point in time which we reached when we flew around the Earth in our helicopter, equating one foot to every thousand years in the past.

It is also rather startling that other evidence has been found to support the idea that somehow everything started in the universe somewhere between five billion and ten billion years ago. A great many of the atoms in the rock of which our Earth is composed are radioactive in nature. This means that every now and then one of these atoms—for example, a uranium atom—decides to emit a particle from its nucleus and change into something else. Scientists have measured these rates of emission carefully. By studying the rate of emission and the intensity of emission at the present time, it is possible to calculate the point in time when the uranium started emitting. Thus we regard the uranium atoms as little alarm clocks. We can calculate the time at which all these clocks were wound up and first started ticking. This point in time is about five billion years ago.

Like atoms, stars also have a life history. A study of the course of evolution of the stars again indicates that there was some kind of initial point at which this evolution started, five to ten billion years ago. So all this evidence, both from the very small (like the atom) and from the very large (like the stars and the nebulae), directs our attention to a kind of *singular point* in time about ten billion years ago. An understanding of the nature of this singular point in time is sure to be one of the keys that will unlock the door through which we can proceed to a far better understanding of the dynamism of the universe.

Especially during the last few decades, cosmologists have devised many models of the universe to account for this singularity, this kind of initial point. Some go so far as to say that this point represents the time when the universe was "created." Such an assertion has overtones that are more philosophical than scientific. But it is clear that in this area philosophy and science are closely intertwined. Professor Hocking some years ago called our attention to the "non-repeatable nature of the universe."

At any rate, these observations raise a number of interesting questions. Will the universe keep on expanding forever? Are we just on our way down a one-way street? Or, on the other hand, is this expansion that we are observing just the upswing of a cosmic tide which may, in a few dozen billion years, ebb and bring us back to a condition where all the stars are touching one another once more? There are even those who deny that this evidence indicates any expansion of the universe at all and try to account for the red shift in the light from the distant nebulae on other grounds. Some of the most famous exponents of this way of thinking are Bondi, Gold, and Hoyle.

I think that everyone admits that at the present time we cannot draw sure conclusions; but both the evidence and the theories are significant enough to emphasize the need for keeping an open mind at the present time as we make an effort to interpret the dynamism of the universe. And I think that it is worthwhile to explore this evidence a little farther and review the thoughts of a number of the cosmologists and philosophers who have meditated on these problems.

The Nature of Time

One of the most recent and authoritative books on the problems of cosmology has been written by Professor Bonner of the University of London. He comments that, "One of the ways in which relativity most outrages our common-sense is the havoc it plays with our ordinary ideas of time."

Time has been one of the most favored subjects for meditation and speculation both with poets and philosophers. We have the feeling that time flows on like a river. We cannot "set back the clock." Time in its course moves inexorably forward. We waver between the view that time has gone on and will go on forever, that the universe has existed and will exist forever, and the opposite view that there must have been a beginning of time and a creation of the universe. Whitehead calls this "the wavering between immanence and imposition." In speaking of Plato, he says that Plato's cosmology "includes an ultimate Creator, shadowy and undefined, imposing his design upon the universe. Secondly, the action and reaction of the internal constituents is—for Plato—the self-sufficient explanation of the flux of the world; nothing was given off from it, nothing entered it—there was nothing but itself."

Certainly one of the most important aspects of the character of time is its beginning and ending. Does time go back infinitely far? Does time go on ahead forever?

One approach to this question is to try to combine both ideas in a paradoxical union. Whitehead at one point says that the universe is both transient and eternal. Niebuhr remarks: "Christianity sees the source and end of history beyond history. This gives the individual a place to stand within a world of meaning."

Let us consider first the problem that is concerned with this *singular point* of time which appears to lie about ten billion years ago, according to so much of the evidence. It is possible to argue that this singular point really represents a creation of the universe. Somehow all matter, all energy suddenly appeared; space was created; time was created. It is relatively easy to write phrases like these, but what do they mean?

Those who wish to see this initial point as an act of creation are faced with the problem of explaining whether by these words they mean that this act was a creation of *something out of nothing* or *something out of something else.* Philosophically one can imagine different degrees of creation. The supreme creation presumably would be creating something out of nothing. Against this point of view there is the doctrine expressed by Sir James Jeans in his book on "Physics and Philosophy": *"Ex nihilo nihil fit."* In other words, from nothing, nothing can be made. Professor Stace raises the question in his book on "Time and Eternity" whether creation was a *temporal* act.

A number of scientists have tried to get a clearer idea about what was going on ten billion years ago from an analysis of the relations between energy and matter, as we observe them both around us today and in the stars. Professor George Gamow has been one of the leaders in this endeavor. He collaborated with Dr. Alpher in a most noteworthy investigation of some of these relationships. The story is that when their report was almost completed, they felt that it would, with respect to authorship, have an unsurpassed symmetry of form if Professor Bethe could be induced to let his name appear as coauthor, thus making a scientific trilogy of Alpher, Bethe, and Gamow. At any rate, that is the way the paper was published. They postulated that the beginning of the universe consisted of an assembly of hot neutrons and outlined the way in which the heavier elements might have been synthesized during the first thirty minutes of existence. Another notable contribution to this analysis of possible initial conditions was made by Abbe LeMaitre, who proposed that the universe started as one big atom. Both of these approaches implicitly assume a sudden appearance of matter with resulting instability, a kind of initial cosmic explosion from which matter and energy fly out, creating in their flight space and time. Thus the term "big bang theory" is frequently applied to the idea of the origin of the universe at such a singular point.

Before exploring further into the paradoxes and contradictions of the origin of the universe, I want to turn briefly to consider the complementary aspect, the terminus of the universe. Some of the cosmological models like that of Einstein and DeSitter involve an initial point but are open-ended, with no indication of any terminus of time. Other models like the cycloidal model imply a terminus similar in nature to the singular point of origin. As I remarked in the previous chapter, it is noteworthy that in scientific literature there is so much discussion concerned with the origin of the universe and so little about a possible termination. Of course, the direct evidence that we have is entirely from the *past,* since we possess no crystal ball with which to look into the *future*. We can only observe trends and make predictions; and with such a long time to wait for their direct verification it is perhaps not an area suitable for scientific analysis. However, if we acknowledge the need for establishing a clear-cut attitude of man toward his environment today, if we agree with Albert Schweitzer that a civilization can only be as meaningful as its philosophy, then I think that there is a challenge to look at the evidence and try to see at least the direction of the path of man's destiny even though we cannot hope to see the end of the road. Reinhold Niebuhr comments in the second part of his treatise on the "Nature and Destiny of Man" that the end of time in eternity is not a point in time. Whitehead calls our attention to the fact that the concept of the infinity of time implies the disappearance of distinctions.

My own response to these question marks on the horizon of both the past and the future is to develop a deeper awareness both of the beginning of time and the end of time as *boundary conditions*. Professor Stace calls our attention to the fact that we are dealing with the extrapolation of orders of pattern, different in kind. Whitehead urges us to explore the boundaries of form.

If we agree with Niebuhr that the end of time in eternity is not a point in time, I believe that it is equally logical to regard the beginning of time in pre-eternity also as not a point in time. I think that we ought to see whether we can develop a concept of a changing *measure* of time to go hand in hand with a changing *measure* of space as one goes back ten billion years. For this reason, I do not think that the figure of ten billion years should be taken too seriously as the *lapse* of time since the beginning of things. As Professor Bonner points out, this involves the assumption of a constant rate of expansion; and one would scarcely think this rate to be constant under the conditions of extreme density when "the stars almost touch one another."

In fact, I sometimes wonder whether some of the cosmologists are not lapsing into the same kind of mental attitude that led Archbishop Ussher of Armagh, Ireland, to assert back in 1658 that the universe was created by God in 4004 B.C., on Sunday, October 23d. Presumably this was Irish local mean time; and the ambiguity of standard or daylight time had not arisen.

If we regard time not as flowing uniformly and unidirectionally like a river but more as a tapestry woven from the relationships between the dynamic forms that constitute the universe, then in this broader framework we are not quite so boxed in with paradoxes. And of course we should keep in mind the distinction between *paradox* and *contradiction*.

Does a dynamic form have to exist in time in order to be dynamic? Is this any more a requirement for its existence than the requirement that light must vibrate *in* something? If electromagnetic radiation is a dynamic form, an eternal verity, in its own right, does it not transcend time? I suggest that we are dealing here with the paradox of unity and diversity. Lovejoy in his treatise on the "Great Chain of Being" refers to these two aspects as the contemplative and the creative in the Creator. If we are willing to accept time as a tapestry, then we have a very different perspective in which to view man's own relationship to time.

The eternal verities, the eternal dynamic forms, are clearly embedded in and participating in man's total dynamism. We have within us the unity of the proton, the duality of electron-spin, and the trinity of carbon. We have vibrant within us the overarching dynamic forms of beauty, truth, and love. The dynamism of the past is present in us, the dynamism of past humanity which is part of our own total dynamism of life. Thus, the total past is vibrant, dynamic, alive, present in us. And by the same token, our present will be living in the future. Again I quote T. S. Eliot:

"Time present and time past
Are both perhaps present in time future,
And time future contained in time past."

Man in Time and Eternity

The stature of man, some six feet, is midway in ratio between the smallest significant distance inside the nucleus of atoms and the largest significant distance, the diameter of the universe; in the same way, the span of man's mortal life, some three-quarters of a century, is midway in ratio between the smallest significant span of time, a pulse in the nucleus of an atom, and the longest span of time, the pulse of the universe.

At this moment, in the hydrogen atom at the tip of your finger, there is pulsing the de Broglie wave that is its reality. In one second of time, from *now* to *now,* this has contracted and expanded almost a quintillion times. If your heart had beat continuously since the origin of the universe, ten billion years ago, it would still not have beat as many times as this little hydrogen atom in your finger quivers during your reading of this single sentence.

Professor Stace speaks of the divine moment buried in man, even deeper in plants, perhaps even in metals. As we see the dynamism of the eternal verities transcending space and time, is not our own dynamism of this same divine essence?

We recognize that when we speak of infinite time past and infinite time future we are faced with a paradox. Niebuhr says that we must accept the contradictions which are the essence of any attempt to place man in the universe. He notes that the only alternatives are to reduce life to the meaninglessness of natural order or to translate it into dimensions of pure reason, that is, pure eternity. He asserts that man's dimensions include both time and eternity.

I suggest that these contradictions begin to dissolve if we can accept both ourself and the universe not as *matter* but as *music*. In music, there is a dynamism which is more than movement in time. In the dynamic form of music, which can be transformed invariant into so many embodiments, both obviously moving and superficially static, we have the underlying dynamic form which in its dynamism transcends time.

In order to apprehend even dimly the vistas which unfold when we view the universe in the perspective of the dynamisms of these eternal verities, we need above all to strive for the *total,* perspective; we need to see the reaches of thought in that dynamism of infinite dimensions that lies in the unity of the universe. We must search the domain of origin, the domain of destiny, the domain toward which Faust beseeched Mephistopheles to direct him. It is the domain of which even the Devil was afraid even to speak:

"in solitude are throned the goddesses.
No space around them, place and time still less;
Only to speak of them terrifies,
They are the mothers."
Faust asks, shuddering,
"The mothers, the mothers, where is the way?"
Mephistopheles replies:
"No way! to the unreachable, ne'er to be trodden.
A way to the unbeseechable, never to be besought.
Through endless solitudes shalt thou be drifted."
No one has phrased the culmination of these thoughts more beautifully than has T. S. Eliot. In "The Dry Salvages," he writes:
"To apprehend
The point of intersection of the timeless
With time, is an occupation for the saint."
And in looking toward the end of time, Eliot looks back to the beginning:

"What we call the beginning is often the end
And to make an end is to make a beginning.
The end is where we start from."

"And all shall be well and
All manner of thing shall be well
When the tongues of flame are in-folded
Into the crowned knot of fire
And the fire and the rose are one."

19

The Unity of the Universe

IN OUR concept of the universe as an interlaced tapestry
of music, we perceive intimations of a unity that is nowhere to be seen in the picture of a cosmos composed
of vintillions of individual particles of matter. When we
focus in the perspective of cosmic harmony, we see clearly
that space and time and their entire contents are all linked
together in a unified fabric of common threads. And in the
intermingling of our own symphony of life with the symphony of the universe, we find a sense of that immanence of
God which embraces every human being. Does this new
vista of the Divine Presence resolve any of the paradoxes
and contradictions inherent in the concept of a God who is
both the Creator and the ground of all being? Can these new
dimensions of faith help us to understand how God can be
infinite and omnipotent and still have a personal love for an
infinitesimal, individual human being?

It is clear from a number of the trends in current religious thought that there are many who feel that the personal aspect of God is vanishing as science extends our
knowledge of the immensity and the intricacy of the universe. They say that it is unthinkable that a God who holds
in his hands a universe of sextillion stars can focus his love
and concern on a human child. They feel that the infinity of
eternity swallows up, disperses, and destroys human individuality. They assert that infinity is incoherence and im-
potence. I believe that their concern stems from their lack
of understanding of the nature of infinity and especially
from their misplaced emphasis on diversity rather than on

unity in the infinite. I believe that these paradoxes and contradictions which trouble them so deeply can be resolved in our new vista of man and the universe as intertwined cosmic harmony, especially when this vista is properly interpreted in terms of infinite order. So as a step toward clarifying these problems, let us take a look at the structure of infinity.

The Structure of Infinity

One hundred years ago the term *infinity* was widely used by mathematicians, philosophers, and theologians but not clearly understood by any of them. To them it had a negative meaning. The very word itself, *in-finity*, means "no limit" or more precisely "that without limit"; and the presence of the negative prefix *in*, this *infection* of the concept of infinity with negation, generally was not recognized when the word *infinity* was tossed around loosely as a synonym for the unimaginably large.

I think that today these three classes of scholars most concerned with infinity all recognize that infinity really is a dynamic rather than a static concept. Take one of the simplest examples of infinity, the infinite class of integral numbers. We can envision the start of the series of numbers: 1, 2, 3, 4, 5, and so on and on, up to numbers so large that it takes many lines just to write down the digits. We can get a rough idea of the magnitude that such numbers represent. For example, as I hope you recall, the digit 5 followed by twenty-seven zeros is the number of atoms in the average human body. The same number of peas would be sufficient to make a layer of peas four feet deep over the entire surface of one million, two hundred and fifty thousand planets each the size of the earth. As another example, the number 1 followed by eighty-one zeros represents the number of atoms in the entire universe. Such a number is usually written as 10^{81}, where the superscript 81 shows the number of zeros following after the digit 1 if the number is written out in full. We also frequently encounter other examples of even larger numbers in the theory of chemical reactions; the *equilibrium constant* for a reaction may be as high as 10^{1000}. There is no illustration that I can think of by which to visualize such an enormous number, since we used up all the atoms in the entire universe when we got up as high as 10^{81}.

Even larger numbers appear occasionally in science, especially when we calculate the probabilities. Imagine an empty five-gallon goldfish aquarium, which is covered with a glass plate, making it into an airtight box. Imagine that, with your magic eyesight, you can see the molecules of air dancing around inside the aquarium. If you watch long enough, someday you will see the air shrink down into one corner of the box, shrink to one-tenth of its volume; but you will have to wait quite a while before this happens. The probability of this event has to be written as a double exponent unless you want to waste a lot of paper, for it is 1 divided by $10^{10^{24}}$. To write this number out on an ordinary typewriter as the digit 1 followed by 10^{24} zeros would require enough paper to cover the entire surface of the earth above five times, because the string of zeros would be so enormous.

Even with such an inconceivably large number we have still scarcely begun our journey to infinity, because infinity is by definition the number than which there is no greater. We can write

$$10^{10^{10^{10^{10^{10^{\cdot^{\cdot^{\cdot}}}}}}}}$$

and keep on writing as many exponents as we have patience for. We can write

$$1000^{1000^{1000^{1000^{1000^{1000^{\cdots}}}}}}$$

We can make our base number as large as we like and put down as many stairs of exponents as we like; there will always be another number still larger. We will never reach infinity. Thus the concept of infinity is dynamic; it involves a continuing process.

There is an anonymous limerick which summarizes this thought quite aptly, some lines of verse probably written by a student at Trinity College, Cambridge, where Sir Isaac Newton served as Master for many years:

"A graduate student at Trinity
    Computed the square of infinity.
        But it gave him the fidgets
        To put down the digits,
    So he dropped math and took up divinity."

I am impelled to comment that this unfortunate graduate student did really jump from a mathematical frying pan into a theological fire, as the problem of infinity in the latter discipline is far more complex and confused than in the former.

The most important step toward the construction of a clearer and more *positive* concept of infinity was taken by the great German mathematician, Georg Cantor, in the late nineteenth century. Cantor proved with convincing logic that there are gradations or varieties of infinity. He first considered the collection of integral numbers as members of a defined set of concepts, since the process for the construction of these numbers can be logically stated. He then pointed out that there are many sets of identifiable concepts which are congruent with, match item by item, the set of integral numbers. For example, one can undertake to construct the set of all fractions lying between zero and one. We can start with 1/2 and add 1/4 and 3/4 and go on to 1/5, 2/5, 3/5, 4/5, and so on, and thus start the list of the fractions lying between zero and one defined with integral numbers in the numerator and in the denominator. Of course, to list all of these, we would have to have an infinite supply of paper, of ink, of time and of patience. But Cantor showed that you can match each fraction with one of the integral numbers 1, 2, 3, 4, 5 and so on in a one-to-one pattern of matching and thus demonstrate that each set contains the same number of members. Cantor called this kind of set a special kind of infinity denoted by the first letter of the Hebrew alphabet, *aleph,* with the subscript zero. Using Hebrew type this is written as ℵ.

Cantor then went on to show that the number of points on a line lying between 0 and 1 consisted of a set with far more than an $Aleph_0$ infinity of members in it. He was able to demonstrate that the series of points which make up the continuous line extending from 0 to 1 not only contains all the members of the set of integral numbers (of which there are $Aleph_0$ infinity members) but, in addition, a still greater infinity of members. These new numbers are expressible as decimal fractions, if one is willing to use an infinite number of digits to express *each* decimal fraction. In other words, the set of points lying between 0 and 1 on a continuous line is far more *dense* than the set of integral fractions between zero and one. He denoted this number of points by the term $Aleph_1$, *a larger* kind of infinity.

We now take this line one unit long and use it to construct a square which has a unit line as each of its four sides. We then think of all the ways in which we can draw a line either straight or curved from each point on the left side of the square to each point on the right side of the square.

First of all, we can connect each point on the left to each corresponding point on the right by a straight horizontal line. Since there are $Aleph_1$ infinity of points on the side of the square, this gives us $Aleph_1$ infinity of straight lines crossing the square. But now we give ourselves still greater freedom and say that we can connect the points on one side to the points on the other by lines which are as wavy, as intricately curved as we wish. So that with each of the $Aleph_1$ infinity of straight lines, we can associate a new infinity of curvy lines. This gives us a still higher order of infinity, the infinity of functions, which we will designate as $Aleph_2$, a *still larger* kind of infinity.

Cantor then proceeded to prove a number of interesting paradoxes involving infinity. Although any finite number added to any other finite number gives a number larger than itself, $(2 + 3 = 5)$, it is easy to demonstrate that $Aleph_0$ infinity added to $Aleph_0$ infinity just equals $Aleph_0$ infinity. Infinity added to infinity is not anything greater; it is still just infinity. On the other hand, $Aleph_0$ infinity *multiplied* by $Aleph_0$ infinity yields $Aleph_2$ infinity. And $Aleph_1$ infinity, *multiplied* by $Aleph_0$ infinity an infinite number of times yields $Aleph_1$ infinity. As you may have guessed, once the process is started for creating a new infinity from the preceding one, it is possible to go on and on forever up through the ladder of $Aleph_3$ infinity, $Aleph_4$ infinity, through all the numbers all the way to $Aleph_1$ infinity.

Of course, this raises a question regarding the nature of the infinity appearing as the subscript. At first glance it would appear to be $Aleph_0$ infinity. But is there not a possibility that it might be $Aleph_1$ infinity? And why stop there? Are there not descending stairs of subscripts just as we had ascending stairs of exponents? We can envision:

Aleph..Infinity

    Aleph..Infinity

        Aleph..Infinity

Aleph.................................Infinity

.

.

.

.

. Aleph   Infinity

Vistas unfold of infinities of infinities of infinities of infinities . . . *ad infinitum.*

I quoted the limerick on infinity from a fascinating article by Martin Gardner which was printed in the March,
1966 issue of the *Scientific American* magazine. Gardner
points out that when Cantor first proposed these new ideas
about the structure of infinity, there was considerable skepticism. Henri Poincarè called Cantorism a disease; Hermann Weyl spoke of Cantor's hierarchy of infinities as "fog
on fog." Jorge Borges referred to these infinities as "terrible
dynasties." On the other hand, David Hilbert said, "From
the paradise created for us by Cantor, no one will ever drive
us out." Bertrand Russell referred to Cantor's achievement
as "probably the greatest of which the age can boast."

As recently as 1963, Paul J. Cohen, a twenty-nine year old
mathematician at Stanford University, discovered an aston-
ishing solution to one of the great problems in the theory of
infinities, which today is commonly referred to as *set theory.*
For years mathematicians had asked whether there might be
a kind of fractional infinity lying between $Aleph_0$ infinity
and $Aleph_1$ infinity. Cohen proved that one can construct a
kind of mathematics where such orders of "split infinity"
exist. There really is Aleph.................................Infinity.

$Aleph_2$ Infinity

There is one supremely important conclusion to be
drawn from this magnificent and monumental mathematical
analysis of the nature of infinity. First of all, the logic demonstrates conclusively that infinity is definitely structured.

There are orders of infinities, each of these having its own unique quality and characteristic pattern. In the second place, the analysis shows that infinity possesses a kind of dynamism. The characteristics of infinity stem from a *progressive* correlation between sets of forms. It is only as we *move* up the stairs of forms rising endlessly into the horizon of immensity that we can grasp the true nature of infinity. In order to see the full import of this new vista we need another and more searching look at the essences of form.

The Structure of Form

In his searching exploration of the philosophical and theological aspect of infinity in his book entitled "Time and Eternity," Professor Stace asks the question: "Does music transcend concepts?" This question parallels another inquiry which appropriately might be made with regard to form: "Is there an essence of form which transcends representations of form?"

The parallelism between musical relationships and mathematical relationships has been known ever since the days of the early Greek philosophers. Pythagoras discovered the simple number ratios between the lengths of strings and the related musical tones which they produce. He also drew far-reaching conclusions about the role of mathematical form in the structure of the universe, conclusions which today are being verified in most startling ways. For we are now able to explore the relationship between music and mathematics more deeply; and we are increasingly aware of the extent to which these two disciplines are intertwined.

As I pointed out in the extended discussion of music in the second major division of this book, the transposition of a musical chord from one key to another illustrates dramatically the quality of wholeness in musical concepts. We can play the major triad chord (*do, mi, sol*) in any one of the sixteen major keys without altering its instantly recognizable

FIGURE I

GROUP NOTATION

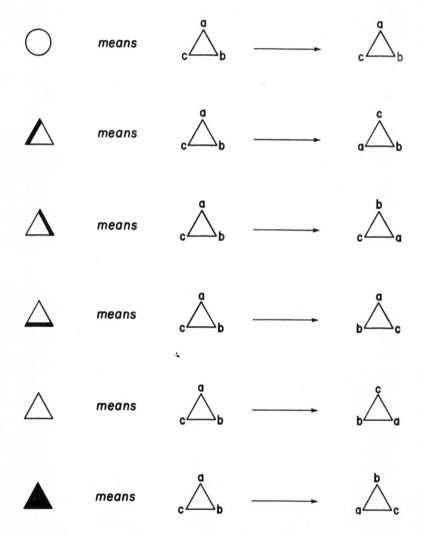

characteristic quality. We can transpose it upward by octaves or downward by octaves; yet always when we hear this chord we identify its total form instantly for what it is, the embodiment of the ratio 4:5:6; no matter in what key it is played, no matter in what range of tone it is played, from low bass to high soprano, it is the voice of a familiar friend. From this we conclude that there is an essence of this form, an underlying reality which remains invariant no matter how the embodiment of the form is transposed from one representation to another.

In the domain of mathematics there is a concept called the *group* which has many features in common with a musical chord. For example, the major triad *chord* is formed from three notes. The triad *group* is a group which can be embodied by the permutations of three symbols which are much like the notes of the musical chord. Mathematicians have recognized for years that there is an essence of the group which transcends any of its embodiments. As the mathematicians put it, the triad group can be *represented* in dozens of different ways; it can be portrayed as the possible cyclic permutations on three letters; it can be portrayed as the rotations of a labelled triangle; it can be portrayed as a set of algebraic matrices; but the group itself is something deeper than, something transcending any of these representations. In the case of the chord, we cannot say that the major triad *is* the combination of the notes C E G any more than it *is* F A C or G B E; in the case of the group, we cannot say that the group *is* the set of permutations, any more than it is the set of rotations, or the set of matrices. We discussed some of these aspects of invariance under transformation earlier in this volume.

In order that you may now have a deeper look into this aspect of form, I have made a series of drawings to explain the nature of the groups associated with the numbers 1, 2, 3, 4, and 5. In Figure 1 the group associated with the number

1 is represented simply by a dot. This group may be said to be the "transformation" which leaves everything exactly as it was before the transformation was applied. This unit group is also a member of every other group.

The group associated with the number 2 is represented by a short, straight line. This symbolizes the exchange of the points that lie at each end of the line. For example, if we have at first a couplet represented by the letters *A B,* and we then transform this couplet by transposing the letters to give us *B A,* then this line represents such a transposition.

The group associated with the number 3 is constructed on the form of a triangle. Let us label each vertex of the triangle with a letter, calling the upper vertex *a,* the lower right vertex *b,* and the lower left vertex *c.* When the triangle is in the position showing the letters located as we have just described them, we write the shorthand for it as *a b c.* In this shorthand we always write first the letter that appears at the top of the triangle. Thus, if we take the triangle as it originally appeared *(a b c)* and rotate it through 120° of arc, then we get the triangle in the new position with the top vertex labelled *c* and we write *c a b* as its designation. If we rotate this position by another 120° of arc, we get *b c a;* and if we rotate a third time by 120° of arc, we get back our original triangle. Our 3-group is a group of *transformations* of the triangle.

To be a true algebraic group such a set of transformations must have four characteristics. First, the set must contain a transformation which leaves everything unchanged, the unit transformation designated by a dot (.). In the second place, for every transformation there must be an *inverse* transformation so that if one is followed by the other, the resulting combination is one in which the second transformation exactly cancels out the first transformation, and we are back where we started, the equivalent of the unit transformation. This all implies that we have a law of combina-

FIGURE 2

GROUP ELEMENT COMBINATIONS

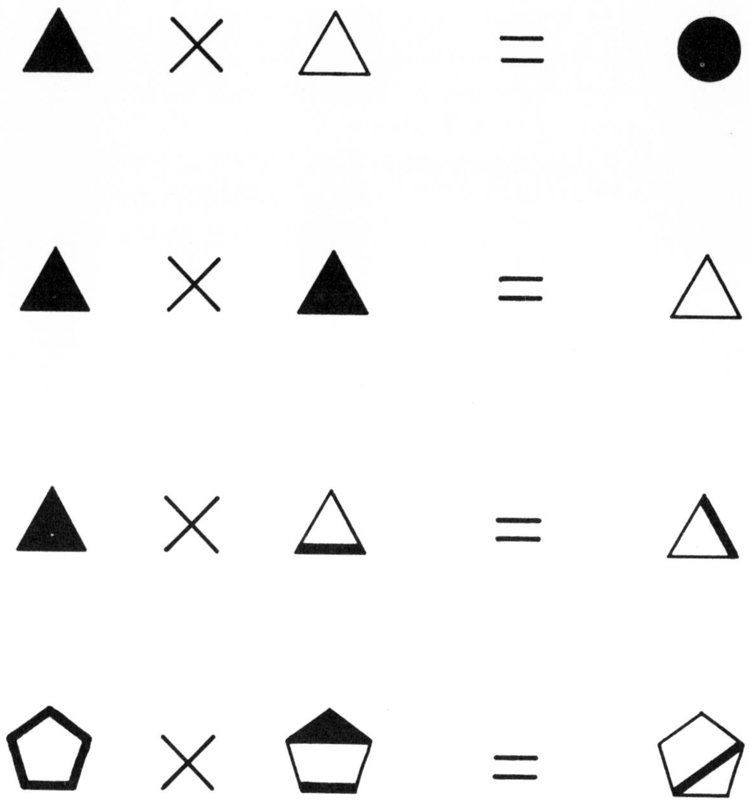

FIGURE 3A

PERMUTATION of GROUPS

GROUP ONE

GROUP TWO

GROUP THREE

GROUP FOUR

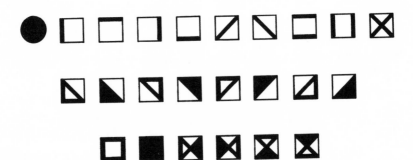

tion allowing us to apply one transformation, follow it by another, and express the fact that the first followed by the second is the equivalent of a third type of transformation. In the third place, every possible sequence of transformations must be the equivalent of another transformation that is a member of the group. Finally, in the fourth place, it must make no difference whether we apply the equivalent of transformation A coupled with transformation B and *then* apply transformation C, *or* apply transformation A and then apply the equivalent of the combination of B and C.

I do not want to turn this chapter into a lecture on group theory but I hope this gives you a little idea of what I am about to demonstrate. In the illustration I use an unshaded triangle (△) to designate the rotation of the triangle clockwise, that is, to go from *a b c* to *c a b*. I designate the rotation of the triangle counterclockwise 120° by the symbol of a triangle whose interior is shaded (▲).

The same notation is used when we deal with the group associated with the number 4; rotations are designated by open and shaded squares. The open square means rotation clockwise by 90° and the shaded square means rotation counterclockwise by 90°. When we deal with the group associated with the number 5, the open pentagon means rotation clockwise by 72° and the shaded pentagon means rotation counterclockwise by 72°. In some of the more complex representations, some parts of the figure rotate clockwise and some counterclockwise; but we continue to use the unshaded part to designate clockwise rotation and the shaded part to designate counterclockwise rotation. Unless you have had some mathematical training you may find this difficult to understand. Please do not be disturbed if all of the details are not clear to you at first glance. If you look at the drawings in the illustration you can follow the main line of the argument without bothering with the details.

The drawing in Figure 3 starts with the designation of

GROUP FIVE

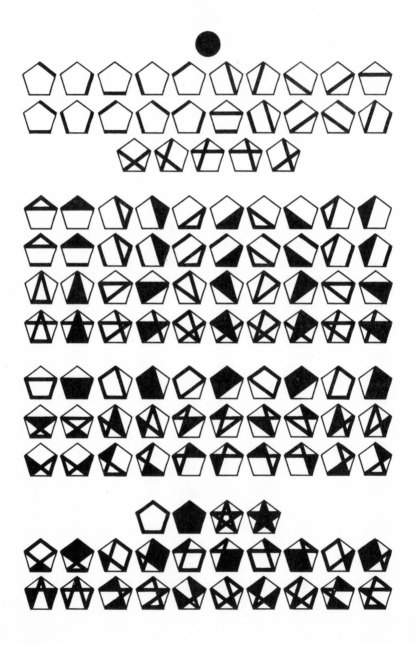

the unit group, which is a single dot. This is followed by the group associated with the number 2, a group having two members: the unit group (.) and the other member of the group which is merely the permutation of the two ends of the line and is represented by a straight line (—). The third part of the drawing deals with the group associated with the number 3. This has six members which consist of the dot, three lines, and two triangles. The fourth section of the illustration deals with the group associated with the number 4. This consists of one dot, six straight lines, three pairs of lines, eight triangles, two squares, and four "hourglasses," making a total of twenty-four members of the group in all.

Our final section portrays the members of the group associated with the number 5. Here we find one dot, ten single lines, ten pairs of lines, twenty triangles, twenty crossed triangles, ten squares, twenty hourglasses, two pentagons, two five-pointed stars, ten single-crossed stars, and ten double-crossed stars, making a total of 120 members of this group. (This begins to resemble the Christmas carol that closes with "a partridge in a pear tree.")

If you remember the definition of factorial numbers you will realize immediately that, in the first group, the number of members is equal to one; in the second group, the number of members is equal to 1 x 2; in the third group, the number of members is equal to 1 x 2 x 3; in the fourth group, the number of members is equal to 1 x 2 x 3 x 4; and in the fifth group, the number of members is equal to 1 x 2 x 3 x 4 x 5. Thus the number of members is equal to the factorial of the number of the group.

Without worrying too much about the underlying mathematical relationships, you can observe several obvious points in this collection of symbols. First of all, you will notice that the unit group, designated by a point, is found in every subsequent group. All the groups contain this component of unity. In the second place, notice that the group associated with the number 2 and designated by the (.) and (—) also appears in every subsequent group. However, this particular aspect of twoness is transformed into many different forms, the variety of its representations multiplying rapidly as we proceed to groups associated with higher and higher numbers. The group associated with threeness, the triangle group, appears for the first time as we might expect in the group associated with the number 3, but also is found *in all subsequent groups* in a richer and richer variety of forms. The same principle holds for the form associated with fourness, the square.

Now I want to call your attention to the similarity between this and the structure of our universe. We have the quality of unity appearing in all forms, from the single particle with its pure unity through the more complex fundamental particles, through the atoms, through the molecules, through the macromolecules, through the cell, and in the organizations of cells culminating in man. We have the quality of twoness as exemplified in the yin and the yang, the complementary spins of the electron, appearing all the way through fundamental particles and the other ascending orders of form right up to man. We have the quality of threeness, present in the three dimensions of space and in the threeness of the carbon atom, appearing again all through the rising complexity of forms culminating in man.

Finally, I want to point out that we can combine two pentagonal forms which are both aspects of the whole in such a way that the combination produces one of the lower forms such as a square, a triangle, a line, or a dot. In other words, the lower forms can be created by the higher forms. And in the same way it is just as logical to say that atoms are *created* through the transformation of molecules as it is to say that molecules are *constructed* from combinations of atoms. Since the whole is *more* than the sum of its parts, since the whole represents a far deeper and richer reality than the parts, it makes sense to think of the parts as created from the transformation of the wholes.

Cosmic Unity

These groups, these forms which I have illustrated, represent just one of many depictions of form and the relationships of form. I hope that these drawings give you an idea of the interpenetration of unity and diversity. If the underlying basic reality of our universe is dynamic form, if it is the melody, the harmony, the counterpoint, the symphonic structure, as evidenced by the recent experimental evidence from scientific laboratories, then in this cosmic symphony, we can discern the omnipresent unity of our Creator, who is both one and many in His infinite aspects. The infinite group will contain all groups within itself and each of these will contain the group of unity.

Again may I remind you that in trying to view the universe in these new perspectives we are still "seeing through a glass darkly," but hopefully this new "lens" of dynamic form perspective is a little clearer, a little more transparent, gives us a little more distinct view of man and the universe than the older "lens" of the particle perspective.

In this portrayal of the universe as dynamic form, we begin to see the truth expressed in the omnipresence of God. One aspect of God is that in a sense He *is* the total universe. Electrons, protons, atoms, molecules, cells, all the way up to man are in one sense part of the totality of the Divine Creator. But in this totality there are these infinite varieties of aspects: the aspect of unity, the aspect of duality, the aspect of trinity. There is also the aspect which we see mirrored in the human soul. There is the divine in man, and *vice-versa,* there is the man in the divine. In this perspective we see in Infinite God an aspect which can only be understood in the terms of the *personal,* which can never be grasped or portrayed in terms of the impersonal.

Just as we thought of man as an ego vector in form-space, we see the Creator of the universe as the Supreme Unity of ego vector in the all-embracing domain of the infinity of infinities.

I want to extend somewhat further the analysis of the relationship of the human to the divine in the last chapter of this book. But at this point I want to summarize the thoughts of this chapter with a few quotations from those who have been the boldest explorers in developing this new way of thinking.

The Divine Ego

In his book on "Time and Eternity," Professor Stace has phrased perfectly some of the thought and attitude embodied in this new perspective of the universe and its Creator in terms of musical form. He reminds us that our words and language can never do more than evoke in us dim intuitions of what lies beyond all thought. He goes on to point out that God is both outside the world and omnipresent throughout the world. This is part of His unity and diversity, embodied in the doctrine of the Trinity. Stace recalls that, in its striving to embrace the infinite, symbolism is the only means of expression in religion. And, of course, if form is the only reality, then symbolism is realism; for after all, symbols are embodiments of form. Stace emphasizes throughout his discussion the constant appearance of paradox as we explore the nature of the infinite. He comments on the nature of unity which multiplied by itself is still unchanging. He goes on to remind us that zero is the unity of addition.

Niebuhr expresses the same thoughts in a slightly different way. He points out that new dimensions are created by a paradox, that it is in the combination of the positive and the negative that we break through to the wider domains of more diverse dimensions. If we are to have freedom there must be the possibility of its misuse, the possibility of sin. It is in the thrust of the ego vector in the domain of freedom that we find the reality of spirit.

Du Nöuy introduces the vivid metaphor of "the wake of the spirit," evoking a vision of the passage of the spirit on the surface of the deeps of reality. This is that deep from which all reality comes, into which all reality goes, where, in the beginning, "darkness was upon the face of the deep; and the spirit of God was moving over the face of the waters," even before God said, " 'Let there be light;' and there was light."

It is in this domain of the spirit, it is in this deep of infinite dimensions, embraced in the arms of Him who is infinity of Infinities, that we must try to envision the unity, dynamism, and destiny of the human spirit. Reinhold Niebuhr writes: "The nexus between the Christian and the renaissance individual is not the protestant idea of the individual's sole responsibility to God but the medieval mystical idea of the infinite potentialities of the human spirit. A straight line leads from Meister Eckhardt to Nicholas of Cusa, one of the great creative spirits of the Renaissance, via the "Brothers of the Common Life" and John Ruysboek. To the mystics who followed Eckhardt, Christ was the symbol of the divine potentialities of man. . . . There is no upper limit for the potentiality of the human spirit: the just soul is like to God by the side of God on a level with God, not under nor yet over. . . ." How the Renaissance transmutes the idea of man's divine potentiality into the concept of individuality and uniqueness is beautifully illustrated in the prayer of Nicholas of Cusa: "Thy true countenance is without any limitations and has neither quantitative nor qualitative, neither temporal nor spacial qualities: for it is the absolute form, the countenance of countenances. . . . every countenance which gazes into Thine own, therefore beholds something not different from its own because it beholds its own truth. . . . Oh Lord, how wonderful is Thy countenance which must be conceived as youthful by the youth, as mature by the man, and as old by the old. In every countenance the countenance of countenances is veiled as in a mystery."

Again we face the paradoxes and the contradictions as we try to discern infinity with finite minds. But we get a gleam of the glory of Him who is all being, all power, and all love, and through whom we enter into the infinity of eternity, not dispersed but fulfilled.

Whitehead remarks that the process of creation is the form of unity of the universe. It is in the surging dynamism of the creativity of the spirit that the soul transcends the limitations of mortality and finds full personal stature in the infinities of eternity, grasping the hand of Him who is in His unity both All-Being and a personal, loving Father.

20

The Meaning of the Universe

E, THE people of the Earth, stand today on the threshold of the last third of the twentieth century, in the midst of one of the most chaotic and crucial periods of history. We are striving frantically to keep the winds of dissension and the waves of destruction from capsizing the frail ship of civilization in whose hold we cower. We are searching desperately to chart a course for the journey ahead to lead us into calmer waters and a safe harbor. But in this searching we are only mortal men with finite minds, trying to scan the infinite.

We gaze through the eyes of science and see that we as human beings stand midway between the infinitely large in cosmic space and the infinitesimally small in atomic nuclei. We must search far and wide, both without and within, if we are to envision our place in the total universe.

We gaze through the eyes of the historians and the archaeologists and have an increasing awareness of our stance between the eternity of the past and the eternity of the future. We realize that we must look back into history and forward into destiny if we are to envision our own significance within the totality of time.

Finally, we gaze through the eyes of the philosophers and the theologians and discern that we as human beings stand midway between the finite and the infinite. We are aware that only in this paradoxical perspective can we understand our own fusion of matter and spirit.

In the preceding chapters I have surveyed some of the thoughts and the perspectives of thinking which have been directed toward this problem of the meaning of man in his spacial, temporal, and spiritual environment. I have written these pages in a mood of deepest humility, aware of my own personal limitations and of the limitations of any finite mind attempting to peep into the mansions of infinity. I am tempted to say with Edgar in King Lear:

"Poor Tom's a-cold . . . Poor Tom hath been scared out of his good wits: . . . Five fiends have been in poor Tom at once!"

There is a component of guilt felt after trying to look where we have been looking. As Whitehead puts it, perhaps Satan fell because of an indecent desire to understand his Creator. But I feel the compulsion, the urgency, the necessity of this kind of looking. As Wycoff says, "No one can afford to neglect the impact of science—and the scientific modes of thought even more than scientific fact—upon the future course of Humanity."

In this final chapter, I want to survey briefly once more the most important facts and features that we have discovered in our search within and without, and summarize the most significant conclusions to be drawn therefrom.

The Meaning of Matter

Through the explorations of science, especially during the first two-thirds of our present century, we have obtained a completely new vision of the structure and nature of matter. We have a new conception of the fineness of matter. We have been able to measure in many ways the size of the atom and to show that it is so small that if all the atoms in an average human body were as large as peas, there would be a sufficient number to make a blanket of peas four feet deep covering the surface of more than one million, two hundred and fifty thousand planets each the size of the Earth.

We have been able to "look" within this almost inconceivably small atom, survey its interior structure, and find that if the atom itself were as large as a football field, then the core of its mass, the nucleus, would still be only a little larger than the head of a pin. We have even progressed in observing the interior of this still more infinitesimal nucleus with vistas of even still smaller "particles."

It seemed at first as if this search were giving us a picture of matter much like the receding hierarchy of smallness set forth in the familiar lives:

> "a flea
> Hath smaller fleas that on him prey;
> and these have smaller still to bite 'em;
> and so proceed *ad infinitum.*"

But suddenly our picture changed from *pointillism* to *holism.* The particles acquired an aura and we discovered that the secrets of their behavior lay in the interpretation of the halos of a new and mysterious kind of waves with which they appeared to be surrounded. Indeed, today we are being forced very far along the road toward the acceptance of these *waves* as the ultimate reality of those aspects of matter which were for so many years described as *particles.*

And as waves have been revealed to our eyes, music has been revealed to our ears. Matter is seen to be a tapestry of related waves of dynamism in a structure of melody, harmony, counterpoint, and fugal intricacy. The deepest reality, the deepest significance is seen to lie in the totality of the pattern. We are forced into a perspective of holism in which we recognize that the whole is far more than the sum of the parts. We begin to see that in many respects the parts are merely shallow, shifting shadows cast by the reality of the whole when it is illuminated by its dynamism.

The static aspect of reality, envisioned as particles *here* and *now,* becomes more and more illusory. And if reality must be expressed not in terms of *here* and *now* but in terms of *harmony* and *melody,* then the perspective of space as a

three-dimensional sensorium and of time as an absolute
flow becomes more deceptive also. The countenance of
reality must be depicted not with dots and lines and planes,
but with harmonic chords in sequential dynamism.

As science probes more and more deeply into matter we
have begun to discover more and more realms of unseen,
unheard, intangible, unsuspected realities. We become more
and more aware of the unseen and the unheard around us
and within us. We become less and less dogmatic in saying
that reality must go just so far and no further, as we continue to find that the road of discovery instead of ending at
the foot of a distant mountain range curves around, up, and
over, disappearing only in the perspective of an infinite vista.

We have found that infinity itself is not composed of undifferentiated limitless repetition. Infinity is an ordered and
structured hierarchy of forms.

All these considerations led us to turn and explore more
deeply the nature of music in order to help us to understand
more clearly this newly discovered harmony of the universe.
Perhaps music may even be the key to an understanding of
infinity. As Stace puts it, perhaps music transcends concepts.

The Meaning of Music

The explosion of new ideas which has characterized our
twentieth century is not confined in any way to science. Both
in the arts and in music, the walls of convention have come
tumbling down, and bold ventures have been made in exploring the fresh fields leading off to the horizon.

In music, it has become increasingly clear that the vocabulary of dynamic forms at the disposal of composers embraces far more than the simple notes of the scale based on
the overtones of the one-dimensional string. We are discovering the new order of infinity of musical forms contained in structured percussion. Pioneered by Stravinsky and
the penetrating interpretations of Stokowski, and inspired

by the imaginative techniques of John Cage and his contemporaries, we are at last breaking through into the domain
of two-and three-dimensional musical form.

We find that there are as many two-dimensional scales
as there are two-dimensional geometric figures. In the same
way, there are as many three-dimensional musical scales as
there are three-dimensional geometrical objects. And each
form has not only its own special scale but its own special
harmony. In the two-dimensional domain there are square
harmony, circular harmony, triangular harmony, and an
infinite number of other varieties. In the three-dimensional
domain there are the harmony of the cube, the harmony of
the sphere, the harmony of the oblate spheroid, and distinct
varieties of harmony for the infinite nameless but distinct
three-dimensional geometric forms. This includes every
statue that has ever been chiseled or cast. There is a special
scale and harmony for the *Hermes* of Praxiteles, for the
Thinker of Rodin, and for the *Slender-Man* of Giacometti.

We see the *gestalt* aspect of music ever more clearly.
There is a reality in the major triad chord which is unique,
distinct, identifiable, no matter how this chord is transposed
into different keys or throughout different ranges of tone.
Thus, in music, we find vivid illustrations of the principle
of reality through invariance under transformation, the
principle which now dominates so much of the thinking in
the new physics.

We now perceive the close relationship between the
domain of music, the domain of art, and the domain of the
atom. The essence of each kind of atom is a four-dimensional
musical chord. It is clear what Teilhard de Chardin meant
when he referred to the ninety-two chemical elements as
notes on an atomic scale.

Since everything living is embodied in atoms, we perceive this new perspective of reality in terms of dynamic
musical form illuminating the nature of life. We see more

clearly what Stace meant when he said that music almost breaks the walls of existence.

The Meaning of Life

The last few decades of experimentation in the life sciences have contributed an unparalleled wealth of new information about the structure of living matter. Viewed in the old perspective of particle physics, this new evidence appeared at first sight to reinforce the materialistic interpretation of the life process. But analyzed in the perspective of matter as dynamic form, this new evidence reinforces the significance of the holistic view of life.

Life is clearly a dynamic process even when viewed superficially. Life is clearly a hierarchy of dynamic forms when viewed in the perspective of our new insight into the nature of matter. We recognize that a total dynamic form embodies within it the lesser dynamic forms in the hierarchy. It is true that the total dynamic form under process of analysis can be made to yield the lesser dynamic forms; but as Teilhard de Chardin has pointed out repeatedly, this does not mean that it is *nothing but* the lesser dynamic forms.

Our most recent knowledge of the most fundamental forms of physical reality, the so-called fundamental particles, points in the direction of underlying realities that are more than the transient representations. We see the analogy with mathematical groups where there is the intangible underlying reality only partly visible in each of a variety of forms as the group is represented in a variety of ways.

Thus, at the most basic level we discern the dynamic eternal verities, the Platonic forms that are interwoven to produce the total tapestry of reality.

Ascending the ladder of complexity, we move from these fundamental forms, up through the more intricate forms of the atoms, through the molecules and the macromolecules, through the biological cells, through the concilium of cells, to man. But nowhere do we find any border post to warm us that *here* the reality of the eternal verity ends. We conclude that man is in essence a supreme eternal verity.

The Meaning of Man

Our study of matter, our study of music, and our study of the life process thus lead us to the conclusion that, in man, the deepest significance somehow resides in the dynamic spiritual *essence* of man—the psyche, the ego vector. The place to look for the meaning of man is not in the depiction of man as a group of particles moving in a space of length, breadth, and height through a unidimensional time. The way to discern the countenance of the spirit is to project the picture of man in the perspective of dynamic form on the infinite dimensions of form-space.

Just as music almost breaks the walls of existence, the ballet comes closest to revealing the true, infinite and eternal dynamism of Man. Here we see the human form projected into the intricate and interlacing dimensions of rhythm, strung not on a single thread of time but woven into a multidimensional tapestry. Viewed in the changing perspectives of science, the ballet is revealed as one of the supreme expressions of the human spirit. The older philosophy of science was based on the concept of matter as particles and on the postulate that in the particle we had the only fundamental reality. The extrapolation of this philosophy asserted that the personality, the psyche, the ego was only a shadow, no more substantial than the dancing shadow cast by a swarm of gnats. At the opposite pole, the new philosophy of science grasps the opposite end of the stick and turns it upside-down, placing the reality of the whole at the peak, and the reality of the parts at the base. The true reality of man is to be found in the psyche which is the total dynamism of his embodiment. And thus in the dynamism of the ballet we find the dynamic embodiment of the reality of man. In the poetry of the rhythm of the human form we have a vocabulary, a grammar, and a syntax for expressing reality, for depicting eternal verity, that far transcends weaving with words or painting with pigments. It is what Schrödinger calls the self-manifestation: light and truth.

As we see the spirit of man as an eternal verity projected beyond time, we see the dissolution of the argument that the spirit of man cannot survive the dispersion of the atoms of his body. We cannot say in finite thought how the spirit of man metamorphoses to the transfinite; but we sense dimly the many ways in which the dynamism of life is projected into the unseen domains of the universe. Through the dynamic halo of invisible rainbows of electrodynamic radiation, through the auras of gravity and probability waves that extend from the body into the infinite reaches of space, we sense the unity of the human soul with the universe; and we can have faith that through the totality of this dynamism we eventually enter into a personal immortality.

Niebuhr reminds us that contradiction is the essence of any attempt to place man in the universe. Contradiction is also the essence of the creation of new dimensions. So it is in the dynamism of the human spirit, in its dynamic freedom, that we see its grasp of the eternal in the infinite. Just as growth is the essence of all animate existence, growth is also the essence of the human psyche; and freedom is the essence of its growth.

Niebuhr comments that innocence is harmony without freedom; mutual love is harmony within freedom; sacrificial love is harmony with God. It is in the mingling of the symphony of the individual soul with the symphonies of other souls to enrich and enlarge their growth and their freedom that the supreme harmony of harmonies is achieved, which brings us at last to communion with our Creator.

Man is made for the infinite, as Hocking points out; man

exists in the infinitudes of dimensions as Whitehead reminds us; and finally, we return to Niebuhr's summary: "Man's dimensions include both time and eternity. The integrity of the spirit has validity in eternity."

Total Meaning

In his treaties on the "Philosophy of Civilization," Albert Schweitzer writes, "There is a necessity for a theory of the universe." Today we see a theory of the universe emerging, based on incontrovertible scientific evidence pointing to the fact that there is far more in the universe than can be accommodated within the confines of common-sense concepts. To understand the structure and dynamism of the universe and man's place within it, we need to fuse the transcommon-sense wisdom of the scientist with that of the philosopher and of the theologian. In so doing, we are truly attempting to breach the ramparts of space, the ramparts of time, and the ramparts of the infinite.

How far can we go before we are stopped by these boundary bastions? The boundaries of man are his birth and his death; the boundaries of the universe are likewise its birth and its death. In this concept Niebuhr directs our attention to the common structure of the dynamism of both man and his total environment. Niebuhr goes on to say that Christianity sees the source and end of history beyond history. This gives the individual a place to stand within a world of meaning. It is Stace's paradox of God outside the world and God also omnipresent. Thus we must look back in history beyond history, beyond time, back to a period before the stars themselves existed, and try to discern within that vastness the infinite mystery of creation.

It is an astounding fact that scientific evidence from astronomical observations points to some kind of singularity in time that is approached when we go back in time about ten billion years (reckoning in our ordinary measure of time). Today we do not have sufficient evidence to depict with any certainty the dynamic structure of this singularity. We can make guesses at the way in which a cauldron of neutrons might explode and coalesce into atoms and into stars. But about the only sure conclusion we can draw is that there is some kind of initial boundary in time beyond which the relationships of time, space, energy, and matter take on a pattern far different from any observed around us today. Although we cannot see the details of the forms at the beginning of the history of the universe, we can have faith that in this original dynamism, in this vortex of creativity, there is the kind of incandescence which illuminates and substantiates meaning in the universe and meaning in man.

We have even less evidence to support any conclusions about the future destiny of the universe. All we can do is observe the structure and especially the dynamism of what we see about us and within us, and extrapolate into the unknown. Again, in this totality of form and its dynamism there is a radiance that lights the sky of the future and gives us faith that we move forward into an eternity of beauty and harmony and individual fulfillment.

Thus, as Whitehead puts it, the universe is both transient and eternal. There is thus involved a grasp of infinitudes, an appeal beyond boundaries. The world is founded on more than transient issues, more than perishing occasions. There is a necessity for recognizing the future in the present instead of relying on the mass of fables called history.

It must be admitted that in this vision of the infinite dynamic boundaries both of man and his universe, we sense both a threat and a promise to man's faith. It is clear that, during the last century, our increasing knowledge of the vastness of the universe has decreased the sense of human significance in the eyes of many. Hocking continually stresses the point that, without something of domesticity, the universe remains hollow at heart. He goes on to comment: "I judge that this is the point on which Bruno seemed to his clerical associates to have missed the truth of things. Infinitude was Bruno's special point of piety, and also his point of heresy. To him, no one who thought God's work less than infinite, thought adequately of God; to his colleagues no one who thought God's world shapeless and devoid of center, as the infinite must be, could think adequately of God. Bruno's world could have no domesticity, and God dispersed everywhere as the 'principle of connection among things' could not be found. It is indeed an incomplete God and an incomplete universe. What it requires, and what all cosmographical physics requires, is a cure for the *illusion* of vastness."

It is in the shift from the concept of a universe of vintillion cubic miles of space, an almost inconceivable vastness which takes thirty-five billion years to circumnavigate at the speed of light, to the universe as an infinitely dimensioned tapestry of music, the cosmic symphony in which all tones interpenetrate, where distance is only difference of tone, where dissonance becomes consonance with a flick of tuning —it is in this shift of perspective that we change vastness to domesticity. It is by this shift that we restore the supremacy of the personal, the personal in man, the personal in God. It is true that we still embrace the infinite. But it is not the infinity of vastness, it is the infinity of harmony.

The religious infinite is the ultimate infinite of all forms. As Professor Stace quotes the Chandogya Upanishad: "In the Infinite only is bliss. In the finite there is no bliss." Whitehead points out the fallacy of divine incompatibility: " . . . a process must be inherent in God's nature whereby his infinity is acquiring realization." In the words of William Blake, it is possible to

"Hold Infinity in the palm of your hand,
And Eternity in an hour."

God is the vast infinite Creator, the infinitely omnipotent;

but in tuning our souls to His harmony of harmonies, we find that within the infinity of infinities He is a loving Father to each one of us, ready to comfort and sustain us when we turn to Him, waiting to embrace us when we enter His mansions of eternity.

The Choice of Stance

As you survey the evidence from science and align it with the wisdom of the past, you must remind yourself that science does not prove the existence of the human soul nor does it prove the existence of God. It is, in fact, part of your supreme individual freedom, part of this essence which is you-yourself, that the final act of acceptance or rejection of spiritual reality must be your choice and yours alone. The facts of science and their interpretation are spread before you together with your own knowledge of the nature of life and the nature of human beings, individually and collective-ly, as you have observed them directly or scanned them in-directly through the records of the past. *You* must make the choice; you must decide whether the total presentation of this evidence points toward meaning for you and meaning for the universe, or whether you still feel that you are only an infinitesimal cog in a cosmic machine.

It seems clear that the outcome of this choice, as you make it and as other millions of our fellow human beings here on Earth today make it, will be a decisive component in determining the future of the human race. Indeed, it may determine whether the human race has any future at all. So it is important to be fully aware both of the significance and the nature of the choice.

In selecting our stance with respect to the facade of civilization and the cosmos, there are important points to keep in mind. We must avoid dogmatic fallacy, as White-head says. We must remember, as Hocking reminds us, that we have an urge to forget what we cannot put into the form of thought. We must accept the fact that, as Stace phrases it, "Either God is a mystery or he is nothing at all." Stace goes on to say that " . . . our words and language can never do more than invoke in us a dim intuition of what lies beyond all thought."

According to Whitehead, we dwell in finitude, which is an island in infinity. But it is exactly on this point where we make our decisive choice. Will we turn our back or our face to the infinite? Will we look down and see only the sterile dust of mechanistic atoms beneath our feet, or will we look up and see beyond the starry sky the prismatic reaches of infinity? Will we retain in our mind the impenetrable darkness of ignorance; or will we open our heart to the rainbows of the unseen and to the harmonies of the unheard so that the strange beauty of the world will be like madness in our blood, as Heraclitus put it?

I plead with you to hold fast to the inquiring mind, to be tuned to dynamism, to be fertile for growth, to nourish creativity.

The Challenge of Our Era

Some years ago, the great Spanish philosopher Ortega y Gasset expressed the thought that engineers must realize that to be an engineer it is not enough to be an engineer. While they are going about their business, history is pulling the ground out from under their feet. None of us needs to be reminded today that there is a shaking of the foundations. For the first time in the history of this planet, mankind holds in its hands ultimate power. This is power which, used wisely, can eliminate all poverty and provide abundant living for everyone everywhere in the world. It is power which can open the door to a stable world of peace and good will among men. But this same power is of a magnitude which, used wrongly, can leave us no world at all.

We must make the right choice in the use of our new

power. To acquire the wisdom to insure the right choice is the challenge of our era.

First of all, in our effort to be wise, we must be aware that many things do not matter. As Whitehead points out, the opposite view has tinged history with ferocity. Theodore Ferris comments: "The statesman cannot create the stream of time; he can only navigate upon it. He must reach for the helm when he hears the garment of God rustling through events."

I submit that our one hope today is to grasp the garment of God. For many centuries, we have tried to operate our world on the principle of *balance of power*. We have tried to balance the physical power of one nation or group of nations against the physical power of another nation or group of nations. For some centuries this worked reasonably well; but as the amount of power in the world has increased, the balance has become less and less stable. The last two world wars demonstrate this conclusively. Today we are tossing on the scales the power of the atom. When we perfect the complete release and control of this power, it will dwarf all other previous sources of physical power on Earth into insignificance. We have passed the point where we can hope to control physical power by physical power. Our one hope for the future is to achieve a new power of the human spirit so intense, so all-pervasive that it will dominate and control our vast new sources of physical power and insure that they are directed toward the good. We must grasp the garment of God that is so clearly rustling through the events of our time.

But can we hope to achieve any greater spiritual power, any greater moral stature in the world today? I believe that our one hope is the fusion of our faith with the new wisdom that science presents to us. In his introduction to "Human Destiny," Lecomte du Nöuy writes that we must fight materialism with scientific arguments. Science leads inevitably to the idea of God. Professor Dewey calls our attention to the moral potentialities of science. Niebuhr admits that the understanding of the human spirit is beyond science but insists that it is a necessary undertaking to inquire into that beyond. Whitehead emphasizes this point over and over again. He emphasizes the weakness of scientific materialism, the strength of scientific spiritualism.

Toynbee poses the questions: "Will history repeat itself? Are we doomed to social suicide?" He suggests that we should attempt to put our secular superstructure back on religious foundations. Religion is the serious business of the human race. Let us not forget, he says, the epitaph of the Roman Empire: "Too late." Du Nöuy adds the thought that civilization is a war against time.

Can we achieve this fusion of the wisdom of science, philosophy, and religion? It is up to us. Teilhard de Chardin writes, "Like meridians as they approach the pole, science, philosophy, and religion are bound to converge as they draw nearer to the whole."

At the end of the treatise on "Adventures of Ideas," Whitehead concludes: "At the heart of the nature of things, there are always the dream of youth and the harvest of tragedy. The adventure of the universe starts with the dream and reaps tragic beauty. This is the secret of the union of zest with peace: that the suffering obtains its end in a harmony of harmonies. The immediate experience of this final fact with its union of youth and tragedy is the sense of peace. In this way the world receives its persuasion towards such perfections as are possible for its diverse individual occasions."

Let us stand firmly on the quarterdeck of our ship; let us grasp the helm; and let us confidently set our course for the Harmony of Harmonies, for the Infinity of Infinities, for the Unity of Unities.

Reference Volumes and Articles

Henri Bergson: "Creative Evolution"
(Translation by Arthur Mitchell)
Random House, Inc., New York, N.Y., 1944.

William Bonnor: "The Mystery of the Expanding Universe"
The Macmillan Company
New York, N.Y., 1964.

Louis de Broglie: "Matter and Light"
Dover Publications
New York, N. Y., 1946.

Peter Debye: "The Atomic Heat of Solids"
Ann. Physik, (iv) 39, 789 (1912).

John Dewey: "Human Nature and Conduct"
Columbia University Press
New York, N. Y., 1922.

T. S. Eliot: "Four Quartets"
Harcourt, Brace and Company
New York, N. Y., 1943.

e. e. cummings: "1 x 1"
Henry Holt and Company
New York, N. Y., 1944.

Theodore P. Ferris: Sermon at Trinity Church,
Boston, Massachusetts
November 23, 1952.

Martin Gardner: "The Hierarchy of Infinities and the Problems
It Spawns"
Scientific American
March, 1966, page 112.

Johann Wolfgang Von Goethe: "Faust"
(Translation by Bayard Taylor)
Houghton, Mifflin and Company
Boston, Massachusetts, 1870.

Sebastian P. Grossman:
 "Discovery"
 May, 1966.

William Ernest Hocking: "Science and the Idea of God"
 The University of North Carolina Press
 Chapel Hill, North Carolina, 1944.

Walter Kauzmann: "Quantum Chemistry"
 Academic Press, Inc.
 New York, N. Y., 1957.

Arthur O. Lovejoy: "The Revolt against Dualism"
 The Open Court Publishing Company
 W. W. Norton and Company, Inc.
 New York, N. Y., 1930.

Arthur O. Lovejoy: "The Great Chain of Being"
 Harvard University Press
 Cambridge, Massachusetts, 1936.

S. Luria: "General Virology"
 John Wiley and Sons, Inc.
 New York, N. Y., 1953.

Andrè Lwoff: "Biological Order"
 M.I.T. Press
 Cambridge, Massachusetts, 1962.

Henry Margenau: "The Nature of Physical Reality"
 McGraw-Hill Book Company, Inc.
 New York, N.Y., 1950.

Bernard S. Meyer and Donald B. Anderson: "Plant Physiology"
 (2d Edition)
 D. Van Nostrand Company
 Princeton, New Jersey, 1952.

Philip Morrison: "A Thermodynamic Characterization of Self-
 Reproduction"
 Reviews of Modern Physics
 April, 1964, page 517.

Reinhold Niebuhr: "The Nature and Destiny of Man"
Charles Scribner's Sons
New York, N. Y., 1946.

Lecomte du Noüy: "Human Destiny"
Longmans, Green and Company, Inc.
New York, N. Y., 1947.

Lecomte du Noüy: "The Road to Reason"
Longmans, Green and Company, Inc.
New York, N. Y., 1949.

José Ortega y Gasset: "The Revolt of the Masses"
W. W. Norton and Company, Inc.
New York, N. Y., 1932.

Ortega y Gasset: "A Philosophy of History"
W. W. Norton and Company, Inc.
New York, N. Y., 1938.

Bertrand Russell: "The Scientific Outlook"
W. W. Norton and Company, Inc.
New York, N. Y., 1931.

Harold K. Schilling: "Science and Religion"
Charles Scribner's Sons
New York, N. Y., 1962.

Albert Schweitzer: "The Philosophy of Civilization"
(Translation by C. T. Campion)
The Macmillan Company
New York, N. Y., 1950.

K. Smith: American Scientist 46, 413 (1958).

W. T. Stace: "Time and Eternity"
Princeton University Press
Princeton, New Jersey, 1952.

Pierre Teilhard de Chardin: "The Phenomenon of Man"
Harper Torch Books
Harper and Row, Publishers
New York, N. Y., 1965.

Arnold Toynbee: "Civilization on Trial"
      Oxford University Press
      New York, N. Y., 1948.

Hermann Weyl: "Mind and Nature"
      University of Pennsylvania Press
      Philadelphia, Pennsylvania, 1934.

Hermann Weyl: "Philosophy of Mathematics and Natural
      Science"
      (Translation by Olaf Helmer)
      Princeton University Press
      Princeton, New Jersey, 1949.

Alfred North Whitehead: "Adventures of Ideas"
      The Macmillan Company
      New York, N. Y., 1933.

Alfred North Whitehead: "Essays in Science and Philosophy"
      Philosophical Library
      New York, N. Y., 1947.

Norbert Wiener: "The Human Use of Human Beings"
      Houghton Mifflin Company
      Boston, Massachusetts, 1950.

PRINTED U.S.A.   93-F-15M-5-67